BACK OFF I

THE STORY OF FRANK DALTON & FRANK DALTON

Written by
Carl Franklin 'Dalton' Holliday
and Cheryl Bartlam du Bois

A Place In Time.Press • Beverly Hills, CA

A Place In Time.Press
8594 Wilshire Blvd., Suite 1020, Beverly Hills, Ca 90211
310 428-1090 or info@aplaceintime.press

This is a work of fiction. Names, characters, businesses, places, events and incidents are either the products of the authors' imagination or used in a fictional manner. Any resemblance to actual persons, living or dead, or actual events is coincidental.

A Place in Time.Press
8549 Wilshire Blvd. Ste. 1020,
Beverly Hills, CA 90211
310 613-8872
e-mail:info@aplaceintime.press
Website: aplaceintime.press

Cover Design & Layout:
Christopher Staser, brandweaver.tv

Special thanks to Mike Wilson for assistance with USMC research.

Library of Congress Cataloging-in-Publication Data is available on file.
Print ISBN: 978-0-9745414-8-8
Ebook: ISBN: 978-0-9745414-9-5
HISTORICAL FICTION
Printed in the United States of America
Our books may be purchased in bulk for promotional, educational, or business use. Please contact your local bookseller or the publisher: aplaceintime.press

First U.S. Edition 2023

WHEN THE DALTON'S RODE

Excerpts have been taken from *When the Daltons Rode,* Written by Emmett Dalton in Collaboration with Jack Jungmeyer and published in 1937 by The Sun Dial Press, Inc., Garden City, New York.

When the Daltons Rode, in its original publication, is a public domain book. No notes or additions from any subsequent publication of this book have been used in this printing.

Pages included from *When the Daltons Rode:*
(pages 40-48 of When the Daltons Rode)
(pages 57-61 & 64-66 of When the Daltons Rode) Chapter 4
(pages 91-100 of When the Dalton's Rode) Chapter 6
(pages 146-149 of When the Dalton's Rode) Chapter 7
(pages 157-158 & 160-161 of When the Dalton's Rode) Chapter 9
(pages 165-167 of When the Dalton's Rode) Chapter 10
(pages 170-179 of When the Dalton's Rode) Chapter 13
(pages 237-261 of When the Dalton's Rode) Chapter 25

AUTHOR'S NOTE
Cheryl Bartlam du Bois

Although some names and detail have been changed to protect loved ones, much of the following story is and accurate accounting of Carl Franklin 'Dalton' Holliday's life—as well as Frank could recollect. As he told me his story I couldn't help but feel heartache for the young boy who suffered such inhumane abuse at the hand of his own mother. At the same time, I was impressed by the man he had become. He is now a happily married, successful, literate man of eighty-seven.

Although I realize that as an author in today's world, it is politically incorrect to write with colloquial dialect, although I felt it necessary to imbue the reader with a true sense of the poverty and illiteracy of the time, in the poor south during the depression and post sharecropper eras.

Regarding the excerpts contained in BACK OFF I'M A DALTON, I have taken them from the Dalton original memoir, WHEN THE DALTONS RODE—1937—Written by Emmett Dalton in Collaboration with Jack Jungmeyer—in its original publication, is a public domain book.

WHEN THE DALTONS RODE is a beautifully written accounting of the Dalton Gang's story––told by the only surviving brother and member of the Dalton Gang, Emmett Dalton, following the deadly shootout in Coffeyville, Kansas on October 5, 1892. His first-hand voice gives his memoir an authentic and accurate voice for the telling of their famous and fateful story.

Since Frank desperately wanted to confirm his ancestral connection to the Dalton boys, I asked my writing partner, who is an expert on Ancestry, to follow the thread. I knew, the minute I discovered that Carl Franklin 'Dalton' Holliday's father was named after the Dalton boys' father, James Lewis Dalton, there was a definitive connection. Indeed, Debra was able to find the direct thread to their blood relations.

In loving memory of my son,
Terry Gene Holliday

Carl Franklin 'Dalton' Holliday

ACKNOWLEDGEMENT

I wish to dedicate this book to my loving wife, Barbara Homsey-Holliday, who has stood by me during difficult times and supported me with trust and love.

She has indeed taught me how to love—a value never instilled in me as a child, and I thank her for all the loving years and memories that our partnership has given me.

Carl Franklin 'Dalton' Holliday

TABLE OF CONTENTS

PROLOGUE

1930s – A Post Sharecropper's South Carolina

Tenant farming and sharecropping took the place of slavery in the South after the Civil War—providing labor for large landowners who had once depended on slave labor. Unable to afford wages to provide enough manpower to grow their crops during the Great Depression, large landowners adopted the tenant farming agreement, and the Southern Tenant Farmers Union was formed, which brought both white and black farmers to farm the land. Most importantly, aside from labor, the tenant farmer came with mules and equipment to plant and harvest the crops they would then share with the landowners as payment for rental of the land. The concept of sharecropping and tenant farming, having come from Scotland, Ireland and colonial Africa, was a workable solution to the south's problem.

Sharecroppers garnered a lower position on the rung of the farming hierarchy as they came to the table with little or nothing more than their ability to work. At the end of the growing season they would be required to share a larger portion of their crops with the landowner farmer. Approximately two-thirds of the sharecroppers were white and the rest black with their arrangement not so dissimilar to that which had existed before the war on the slave plantations. The sharecropper would also receive the lowest of the housing options to be offered by the farmer/landowner and the shacks often came with broken windows and drafty walls—very few had electricity, running water, or bathrooms.

The South in general survived in a permanent state of poverty during those years following the emancipation of slaves—leaving it the poorest region of the United Sates. Then along came the Great Depression of 1929, which even further confirmed the poverty of the already harsh living conditions of the South.

There was little employment as farms and factories failed and workers were forced to live on unemployment benefits, or earnings from extremely low-paying jobs. Most farmers abandoned the land to move closer to the cities, seeking any kind of paying jobs available and whites called for blacks to be fired so that they might have the limited number of paying jobs in their community. Lynchings rose and racial violence grew as the south struggled to survive in the impoverishment of the decade.

In 1933, Franklin Roosevelt's New Deal began to rescue cotton and tobacco farmers in the Carolinas however, tenant farmers and sharecroppers lost out on payments and that plus the rise of mechanization, would eventually end the existence of tenant farming—meaning the landowners only needed laborers for harvest, creating the migrant farmer who transitioned from region to region as crops came to harvest. Then the advent of chemical farming, to eradicate weeds, would eventually dispense with most hired labor all together.

On a very hot Wednesday afternoon, on August fourteenth 1935, a baby was born to Virginia Alexander Dalton and James Lewis Dalton in Pickens, South Carolina. On an unkempt abandoned farm, Virginia gave birth in a rundown sharecropper's shack, surrounded by poverty, tall weeds and cotton, as well as windows stuffed with newspaper. Tina Webb, the local Negro midwife, delivered the child and handed him to his mother, who refused to take him. He was named Carl Franklin Dalton, after his distant ancestor, James Franklin Dalton—the infamous U.S Marshal. The truth grows blurry after that as to the disappearance of Virginia and James—some say she went to prison for the next four years, but the only fact that we know for sure is that little Franklin was left with his poor grandmother, nicknamed 'Bessy'—Nancy Elizabeth Sloan Alexander—to raise. Trying to stay alive, she lived in an old rundown farmhouse with her two youngest sons, Coleman and Earl—Virginia's two youngest brothers.

By the time Frank was five, most schools were closed in rural South Carolina as unemployment soared and funding for schools was close to non-existent. Farmers struggled to pay wages for labor and children were put to work on farms and in factories for substandard wages.

CHAPTER ONE

A Carefree Childhood

1941 – Kirksie Farm, Pickens County, South Carolina

Frank Dalton's earliest memory was sitting on the front steps of his grandmother's whitewashed, but weathered, wood-frame house in rural Pickens County, South Carolina, on the Kirksie farm, shooting at lizards with pebbles from a homemade slingshot. Cicadas cranked their loud percussion song in the trees as a slight breeze blew the tall, uncut cotton stalks growing wild in the no longer farmed fields. The cotton had been picked long before and the stalks left to sway in the wind as a quiver of heat drifted above it as if it were baking in the ninety-degree sun. All signs of a prosperous farm and community had faded long ago and left nothing but poverty and abandonment in its place.

It was Frank's sixth birthday and he competed with his uncle, Coleman, only a year older than Frank, to see who could kill the most lizards with his slingshot—a new birthday present made from a tree branch and an old inner tube by his uncle Coleman. The boys were drenched in sweat, but the heat and the glaring sun didn't seem to bother them as they laughed and hunted for more ammunition in order to beat the other with their keen marksmanship. Frank's youngest uncle, Earl, only four years old, cried unattended from somewhere inside in the house because the boys wouldn't let him play with the slingshot. Frank's grandmother, Bessy, worked in the hot kitchen baking pies from apples and berries the boys had picked earlier that day. She took note of the nearly empty flour sack on the counter as she measured out the rest of the dough for the top crusts. Bessy was a middle-aged, petite woman, who appeared as though she couldn't have birthed one child, let alone two short of a baker's dozen. Aside from her tobacco-stained teeth, there was truly nothing noticeable about her.

Outside, Frank looked up hearing a car coming down the long, dirt drive as the disturbed dust forewarned of its arrival. Frank ran towards the new, black Buick Roadmaster, sporting wide whitewall tires as he recognized his uncle Mack's car approaching the house. He'd been told that Mack was really his mother's uncle, however he had no idea what that meant. In fact, he didn't even know who his mother was, or where she was, since no one spoke of her much and there were no family pictures of her in the house. No matter, Mack Hurt was his favorite relative, since he was always nice to him when he came once a week or so for his visits to bring Bessy either provisions or a few dollars.

Mack pulled the car up near the front porch and got out of the air-conditioned automobile wearing a black three-piece, pin-striped suit and tie, as well as a fedora and black and white wing-tipped shoes in the hot sun. He was a tall, stately man who looked as though he meant business. Carefully, he took off his hat and laid it on the back seat, then removed his jacket, and hung it on a hanger in the back. The boy's eyes grew wide at the site of his pearl-handled revolver in a leather chest-holster, strapped over Mack's vest, conjuring the ideal image of a 1930s gangster. The boys looked at the handgun in awe as he unbuckled the holster and placed it on the back seat next to his hat.

"Uncle Mack, Uncle Mack!" the boys squealed in unison running to him.

Another tough looking gangster climbed out of the passenger seat of the car and silently surveyed the area. Mack smiled and walked around to lift the two boys off their feet—one under each arm—and swung them around like a helicopter. The boys squealed in delight as if they might take flight like a dragonfly on the wing. Mack set the boys back on their feet and staggered as if he were dizzy and the boys laughed harder rolling on the ground, watching his antics.

"What did you bring us?" both boys screamed jumping back to their feet.

"Now who says I brought you something?"

"But you always do," pleaded Frank.

Then Mack plunged his hands in his pants pockets and pulled out two fists squeezed tightly together, holding them out in front of the boys. "Pick one," Mack demanded as the boys each grabbed a fist doing their best to pry it open as Mack squeezed them tighter and tighter. Finally, he pretended to lose his grip, "Boy you guys are getting stronger every time I visit," insisted Mack as he gave up the fight opening his fists to reveal a shiny penny in each hand. The boys squealed again with delight as they each grabbed a penny from his hands.

"A little bird told me it's your birthday Frank. Is that right?"

"Yes, it sure is uncle Mack. See what Coleman made me," Frank boasted, holding up the slingshot like a prize possession.

"Wow, that's a good one. Coleman's always been good at making things," Mack exclaimed.

Maybe on my next birthday I can get a six-shooter like the Dalton boys?" questioned Frank.

"Is Betsy still reading you the book about the Dalton Gang?"

"That and the Lone Ranger. You know I'm named after Frank Dalton the US Marshal," insisted Frank.

"I've heard that story once or twice." Mack replied. "Maybe one of these days when you're older you'll grow up to be a law officer."

"You bet I will Uncle Mac!" exclaimed Frank. "How many pennies do you think I need to buy myself a six-shooter?"

"A few Frank, it'll take a few more of those."

The screen door slammed as Bessy walked out with beads of sweat running down her face. She wiped her hands and face on her dishtowel and approached Mack, giving him a big hug. "Hope you're plannin' to stay for dinner."

"As a matter of fact, I brought dinner," Mack said as he opened the trunk to reveal a dead chicken. "Hit it on the road driving here as luck would have it."

Bessy just looked at him as if to say, 'Whose chicken did you steal?' Then she shook her head and said, "Give me that thing. I'll go pluck it and put it in the oven. It'll taste good with poke sallet and biscuits. Too bad you didn't run down a few potatoes while you were at it."

"As a matter of fact...." Mack pulled a small sac from the trunk making Bessy's stern expression brighten to almost a hint of a smile.

"Boys, go pick us some butter beans and tomatoes for dinner. Looks like Franklin's going to have a real birthday feast tonight."

"Oh boy! And, Grandma even baked an apple pie for my birthday!" crowed Frank in his deep southern accent, licking his lips at the thought of hot apple pie. "Come on Coleman....let's get some of them tomatoes and those sweet purple grapes!" Frank said as he ran off to the garden with Coleman hot on his heels.

Bessy shouted after them, "Now don't eat all them tomatoes before you get 'em back to the house ya'll hear?!"

"Yes ma'am," shouted Coleman over his shoulder.

"Where's Marshall?" Mack asked Bessy.

"Oh likely getting into some sort of trouble somewhere in town. You know that oldest of mine, Austin is a bad influence on the younger ones. And, you aren't much better, Mack. My boys idolize you and you don't always set the best example comin' 'round here wearing that gun. Someday you're gonna end up in jail for stealin' or killin."

"Now Bessy....that's just plain old nonsense you've been

hearin'.'" Mack pulled out a few dollars and handed them to her. "Now how could I help you when you need it now that Christopher's gone, 'less'n I be creative?"

Betsy took the money and pulled a well-worn tobacco sack from her bra. She slid the folded bills into the pouch and stuffed it back into her bra. "Damn shame the man had to go and defend my honor....got him murdered," she said, shaking her head. I'd rather had him living than have my reputation intact."

"Yeah he was a principled man and see what principles will buy you....? A bullet in the chest is all. You see now my principles in bein' a creative businessman affords me the ability to avoid that kind of trouble."

Bessy laughed sarcastically, "You're creative all right, at tellin' stories." She turned to go inside—then turned back. "I'm gettin' low on flour and sugar....you think you could scare up some for me next week?"

"Sure thing Bessy....I will do my best."

"Maybe you can find some that fell off the truck like last time," Bessy trailed with a sarcastic look as the screen door slammed behind her.

Since Bessy's husband had been murdered working at the logging camp in Oconee County five years prior, things had been tight. Bessy was busy at home tending to her nine children, as they came and went, as well as her daughter Virginia's son, Frank and so she was unable to work to earn any kind of a living. Hendrix, the man who had shot her husband stood trial in Pickens County for Christopher Alexander's murder, however his attorney, a man named Durham, had blasted and bad-mouthed Bessy terribly in court, stating that because of her bad behavior their fight had escalated to "....a murderous affair between the two men....only Mr. Hendrix here was a quicker shot."

The older Alexander boys, Austin and Marshall, as well

as their cousins the Orr boys from down the road, Huey and Duey—both professional boxers in their own right, waited for the attorney to leave the courthouse and beat him so severely for bad-mouthing Bessy Alexander, the trial had to be delayed for a week until he got out of the hospital. Ultimately, Hendrix was found guilty of murder in the first degree and sentenced to life in the state pen. The family found him to be a constant reminder of their loved one's murder when they saw him working on a chain gang on the local roadways around town.

For an income-less family, the two-bedroom house fared on the luxurious-side boasting finished walls and ceilings inside—unusual for old farmhouses in the south, even if it lacked electricity and plumbing. Bessy was an educated woman and oil lamps sufficed at night when she read books to Frank and her children. She wanted them to learn as much as she was able to teach them, even if they couldn't go to school, since it was closed much of the time due to lack of funding,

Out back of the old farmhouse was a pump for water and an outhouse for a toilet. In the cold winter months, a chamber pot was kept in the bedrooms to prevent one from going out to relieve them-selves in the freezing night air. The screened-in back porch served as their dining room in the heat of summer after cooking dinner on the kitchen's wood stove and the house had heated to an unbearable temperature on a steamy, summer's night. Most nights in the summer months afforded barely a breeze through the old tattered and repaired screen, which failed to keep out all of the summer night's mosquitoes. As the sun set and the sky grew a bright shade that resembled Mecurochrome, the bats swarmed the sky from the hayloft in the old barn. Outside the old rusted screen twinkled brief and numerous flashes of greenish light from hundreds of fireflies, or lightning bugs, which flitted through the tall brush in the backfield. Frank looked up and noticed a bat hanging upside down from the screen door, "Look....there's an air-mouse hanging from the door."

"Get rid of that diseased thing," Bessy pleaded as Mack took the fly swatter and whacked the thing so hard it flew from the screen and fluttered off to meet its clan as they circled the barn in the now-purple haze that was settling into night.

That night the smell of roast chicken and gravy wafted through the house onto the porch and Frank thought it was the best birthday he'd ever had—not that he could really remember any others.

"So Frank," interjected Mack interrupting Frank's intoxication with the smell of the roast chicken steaming from his plate. "What are you going to do with all those pennies you've been saving?"

"I'm going to town to buy one of those Coca-Colas you drink uncle Mack. I hear I can get one for five of them pennies." Frank sighed. "And it's going to taste soo good."

"I thought you were saving up for one of them six-shooters like the Dalton Gang carried?"

"Yeah, you're right," Frank sat thinking. "But I think that'll take way too long. Why wait when I can enjoy the Coke now? Maybe I should get me a job so'en I can buy the six-shooter."

Mack just smiled at the boy, "Maybe so someday....but not just yet."

That night after the meal was finished and the dishes sat washed in the old porcelain sink, Frank and Coleman took the few measly table scraps left from their feast out to feed the two hogs in the back pen. Come cold weather it would be time to butcher the oldest hog, and then their nightly dinners would include some fatback, cracklings or bacon added to their nightly poke sallet and biscuits.

That night Frank pleaded with his grandmother to read

another chapter of *When the Dalton's Rode*, to them. And even though Bessy was exhausted from a long day's work around the house, she never could turn down a request for learnin' from her brood. So she settled herself on the porch next to the kerosene lamp with the three youngest of her pride gathered around. "What you want me to read tonight?" she asked.

Frank shouted, "The part about Frank Dalton!" He pleaded.

"Okay, okay," agreed Bessy. "Since it's your birthday I'll read it, but tomorrow we have to do some catchin' up on our bible studies.

Bessy sat down in her rocker with her snuff and an old tomato can and after dipping a wad, she opened the book to her crocheted bookmark in the shape of a cross. "Let's see here where'd we leave off?" She started to read....

"*'The first gunshot that crashed loud with personal significance in my young manhood snuffed out the life of my brother, Frank Dalton. '*"

Frank sat up straight in his chair—his attention piqued. Bessy continued....

"*'In 1884 he had been appointed United States Deputy Marshall out of Fort Smith, Arkansas.*

"That's my distant cousin!" Frank announced with excitement.

"Now Frank if you want to hear the story, you have to let me read," Bessy insisted.

"Yes Ma, sorry."

He deserved and won great respect as a peace officer. To us younger brothers who were for a time to follow in his footsteps—Grat, Bob, and myself—he was an heroic and exemplary figure; a rock of courage, integrity, and disciplined behavior. As long as we were within reach of his voice we regarded him as our family leader and counselor...."

Frank sat quietly in the chair beaming, listening to the story.

CHAPTER TWO

Frank Dalton United States Deputy Marshal

Born March 12th, 1859 – Killed November 27th, 1887

Bessy could see that Frank was enthralled by the story but it was getting late and her eyes were tired.

"Ma please don't stop!" Frank begged.

Coleman and Earl also piped in pleading for Bessy to continue.

"Alright then....just one more chapter, then it's off to bed with the lot of you. I swear, my eyes are getting so weak, you're going to have to learn to read soon so you can read for me," she complained shaking her head. "Okay..."

"'It was in 1887 that Frank Dalton and another deputy, Jim Cole, attempted to arrest three whisky runners in the Arkansas River bottoms across from Fort Smith. The bootleggers resisted. In the ensuing battle Frank was shot down in the first exchange of bullets and was then killed, as he lay helplessly wounded, by a youth named William Towerly. Two of the smugglers, Smith and Dixon, and Smith's wife, who had struggled with the deputies, were killed by the officers. Towerly escaped and was later killed at Atoka by pursuing deputies, but not before he had exacted another officer's life.'"

"You mean the Frank Dalton I was named after was killed that quick in the story?" Frank lamented.

"That's the way it happened. Now would you like me to stop here or keep on reading?" Bessy questioned, ready to put the book away.

"No!" The three boys replied in unison. "Keep reading," begged Frank.

"Okay so stop interrupting then...."

"'The peace officer in the Indian Territory had to wear his life lightly. It was a hair-trigger realm. It became, in fact, the six-shooter center of the United States, this tramping ground once called the Nations, where ill-assorted Indians dwelt in uneasy neighborhood within arbitrary bound; where cattlemen fought over choice pasturage as the aborigines had disputed prized hunting grounds; where assorted men of lost names and furtive aliases and expedient morals jostled dangerously. The halfway station of horse- and cattle-thief trails, it was, and haunt of whiskey peddlers whose traffic was forbidden among the Nations. An island in the stream of westward migrations, upon whose shores much flotsam was cast; an island deluged by those land-crazed hordes who stormed in upon the region when it was opened to homesteading, finally to be made amenable to civil law under the statehood of Oklahoma after the great stampede of 1889. Under federal jurisdiction it required half a hundred Deputy Marshalls working out of Fort Smith and Wichita to patrol the territory and to keep even a semblance of order. Blazing defiance made frequent gaps in the ranks of these officers and the posse men they impressed.

Into this organization of border marshalls Brother Frank had led the way for us. Bob had already followed as a guard of prisoners and posse man. Grat was soon to accept service. Following Frank's death, Colonel John Carroll, Marshall at Fort Smith, appointed Grat to fill Frank's boots. Bob immediately joined Grat as posse man and soon thereafter was himself appointed United States Deputy Marshall by Colonel Yoe, who succeeded Carroll in the Fort Smith district. Following my brother's footsteps, I left the Bar-X-Bar to work as guard under Bob.

Deputy Marshalls in those days were paid by the fee system. They were allowed ten cents per mile, one way, when serving papers or bringing in prisoners; forty cents a day for feeding a prisoner en route; two and a half dollars for reading a warrant, the same amount for the commitment, and proportionate fees for other services. The guardsman, paid by the deputy, usually averaged about two dollars a day.

Thus I became intimate with the law and its processes, sworn to uphold it, riding its shifting and far-flung firing line. The .45 Colt in my scabbard and the Winchester rifle in my saddle were indeed the very badge and voice of authority, subject, of course, to the orders of my superior. For a time my fighting was the orders of my superior. For a time my fighting was to be official.'

<u>*Herdsmen of the Law*</u>

Deputy and guard, Bob and I began riding together in danger-fraught intimacy. With us rolled the wagon of the law, to transport captives, a sort of prison caravan; a chuck wagon, and extra horses comprised the rest of the equipment for the hard, grueling dashes or the patient trek after fugitives over a vast region of wooded hills, long grass pastures, creek bottoms, lonely houses and corrals, Indian wigwams, and raw young prairie towns.

Strange, exciting journeys, these, making me familiar with the ways and wiles and resistant toughness of hard men in trouble, and how they stood up to it or cringed when the time came for showdown. Simple and not very dramatic, I thought our enforcement journeys at the time. A summons here, an outright arrest there—the nudge of the law for trifling or serious offenses. A human roundup, much like finding mavericks on the range, butting them out, herding them back to Fort Smith for the branding or for the short and strangely knotted rope. Herding men to iron corrals.

Bob was already a veteran—seasoned, imperturbable. I was not yet so sure of myself. Often I sat a little apart, rifle across my knee, in the dusk about supper campfires, watching and appraising captives on their way to pay the fiddler. Trying to read their thoughts. Watching them as they carelessly ate their beans and made some coarse joke about a trifle. Observing them a they stared sullenly into the fire or with dismal gaze eyed the prairie where they would rove no more. Minding them as they snored in their blankets, callous of tomorrows, while the crickets chirruped in the weeds, or a coyote yapped from the hills.

Sometimes there would be boys like myself under guard, scared, or trying to be unconcerned. Perhaps I strutted a bit. I was on the right side, the strong side. I was part of the law which heretofore had been so vague and extraneous. Now it lay in my hand—a gun with a warrant behind it, applied by the authorized power of my brothers and myself. Perhaps this sense of power and responsibility should have awed me. Instead, it gave me a sense of exhilarating importance. The law, I perceived, was men like me flanking the prison wagon as it jolted across the wild lands whose green mane was so often stained red by violence. Just ordinary human beings, told to go and get somebody. And so, gradually, I came to think no longer of any majestic envelope around the instruments of justice. Only a sense of personal power and fitness remained. I was developing the assured manner and the knowingness of the man who has been behind the scenes of mystery to see the ropes manipulated; I was backstage in the play of the law; something which was to have its effect in the day when I would be hunted by other fellows like myself.

Now and then, when we had gathered an exceptional load of prisoners, some of the petty offenders would be given guns and permitted to help me guard the others. This was within the wide discretion of the deputy who was at times virtually court and jury.

It happened frequently that it was the son of a farmer we came to take. This might result in odd parlays between the Marshall and the head of the family. The hay was being cut, perhaps, or the sod broken for the new grain field. The boy would be needed to help with the work. If the officer didn't mind, the farmer would pledge to have his son on hand at a certain time to take his medicine. Couldn't the Marshall make out to wait a spell, under the circumstances? Yes, the Marshall could wait. And thus it would be arranged. Strange pride and stern self-respect behind this pledge. And at the appointed time the sons would be brought up to judgment at Fort Smith by these austere patriarchal Abrahams of the frontier.

In this stoic adherence to their given word the good folk of the prairie land were emulating the code of their red neighbors—the Chickasawa, Seminoles, Choctaws, Creeks, and Cherokees. In the so-called Nations here the high pitch of aboriginal American pride, dignity, and equitable dealing had been reached by the five Civilized Tribes. At the top stood the Cherokees, among whom self-government of a modern character was highly developed. If among them one were condemned to death and would pledge himself to return for execution on a certain day, he might be permitted unwatched freedom so that he might set his house in order. On the given day he would appear. He had given his word, the supreme law of his race. Pride rose above death.'

'If the blood of red man and white intermingled rather freely to produce a physical blend, the close and constant mingling of the races in neighborly contact also had its decided reciprocal effects on character, code, and conduct in the melting pot. Sometimes for better, sometimes for worse.

You are not to think that this reference to the Oklahoma Indians is a mere vagrant detour in the story that tells the shaping of the Dalton band and those other desperadoes whose trail so frequently crisscrossed with ours in days to come. The mutual impact between Indians and whites had a great deal to do with the nature of the lawless breed that roved between the Kansas border and the Red River, the Missouri-Arkansas frontier, and the Rockies.

Within fifty years, under pressure, the civilized tribes had progressed farther than the Anglo-Saxon had developed in twenty centuries. The skin-clad hunter who burned his captives at the stake had by the time of my young manhood become a pastoral man. Here was primitive stock of amazing capacities. This strain, fused with white blood, produced individuals of high and honorable distinction. And occasionally it begot savage throwbacks who wrote a darker legend.

At the upper end of the scale it boasts of men like Will Rogers, celebrated cowboy wit and philosopher, who is proud of his trace of Cherokee. Robert L. Owen, former United States Senator from Oklahoma, is another example of the best of this mingled Cherokee lineage. Owen is one of the few United States Senators who ever refused to run for continued office after serving several terms with distinction. He was also an ardent "dry" at a time when the Indian's love of firewater was a byword. Many other men of my acquaintance high in civil official life trace their pedigree back to these First Families of America.

At the other end of the scale are recorded such men as Henry Starr, noted Oklahoma outlaw, who sprang from an honorable old family prominent in Indian politics since tribal days.'"

With tired eyes Bessy closed the book to moans from the boys, especially Frank.

"Please Ma jus one more chapter," Frank pleaded.

"Not tonight. It's past your bedtime and I can barely see the pages anymore. Now go wash up and good night," Bessy declared as her final word.

CHAPTER THREE

An Unexpected Visitor

1941 – Kirksie Farm, Pickens County, South Carolina

The next morning, the sun was just rising in the orange and saffron skyline when Frank walked out the front door of his grandmother's house, making a beeline across the field to the old barn. He was on a mission to build something—he'd remembered that old wagon wheel hub he and the boys had found in the barn. Frank navigated the cotton stalks that were nearly over his head with a long stick, poking the ground ahead of him so as not to step on a snake that he couldn't see in the deep undergrowth. It was that time of the year that rattlers and cottonmouths were as plentiful as the mice, moles, and frogs they feasted on. But the worst of them was the copperhead—a fact that Frank had learned early on while playing on the farm. His older uncles had taught him how to tell them apart and although the rattlesnake gave fair warning of its presence, the others were silent and deadly. He'd seen how fast his uncle's old hunting hound had died the day he'd been bitten by a copperhead. It was no matter that the black racers and rat snakes were harmless—to Frank, they were all snakes and he hated them all with a passion. So he continued on carefully to the big old two-story barn with a hayloft above. He was on a mission that day to build himself a toy that he could share with Coleman and Earl. Struggling, he pushed the big door open far enough to slip in and looked around in the heavy shadows.

The barn no longer housed the horses used to plow the fields when the farm produced cotton, as did most of the neighboring farms. It was now home to only a few feral cats, rats, mice and a couple of chickens for eggs. Dust wafted through the light strikes coming through the windows streaking long illuminated patterns on the floor. Once Frank's eyes adjusted to the dim light, he searched for the materials he would need for his project. Off in the far corner sat the old abandoned cotton gin machine that had been used at one time to separate the cotton from the seed. But that wasn't the prize that Frank was after for his contraption. In the opposite corner sat the old broken wagon wheel hub that was about nine inches in diameter. He'd remembered seeing it many times and he knew that one day he'd find good use for it. Wheels and automobiles fascinated him and he wanted something that he could pull or drive around the yard. Near it was an old, metal grounding wire for a lightning rod and he went to work to make a push-toy out of the wreckage of the past. Frank was an industrious child and always seemed to find some project or activity to occupy his time. By lunchtime he looked upon his new toy with pride and decided it was time to show it off to his uncles. He carried the wheel out the barn door and ran across the field totally forgetting about the snakes.

"Coleman, Earl! Come see what I made," he shouted at the boys playing on the front porch with a bumblebee, which was flying in circles—a string tied to its leg.

Frank arrived at the step with his prized invention in tow and the two boys looked on in awe at this wondrous new toy.

"BOYS!" Bessy's voice called from the house.

Suddenly, Frank realized his grandmother was calling him and he decided it best to wait to reveal his new invention until he'd finished the chores he'd shirked that morning in lieu of construction of his newest project. He shoved the new toy under the porch, "Tell her I'm comin'!" He shouted over his shoulder and ran to the apple tree to quickly pick some apples for his grandmother, not wanting to show up at the house empty-handed.

Breathlessly, he ran to the back porch and swung the screened door open, panting, "Sorry Ma.... I was pickin' apples for you."

"Since dawn it took you to pick them apples, boy?" Bessy asked sternly. "Did you clean out the hog pen like I asked."

"I'm sorry I was workin' on somethin' for Colman and Earl to play with."

"Well 'round this farm the workin' comes first, then the playin."

"Yes ma'am, I'm sorry Ma."

She insisted, shaking her head, "No matter....go an' clean those ears and your face and hands and give me that filthy shirt to wash. We have a visitor coming later today. Someone you haven't seen in a while and I don't want her to think I raised a little ragamuffin."

Frank tore his shirt over his head and dropped it in the washbasin on the counter, then ran out back to wash himself at the old pump. A sliver of lye soap sat dried in the sun on the washboard and he scooped it up and did as Betsy had ordered, scrubbing himself well to wash off all of the dust and grease from the barn. He thought it must be important if he had to get all cleaned up for their visitor on a weekday and he wondered who it might be, and if they were bringing something good with them—even another birthday present. He glanced to the east at the dark storm clouds billowing higher and higher in the distance like foam bubbling from a pot of boiling crayfish. Rain was coming soon, which disappointed him since he couldn't wait to show off his new invention to Colman and Earl.

What Frank didn't realize was that the storm brewing on the horizon was a world of hurt about to pour down on him with the arrival of that so-called visitor who was bringing nothing good for him—only misery, pain, and suffering. His simple, little world was about to be turned upside down and he would never feel the same again.

The rain came in hard and beat down on the tin roof and windowpanes with a few leaks dripping a steady rhythm into pails around the house. A terrible thunderhead passed overhead tossing lightning bolts violently at the ground surrounding the house. One even hit the lightning rod atop the barn roof, lighting up the yard as if an atomic bomb had struck it. Luckily, it was grounded well and didn't cause the old structure to catch fire, but it did manage to break a few windowpanes as the electricity surged down the grounding-wire into the earth below. Folks inside the house jumped to their feet and ran to the window to see if that old barn was still standing. Slowly, the thunder faded away into the distance as the lightning took longer and longer to light up the sky. As the midday sun eased from behind the clouds the massive puddles standing in the yard began to steam from the heat and birds flapped their wings and washed their feathers in the water. Coleman and Earl begged to go out to play in the rainwater, as did Frank, but Bessy insisted they sit at the table for a lunch of poke sallet, fried apples and a few leftover biscuits from dinner.

After lunch, Bessy took Frank aside and gave him a hug, which frightened him, since he'd never been hugged before that he could remember. "I just want to say goodbye boy." Bessy looked him in the eye. "I know it won't be easy, but try to be good boy you hear?"

"But where are you going Ma?"

"It's not me that's going dear." Bessy just looked at him and shook her head. "Your mama's coming to get you today. She's back and wants you with her."

"My mama? Who's my mama? I don't understand. I thought she'd gone away fur good."

Bessy looked up, "Heaven help me, but I almost wish she had my dear Franklin. You just try to be strong and you'll survive. She's not the easiest person to get along with, but you'll find a way. I'll make sure Uncle Mack checks in on you as often as he can. Now go and pack your things up in a pillow case."

"But why can't I stay here with you and Coleman and Earl? I don't wanna go nowhere!"

"It's not up to me I'm afraid Franklin....I'm your grandma not your mama. My daughter, Virginia, is your mama and when she wants something she's gonna make damn sure she gets her way."

Frank just looked at her confused and backed away. "But I thought you were my mama now!" He turned and ran to the bedroom and threw himself on the bed.

Bessy sadly watched him bury his head in the old quilt and wondered how such a sensitive young boy would survive her daughter's untamed temper. Although she would have fought to keep him, Bessy knew that she couldn't afford him. After all, she had given birth to two short of a baker's dozen with three dying at birth. The eight who lived—the oldest being Austin, then came Virginia, Geneva, Jeanette, Hank, Eliga, Ralph, and Marshall—all old enough to be out on their own earning a living elsewhere, however she still had her two youngest, Coleman and Earl, at home with her. After all those years of childbearing and raising her brood, she was tired. It was all Bessy could do, now that Christopher was gone, to feed Coleman and Earl.

Coleman walked in the living room and saw Frank lying on the bed crying. "What's wrong with Frank, Ma, is he feelin' bad?

She said shaking her head, "He's not yet but he's sure gonna be when he gets to where he's going. In fact, I sort of feel as though I'm leading a young lamb to slaughter."

Later, the screen door into the living room slammed loudly rousing Frank. He heard heavy footsteps into the kitchen and a woman's harsh voice speaking to Bessy. He got up and eased his way to the back of the bedroom door, covertly listening through the opening.

He could see a tall, sturdy-looking woman—attractive but hard, standing next to his grandmother, wearing a dirty smock and shoes muddied from the rain.

"Where's Frank?" the woman demanded of Bessy, "Mack was supposed ta tell ya to have him ready."

"And it's good to see you too Virginia."

"Well, nothin's good about spendin' four years in lock-up."

"I certainly hope you got some help in controlling that temper of yours. Trying to shoot that man for killing your daddy certainly didn't bring him back now did it?"

"No but he got his. I seen him out on that chain gang breaking rocks for the new county road. He'll be rottin' in jail for the rest of his life."

"You should have had faith in the system. All your actions did was to cost you four years away from your son," Bessy continued.

"Uhump! A Dalton ain't no son of mine. But he's grown enough now to be a big help around the house."

"Don't you and that Wes Holliday you married, hurt that boy."

From behind the door Frank swallowed hard, waiting for his mother's response.

"That's not for you to say, now is it, Ma? Don't you be worryin' 'bout it no more. He's my problem now." Virginia turned to the bedroom and hollered, "FRANK! YOU GET OUT HERE NOW, BOY!"

Frightened, Frank backed away from the door and quickly grabbed the pillowcase from the bed. He opened the drawer and stuffed his meager clothing and five pennies into the sack. Maybe he could still sneak out the window and run away before she saw him. He could go in search of his Uncle Mack, who he knew would save him from this woman. But before he could turn back to the open window Virginia was standing in the doorway with an angry scowl on her face.

"Is that any way to greet your mama, boy? Haven't seen

you in four years and you couldn't be ready and waitin' for me when I called? You're a scrawny thing....guess'n you won't be no good for heavy liftin' around the farm for a while."

Frank took a step backwards determining if he could make it out the window before she could catch him.

"Let's get one thing straight right now Frank. You can't get nothin' over on me. And I ain't gonna tolerate any kinda lip from you, do you understand me?"

Frank just stood there, frozen like a fawn in the headlamp of an oncoming train.

"Come now ya hear me. It's time to go to your new house!"

"But I like it here," Frank's voice quivered realizing he'd made a mistake by offering this woman such ammunition against him.

"Well in that case, say good bye to your grandma and uncles cause you won't be seein' them any time soon. Now get out that door," she demanded pointing at the front door.

Frank's head dropped and he did his best to walk around her without getting too close, but she still managed to swat him good on his backside sending him flying through the living room and out the front door, with Virginia close on his heels.

Coleman and Earl stood playing in a puddle with mud up to their necks, watching the spectacle.

Once outside Frank remembered the toy he'd made. "I've got ta get somethin' from under the porch."

"What's that?"

"It's a toy I made."

She laughed, "You ain't gonna have time for toys boy. I've got plenty of work to keep you busy....now get on," she said pointing across the field. "And pick a good strong switch while you're at it." Grabbing him by the wrist she dragged him into the field, breaking off a strong stalk herself.

Bessy stood in the doorway watching them go with her two boys looking on confused about who that woman was and where she was taking Frank. If only Christopher were still here, Bessy thought, she would fight her daughter to keep Frank with her.

"What about snakes?!" Frank cried out as she pushed him forward through the stalks.

"What about 'em? I'm the only snake you need be worried about boy, you hear me?" As she strapped him hard across his bare back, raising red welts almost immediately. "When I tell you something you'd better do it!"

Virginia whipped him all the way across a fifty-yard field till they came to the old sharecroppers's house at the far end of the farm.

When they arrived at the old unpainted, clapboard shanty with many broken windowpanes, Frank stopped at the front door afraid to go in. His back was now crisscrossed with red stripes, from her many lashes, and tiny droplets of blood were spattered across his tanned skin. Somehow the trepidation of crossing the threshold of that house meant no returning to the only life Frank had known with his grandmother. No matter, Virginia opened the screen door and pushed him inside, shoving him to the floor. He pulled himself up standing in the tiny living room, which doubled as a kitchen. He looked around in the dim light cast through the few remaining glass panes—the rest of the windows were covered with wood or stuffed with paper and rags. The house was much smaller than his grandmother's and the walls were unfinished and streaked with stains. The ceiling was nothing more than tin that did a substandard job of keeping the rain out as water still dripped from the ceiling into buckets throughout the house. One small room with a double bed adjoined the

main room, which was furnished with an old tattered chesterfield and a small table with two chairs. Stretched out on
the old, tattered mohair sofa slept a man of about thirty
years of age, snoring away in the middle of the day. His un-
shaven face and greasy, unkempt hair spoke volumes about
his lack of hygiene and he wore nothing more than a dirty
pair of white cotton boxers. Dirty dishes were stacked on
the kitchen counter and the house reeked of the peppery
smell of mold and the full chamber pot in the bedroom.

Virginia batted Frank up the side of his head, whisper-
ing, "You be quiet now and don't wake your daddy."

Frank just looked from the man on the sofa to his mother, confused. "Is his name Dalton?"

"We ain't gonna be havin' no Daltons around here boy.
As far as you're concerned, this man's Wes Holiday. He's
the closest thing to a father you're ever gonna have so remember that and you be sure to call him Pa, you hear?"

Frightened of this woman Frank just nodded his head
acquiescing. He kept his eyes glued to the floor—afraid
that if he looked at her too long or the wrong way she'd hit
him again. The welts all over his back already marked his
mother's signature of ownership over him. The stinging
pain made him grimace, especially when one of the many
no-see-ums, mosquitoes, or deerflies feasted on the bloody
welts on his back, raising bites on top of them.

"From now on you're Frank Holliday do you understand?"

"But I thought my name was Dalton," Frank replied,
confused. "You'll be startin' school in a few weeks and
we'll be enrollin' you as Frank Holliday. I don't want to
hear no nonsense about bein' related to Frank Dalton. Your
grandma has filled your head with lies and it's gonna end
right now."

"But Ma don't lie," Frank insisted.

Virginia stepped in front of the boy and grabbed his
chin yanking his head up so hard it nearly gave him whip-

lash. "Do you understand me?"

"Yes ma'am....where am I supposed to sleep?" Frank looked around confused.

"Go make yourself a pallet in the corner of the bedroom with them old quilts over there," she pointed to a pile of dirty quilts and old clothes that were tattered and frayed. "Then get out back and wash them dirty dishes next to the pump and then you can do the ones on the counter."

Frank just nodded and walked to the pile of bedding, dragging it into the bedroom.

That night dinner was stale cornbread and milk, which Frank ate sitting on the floor in front of the chesterfield, while his mother and newly acquired father sat at the table eating fresh cornbread with pork cracklings. Until that point, the man that had been designated as his newly acquired father, had spoken nary a word to Frank. He just stared at him with utter disdain from the table. There was no radio and even less conversation in the room as the sun started to set into a puddle of hazy blue-pink. As the sound of the cicadas grew dimmer and dimmer, the mating call of the tree frogs took over the loud cadence high in the branches—starting as a soft serenade and slowly growing to a high pitched decibel as if they were in competition with the cicadas to see which species could outdo the other.

Finally, the silence in the room was broken by Wes' order to Frank, "Make yourself useful boy, and pour me some more milk."

Frank looked up seeing the jug of milk sitting right in front of the man, but he knew better than to question his request. He walked to the table to obey his wishes, taking his own glass with him and after filling Wes' glass he started to pour himself a second glassful.

"You don't drink anything around here until we've had

our fill!" Virginia slammed her hand down on the table and shouted, "Now you pour the rest of that in here," she demanded as she shoved her glass at him. Frank simply remained silent and poured the last of the milk into her glass. "Now you take your plate and glass outside and wash 'em!"

Frank just looked at his unfinished cornbread, "But I'm not finished."

That's all it took for Virginia to backhand him across the face, giving him a split lip. "You better learn quick not to backtalk me boy," she snarled with look of hatred in her eyes.

Quickly, Frank backed off, grabbed his plate and glass and flew out the back door.

"I'm going to live to regret ever givin' birth to that boy," Virginia snarled to Wes who reserved comment—evidence that his wife always required the final word. "He reminds me too much of his no-count father."

That night Frank lay on his pallet on the floor and stared out the single unboarded windowpane at the stars. He heard the sound of the whippoorwill calling his mate, accenting the first and last syllable with a tremulous trill in between. Frank loved that call more than any other bird since Bessy told him it was a papa bird serenading his wife. His reverie was broken by Wes' snorting and snoring, causing Frank to painfully miss the sound of the soft breathing of his two uncles sleeping either side of him. His only hope was that his Uncle Mack would come to rescue him from his nightmare. His life with his grandmother had been a modest one, but he'd always felt loved and cared for. Here, he'd quickly come to understand the meaning of true poverty and malevolence. The house seethed of a festering energy of meanness and indifference and he longed to return to Bessy's care.

The next morning Frank was surprised to see Wes shave and comb his red hair and dress in clean, yet tattered clothing. Around nine an old beat-up A-Model Ford pickup pulled in the yard, driven by Wes' brother, JD, who was about Wes' age and looked just like him. JD was there to drive Wes and Virginia to apply for jobs at the dairy so they could find a new place to live for the winter.

Frank had overheard Wes and his mother discussing the need to find a better place to live before the onset of cold weather—seeing that the sharecropper's house had no source of heat or insulation and by November it would be impossible for them to stay there.

"Frank you get your chores done while we're gone, you hear?" commanded Virginia, shouting at him from the front seat of the truck.

"Yes Ma," answered Frank suddenly realizing they were actually going to leave him alone. He watched as the truck struggled up the long dirt driveway with the transmission grinding as it shifted from first to second gear. It finally reached the top of the hill and turned onto the state road toward 6-Mile Mountain. Quickly, Frank took to cleaning dishes and doing wash, hoping to walk to town to buy himself a Coca-Cola. Once he'd finished a noticeable amount of wash and hung it out to dry, he quickly hiked up the long dirt drive to the road and made a beeline toward the local filling station with his five pennies burning a hole in his pocket. He walked for what seemed like hours, under the quickly rising sun, before he caught site of the station and market. Several old men sitting in chairs on the porch nodded to Frank as he marched through the door grasping the pennies in his pocket tightly in his fist, as if he feared that someone would attempt to steal them from him. Next to the register sat the prize he awaited—a tub full of Coke bottles in rapidly melting ice. An old, oscillating fan blew a warm breeze his way expediting the demise of the blocks of ice in the tub. Frank quickly scooped up a somewhat cold bottle and stepped to the register sitting it down loudly on the worn, wood counter. The older salesman looked over his spectacles down at Frank, debating whether or not this boy could actually afford to pay for the soda pop. Before he could say, "That'll be five cents," Frank slapped the pennies on the counter in front of him. The salesman raised his eyebrows, impressed that the boy had the money. He rung up the sale in the register—dropping the pennies into the till. "Would you like me to open that for ya?" questioned the clerk.

"Naw, I'll take it like this," replied Frank not realizing how hard it was going to be to get the lid off the bottle. As quick as he'd come, Frank exited the store and set off back down the road to the farm. Of course, on the way back he had to pass his grandmother's farm and he was tempted to stop and tell his grandmother how much he hated living with his mother, but he was more afraid of the possibility of his mother arriving back home before him. So, he sped up his pace practically running most of the way—all the while shaking the bottle of Coke that was getting increasingly warmer by the minute in the hot sun. When he finally reached the driveway, he took off at a sprint praying he'd made it home before them. Out of breath and drenched in sweat he arrived at the porch and tore open the screen door to find the house empty. He breathed a sigh of relief and ran to the kitchen to try and find something with which to open his prize. He tried pretty much every type of utensil in the old cabinet, but a church key or some other type of bottle opener was just not part of their arsenal of old spoons, knives, forks and other strange objects he found in the drawers. He was getting pretty frustrated and a bit desperate when he heard the old truck rattling down the drive.

Quickly, he hid the Coke bottle under the remaining dirty laundry since he knew his mother would never look there. He grabbed up some more dirty clothes and went out the back door to look as busy as possible when they arrived. He heard voices around the front of the house and then the door to the truck clanged shut. A few seconds later the front screendoor slammed." FRANK!" shouted Virginia. "Where the hell are you?"

"Out back doing laundry Ma!" Frank answered.

Virginia saw the clean dishes on the counter and headed for the back door, surprised to see clothes drying on the line. Frank was busy scrubbing a pair of britches on the washboard in the tub next to the old pump. "Well, well," retorted Virginia sarcastically. "Damn....would've guessed you to be a dog that wouldn't hunt, but you surprise me boy."

"What dog you talkin' 'bout Ma?"

Virginia just shook her head and walked back in the house and started talking to Wes about their new jobs at the dairy for the coming fall and winter. They also discussed the fact that they couldn't move to the bunkhouse at the dairy for a week and Frank would have to stay home alone while they worked. Frank liked the idea that he'd be left alone to fend for himself, however he knew better than to show his excitement. He was thrilled that if he was going to be on his own, they'd be none the wiser if he were to slip over to Bessy's house for a visit every now and again. In his mind he started making plans to play with his uncles as he rinsed out the wash under the hand pump. Then he suddenly realized that when they moved closer to the dairy he'd be too far from Bessy's house to ever see them. Struggling with a large pair of pants he wrung the water from them and dragged the old stepstool under the clothesline so he could reach it to hang the britches. He clipped the pants to the old galvanized wire with two weathered, wooden clothespins and as he turned to step down he found himself eye-to-eye with his mother. In one hand she held his Coke and in the other she held the rest of the dirty laundry, which she shoved at him. "No wonder you didn't get all the wash done while we were gone."

Holding up the pop, she demanded, "Where'd you get this pop? Did you steal it?"

Frank just froze unable to answer her.

"I asked where you got this! Did Uncle Mack come by?"

Frank just shook his head, 'no.'

Virginia grabbed him by the arm and yanked him from the stool making him tumble to the ground with the pile of dirty laundry. "I said, where did you get this?"

"I got it at the store."

"You expect me to believe you walked all the way to the store and had the money to pay for this soda pop?"

"Well....yes ma'am," Frank whispered meekly. "I had five pennies I'd saved that Uncle Mack gave me. But, I couldn't get it open to drink it."

Virginia propped the edge of the cap on the wooden pump stand and slammed her fist down on it sending the bottle cap flying. Like a small geyser, the hot, shaken sofa spewed out, leaving only half of the liquid. Frank was horrified to see his prized Coca-Cola pour all over the ground, but before he could say a word, Virginia chugged down half of what was left and shoved the bottle at him and walked away. At the door she turned and demanded over her shoulder, "Now get that damned wash done and hung up before the rain comes, you hear?"

Frustrated, Frank sipped the last remaining inch of soda from the bottle and threw it out into the field. Picking up the clothes from the dirt he started scrubbing the garments one-by-one on the washboard wondering what he'd done so wrong to deserve to be the son of someone so mean. Why couldn't she have just stayed wherever she was and then he would have been able to keep living with the woman he considered his real ma.

Virginia opened the door again and set a full jug of milk on the back steps. "Take this milk and put it in the creek before it spoils!"

Frank just looked down and nodded that he understood.

He walked over and picked up the jug, welcoming the opportunity to head down to the creek. Maybe he'd find Coleman there trying to catch fish with their net.

Frank's freedom to visit Bessy and his uncles only lasted a week before the family moved to the bunkhouse at the old dairy farm. In the meantime, Frank took full advantage of his free time by exploring the creek at the bottom of the farm with his cousin, Coleman.

One of their favorite things to do was to pretend to be the Dalton boys—Frank, of course, always playing the role of Frank Dalton, the U.S. Deputy Marshal, with Coleman and Earl posing as the bank robbers or whiskey runners or Indians. For guns they would tie several sticks together to make it look like a gun and they'd hide in the barn and pretend to have a shoot-out. Once in a while, they would change the outcome of Frank's encounter with the whiskey runners and he'd pretend to kill them instead of dramatically taking the fatal fall.

The boys loved playing down by the creek and they discovered that if they created a small dam by piling up rocks, they could easily catch brim. They would use a potato sack, which they would turn into a makeshift net, to catch the fish for Bessy to cook up for lunch in her cast-iron skillet. On their way down to the creek they would stop and pick the fat, purple grapes from the old grapevines along the broken-down fence and squeeze them into their mouths, then see who could spit the seeds the farthest. By the time they reached the creek their faces and hands would be covered in sticky grape juice and their shirts covered in purple stains. They would splash around in the water to clean themselves and to scare the brim to the little basin they'd built behind the damn.

Of course, the rat snakes in the trees near the creek gave Frank the willies, but he did his best to steer clear of the ones that liked to climb trees and sun themselves on the branches that hung over the stream. Before the week was over, Frank and Coleman had caught enough fish for lunch and dinner every day, and then some. Bessy made Frank's dinner early so he'd be back home before his Ma got home, being none the wiser of his day spent with this grandmother.

The first day Frank sat at Bessy's table for lunch without his shirt she saw the red marks remaining on Frank's back from Virginia's switching, not to mention the split lip as well as a numerous other bruises across his cheek and around his wrists. "Who did that to your back and face, boy?" Bessy asked before the other two boys slammed through the door from washing up at the pump.

Frank just looked down as if he'd done something wrong.

"It's not your fault if someone hit you, dear. Did my daughter do this to you?" she asked as she rubbed some butter on his back.

"Yes Ma....I mean....Grandma. Why is it you can't be my ma no more?" he asked and grabbed her around the waist, hugging her tightly and burying his face in her apron to hide his tears.

"It's just the way of the world, Franklin, my boy," she said rubbing his head. "I sure wish I could still be your ma."

Frank pulled away, wiping his eyes as Coleman and Earl ran into the kitchen.

"Sure smells good Ma!" shouted Colman excitedly as he plopped himself at the head of the table.

Bessy shook her head and took the frying pan full of fish off the stove and served up Frank the biggest piece in the pan before she served her own boys.

"How come Frank gets the biggest one?" Colman questioned sizing up the piece Bessy dropped on his plate.

"Just cause," she said. "You won't be seeing so much of Frank when they move to the dairy."

The boys just looked at Frank—their smiles falling from their faces. They were going to miss him, but not nearly as much as Frank would miss them.

The last day before Frank was to move with his mother and Wes to their new place at the dairy, he quickly finished his chores around the house and ran through the field, totally forgetting all about the snakes. He stopped and shimmied up the apple tree to pick as many apples as his shirt would hold and then ran to the backdoor of Bessy's house. Out of breath, he threw open the screen door and rolled the apples out of his shirt onto the kitchen table. Bessy was busy baking biscuits and thanked him for picking the fruit for her.

"Where's Earl and Coleman, Ma?"

"They're in the barn. I guess one of them feral cats had kittens last night."

That was all Frank needed to hear as he bolted out the front door and headed across the field to the old barn. He ran through the door, "Coleman, Earl....where are you?!" he shouted, out of breath.

Coleman looked over the railing three stories up in the hayloft "Get up here and look at this!"

Quickly Frank climbed the stairs to the second floor, then shimmied up the ladder to the hayloft. The two boys were bent over studying something nestled in the hay. Frank leaned over to see what they were looking at. There, burrowed in the hay were a bunch of tiny, grey, wiggly things with their eyes squeezed shut. "Ma said you was looking at a kindle of kittens."

"Naw we just tole Ma that. These are baby rats and you know they call 'em kittens. Maybe we can sell em. "

"Now....who'd buy a baby rat?" questioned Frank.

"I've heard people keep 'em as pets."

"No way....who'd keep a rat for a pet?"

"Come on let's try. Maybe Uncle Mack'll buy 'em from us. He's got lots of money and Ma says he's comin' by for a visit today."

"Oh boy, I need to talk to have a talk with Uncle Mack!" Frank said relieved.

With that, Coleman and Frank scooped up four each of the little rodents, stuffed them in their pants pockets and climbed down the ladder.

A few hours later Mack's Buick turned into the drive and Frank was already waiting for him at the top of the driveway. Mack pulled up next to him and rolled down the window. The cool air wafted from the car's air-conditioning and Frank closed his eyes feeling the relief from the heat on his face.

"What's up little man?" asked Mack.

"I gotta talk to you!" Frank spewed frantically.

Mack opened the door and pushed his seat back some. "Okay hop in and tell me what's so important. You wanna drive?" He nodded at his partner who stepped out of the passenger side and closed the door.

Frank's face beamed as he climbed into Mack's lap and took hold of the wheel. Mack closed the door and took his foot off the brake. "You got it?"

"Yeah! Look at me...I'm driving!" he cooed as they slowly coasted down the dirt drive with Frank on Mack's lap steering the car—doing about three miles an hour.

They rolled up in front of the house and Mack stepped on the brake and shifted the car into park.

"So now....tell me what's wrong."

"It's Ma. Not my grandma....my real ma." He pulled up his shirt and Mack saw the child's scared back.

Mack started fuming and set Frank on the seat next to him. "Guess she also did that." Mack rubbed Frank's split lip. "Don't you worry 'bout nothing. I'll have a talk with Virginia."

"But you can't let her know I was here. She'll beat me again."

"We'll just say I dropped by your house for a visit today. How about that?" Mack offered.

Frank nodded his head, relieved that his Uncle Mack was going to save him. "You gotta take me away....make her let me live here with my real ma."

Mack just looked at him sadly, "That I'm not sure I can do. But, I promise you that you won't get hit again."

When they got out of the car Coleman ran over to Mack with his handful of rats. "Uncle Mack do you want to buy some pet rats?"

Bessy shrieked, "Get rid of those vermin Mack!"

Mack pulled out two cents and held out an empty hand for Coleman to give him the rats. Then he deposited the two pennies in place of the rodents. He pretended to put them in his pocket and walked in the front door. When the boys weren't looking he opened the lit wood stove and dropped them into the fire.

He turned to Bessy, "Good thing the boys didn't see you do that," she said. "I've gotta talk to you about Virginia."

"No need I saw the boy's back. I'll take care of it." Mack just shook his head and went out the back door to wash his hands at the pump.

That afternoon, Mack took Frank to the general store and bought him a cold cola and a Moon Pie, totaling ten cents. This time Frank made sure to drink the Coke on the spot and he thought nothing ever tasted so good. Mack drove him back home and waited for Virginia to get there.

When she and Wes pulled up in the old pick-up Mack was sitting on the front porch step next to Frank, who wasn't wearing a shirt. Virginia climbed out of the truck,

"What're you doin' here Mack?"

"Come to see you, Virginia."

Virginia shouted at Frank, "You go on now boy....I'm sure there's something you should be doing other than sittn' around on your useless behind."

Frank jumped up and she swatted him on the back as he ran in the house. Mack stood and blocked her way.

"You and me need to have a talk, Virginia," Mack said sternly nodding to his partner who was standing by the Buick. He opened the door to the back seat for Mack and Virginia to get in. "Let's go for a little ride."

Virginia glanced nervously over at Wes who was standing by the driver's door of the truck talking to his brother.

Virginia looked concerned as Mack took her by the arm and escorted her to the back seat of his car. Wes just looked away and continued his conversation. Mack's partner walked around and got in the driver's side and started the car, then slowly drove out the driveway trying to not stir up the dust and dirty his car.

An hour later Virginia walked in the front door of the house and never even looked at Frank. She just went straight to work putting fresh cornbread on three plates and pouring three tall glasses of milk. That night dinner was as quiet as it'd ever been, but Frank got fresh cornbread with cracklings and two glasses of milk.

Later that night Virginia got the surprise of her life when she crawled into bed and found the four baby rats Frank had forgotten were still in his pocket. He smiled to himself as he heard her scream and rip the covers from the bed, rolling Wes onto the floor. She then went outside and launched the rodents as far out into the field as she could toss them. That night, Frank slept like a baby.

CHAPTER FOUR

The Language of the .45

August 1889

That night Frank dreamed about the chapter that Bessy had read to him from his Dalton book earlier that day....

"'In August, 1889, Bob Dalton narrowly missed death in attempting to arrest Charley Montgomery, a local gun rowdy who fancied himself as a bad man, at Timerberhills, Oklahoma. Previously accused of horse stealing and whisky running, he was now wanted on a warrant for robbery of Jake Bartle's store. Bob had Al Landers with him as posseman. After an all-day search they had discovered Montgomery standing in front of Lon Brown's cabin. Bob and Landers were prudent. Montgomery had plenty of nerve. As the officers crawled toward him he whirled and fired at Landers, then ran around the cabin. Bob, coming around the other way, ran into him pell-mell. Simultaneously and almost point-blank the two fired. Montgomery fell dead, Bob was unscathed, but the belch of the outlaw's gunpowder burned his face. Narrow escapes like this were just the breaks of luck.

In those days a deputy was required, at his own expense, to bury any man he was forced to kill, provided the victim had no known relatives. Montgomery's funeral cost Bob eighty dollars. It paid to take a man alive, if possible. A deputy also had to bring his man in—arrest and transport him safely to court, or serve the papers in lesser cases—or he got no fees or mileage allowance. The Indian Territory officer nearly always got his man, although he didn't make a corps' boast of it as did the Northwest Mounted or the Texas Rangers.

In April, 1890, Deputy Marshall Cox was shot and badly wounded by Alex Cochran, one eighth Cherokee Indian, at Claremore. Cochran was considered a good man when sober but very dangerous when drinking. He had escaped. Bob, Grat, and I had been assigned to the pursuit. On the streets of Claremore we met one of the leading merchants.

"Looking for Alex, I suppose?" he greeted.

"Yes," said Bob, "and if he'll come in and surrender I'll not even look him up."

"No chance of Alex surrendering," declared the merchant, "until he finds out how Deputy Cox comes out. That 'breed is on the warpath."

A number of town idlers had gathered. With ill-concealed antagonism they began making insinuations as to what Cochran would do to any officers trying to take him. Emboldened by these satellites, the merchant grinned derisively.

"If you want Alex so bad, Bob why don't you take out after him? He was in my store a few minutes ago buying a box of cartridges. And there," indicating a distant horseman, "he goes riding down the road. Riding kinda slow, too, if you'll notice."

"You sure that's him?" asked Bob.

"Sure—don't I know his old roan mare?"

Commandeering a horse from a hitch rack, Bob swung up, told Grat and me to get mounts and follow, and charged off after the disappearing rider. Racing up to within a hundred yards of the fugitive, Bob yelled to him to halt. Instead the man spurred into a run. Bob dismounted and fired. The Indian wheeled and put on more speed. Twice more Bob pumped his rifle. Horse and rider fell. By this time Grat and I had come up. We found the man badly wounded; the last shot had taken him at two hundred yards. But it was not Alex Cochran. It was Alex's son, an innocent victim of the merchant's ghastly notion of a practical joke on the Marshalls. The townsmen may not have anticipated actual bloodshed—may have figured only on sending us on a wild-goose chase—but they had wanted a laugh at the officers' expense.

This unfortunate occurrence first served to impress upon me the widespread hostility, sometimes open and sometimes dissembled, through which an officer of the law must move in pursuit of his duty. Here, as in all places, there was a large class of citizens who hated the type of citizen who is first to yelp for legal help when his own feet are trodden on. This hatred or contempt is a galling discovery to the young officer. It rasps his pride of craft. It serves to lower his cool, dispassionate devotion to duty to the level of personal grudge. It puts a chip on his shoulder, and is the secret cause of much bullying and violence in the name of the law. The seasoned officer learns to ignore public animosity, more or less—men like my brother, Frank, whose tolerant and broad humanity could disregard this yapping at their heels.'"

"'Most of the scores of deputies with whom I came in contact merited and preserved general respect, officers who dies like men when the time came. But there were not a few whom even their fellow officers detested, men whose passing caused no lament.

Indian outlaws, as a rule, were hard to take. Fort Smith, with its graveyard of desperadoes, inspired them with such terror that most of them, even if wanted for comparatively small offenses, preferred to shoot it out rather than go to trial. Hanging, furthermore, was for the red man a disgrace which followed him beyond the grave. If an Indian had committed a capital crime you were almost certain to have to talk to him with bullets.

Bill Pidgeon, a full-blood Cherokee, previously of good repute, was charged with the murder of a Negro who had stolen his hogs. Pidgeon took to the Flint hills, a trackless wild, sending back the warning that he would not be captured alive. And so feared was he even by his own tribesmen that none dared to tip off his lair. Occasionally, however, after the first hunt had died away, Pidgeon would come down to his cabin. Here it was thought he might some time be caught off guard and arrested.

The crime was two years old when Jim Richardson, former Texas Ranger and tough officer, joined the territorial Marshalls. Richardson was sure he could get Pidgeon, and was given the old warrant. My brother Frank went with him. Rich-

ardson, boastful but fearless, had twisted the service about its failure to nab the full-blood.

As it happened, Pidgeon was in his cabin when Frank and Richardson crept up to it. They took him before he could lay hands on his Winchester. Richardson chuckled complacently.

"This," he boasted, "is one of the easiest arrests I ever made. You fellers musta been playin' hide and seek with this Injun."

One evening in camp where Pidgeon had been herded with other prisoners of a general roundup, the Texan swaggered up and down before the Cherokee, plying him with studied taunt and insult. He treated the captive with unnecessary roughness.

"You'll make mighty fine crowbait, a-dangling at the end of a rope in Fort Smith," he laughed callously at the killer.

"You fellers don't know how to treat Injuns," he snorted when Frank tried to interpose. "I cut my eyeteeth down along the Rio Grande. You got to handle redskins like we handled bad greaser!"

Richardson was washing his feet in a pan near one of the wagons when Pidgeon made a desperate break and got away, in the face of a full fusillade from the officers. Again the Texan and Frank took the trail. And once more they found Pidgeon at his cabin in the brush. The deputies were riding abreast at a gallop as they came up. Frank noticed the cabin door slightly ajar.

"Look out, Jim!" Frank shouted, and on the instant whirled his horse aside. Richardson jerked his horse up sharp. As it reared Pidgeon's first shot caught the animal squarely between the eyes, just where the deputy's head had been a second before. The horse, falling, pinned Richardson down for a moment. He managed to disengage himself and tried to use the horse as a breastwork. But the animal's threshing death throes exposed him. Before Frank could get into action the Indian's second bullet killed Richardson. Frank and Pidgeon exchanged a number of shots. Realizing that he could not take *the Cherokee alone, Frank finally retired for help. Once more the full-blood retreated far back into the vastness of the Flint Hills. He was never again caught. But after a time he sent word down to the officers.*

"Me have big show kill Frank Dalton time we fight," ran his message. "Me no shoot 'um. He good to me. Other feller I kill. He bad man. Maybe so now crows eat him."

There was a crude but inviolable standard by which the conduct of the man hunter was judged. A Marshall might be admirable, honest, faithful, and brave, but he must not offend the personal dignity of even the meanest and lowest of his captives if he wished to retain good repute and put some slight value upon his own life. "

Bob Dalton now organized the Indian Police for the Osage Nation, and appointed me his posse man. This Osage corps, numbering eighteen to twenty splendid and seasoned men, all mounted and with Bob at their head, patrolled the north central region of the Territory. I could now count myself a seasoned line rider of the law.

The first rift which split one segment of the Daltons from law enforcement to law defiance was near at hand. It was not a sharp cleavage, but rather a gradual defection. In the Osage Nation Bob and I were in the jurisdiction of the Wichita, Kansas, federal district. Pay for Bob's official duties began to be deferred. The United States Marshall proffered many excuses why these dues were not forthcoming; the government had not made the appropriation; the money would be along soon, and so on. In fairness to the Marshall it must be said that he was only a symptom of conditions then existing. Indeed, he himself was often the victim of governmental clumsiness in handling territorial law enforcement. The red tape was particularly complex and aggravating. It alienated many good men from the service. Devices intended to check possible graft in fees and mileage not infrequently played hob with honest officer.

The amount finally coming to Bob ran up to hundreds of dollars, a considerable amount for those days. Protests and pleas and polite demands were of no avail. Worried at first,

Bob finally became bitterly disgruntled. That unpaid sum represented hard, dangerous work. Turning over his account for collection to a good friend at Pawhuka, Bob resigned his commission. The money was never collected. It was a debt for which, among other things, Bob Dalton eventually took compound interest in vengeful retaliation.

At about the same time Grat Dalton also became disgruntled with his work as deputy out of Fort Smith. He, too, resigned.

Thus the three of us, Bob, Grat, and I, said farewell to official arms, at a time when the entire Western country was passing through a singular pandemic of lawlessness. It was not alone in the law enforcement agencies that laxity and inefficiency were evident. The fiber of the whole country was growing temporarily flabby. It was a time of national and moral ebb. Graft was rampant everywhere—Graft, that fifth dark horse which the Apocalypse might have mentioned, and which rides 'drag' for a generation on every great war. There was widespread corruption in business and government. Predatory rings multiplied. Legislatures abetted notorious pillage. A time when men were inclined to take back their delegated powers, turning again to the personal force of wit or gun. It was an outstanding example of how easily crime can become democratic, and it is being repeated in the present 'racketeer' era.

In the East the period produced a Boss Tweed, and all his breed of emulators, big and little. In the West it incubated a large nest of outlaws. On the one side railways, banks, and great corporations, many of which were lawlessly maneuvering for privileged booty; on the other side train and bank robbers who lobbies with six-shooters. Here in the Indian Territory the infection was rife. It required a sturdy moral nature to stand up against the insinuating temptations of the unscrupulous 'eighties, hereabouts.

It was at this juncture that Bob suggested the westward swing through New Mexico which gave us our baptism in out-

lawry, as I related at the beginning of my story.'"

Frank woke from his revelry of the wild west that morning to Virginia screaming to get up and pack up his things. His rerun of the Dalton story had left him still wanting to become a lawman when he grew up—no matter the danger and the pitfalls experienced by his relations, the Dalton brothers. Knowing that he would be leaving the next day, Bessy had packed his beloved book, *When the Daltons Rode* in with the last of his things still in her keeping. Frank still was unable to read, but he now had a reason to learn. He had made certain to hide the book well amongst his bedding so as not to be discovered by Virginia, who would surely destroy the precious book.

CHAPTER FIVE

Attempting an Education

August 1941 – The Dairy, 6-Mile Mountain, & Mill Hill House

Frank rode in the back of the old Ford pickup atop the comforters, from his bed, which were strewn across the old mattress and chesterfield. The warm wind whipped his untrimmed hair into his eyes as he squinted in the midday sun. As the truck rolled down the two-lane road, passing a number of run-down houses and derelict farms, they traveled far enough for Frank to know he wouldn't be walking to visit Bessy and his uncles anytime soon. Finally, the truck turned into a rutted dirt drive, nearly bouncing Frank off the back as it passed the owner's two-story, white farmhouse, the dairy barns and rows of cow pens, that reeked of manure. The old truck bumped to a stop in front of a bunkhouse that had seen far better days. Frank stood and looked around, trying to get used to the stench of the methane infested air. Off in a pen opposite the bunkhouse, a bull mounted a heifer doing his duty to happily inseminate the cow that would soon become one of the cogs in the wheel at the dairy farm, once she gave birth and her milk came in. Frank stared at the copulating animals with awe since he'd never even seen a cow up close before and certainly not a bull.

Wes opened the tailgate as Frank climbed down from the truck. "Got me some of that wooly booger last night whilst you was'a sleepin," Wes said with a vile grin on his face, laughing at Frank, whose eyes were still trained on the bull getting his wooly booger. Frank knew what the colloquialism meant since his uncle Ralph had explained the birds and the bees to the boys when they saw two dogs going at it one day while walking back from the store. The concept of Wes getting wooly booger confounded Frank who found it hard to imagine Wes with one of those heifers.

Uneasy with Wes' sudden need to discuss the cows having what Ralph had called sex, Frank wandered over to the fence where several black and white Holsteins were grazing. In the opposite field grazed brown and white Guernsey cows. Frank was fascinated by their size and docile behavior, almost like a great big dog, he thought. He lazed along the fence-line touching the soft noses of the beasts that seemed to be equally interested in him. Overhead a bi-plane was making a turn from writing its message which read "Pepsi" against a robin's egg-blue sky, as it flew back towards town.

"What do you think you're doing?" shouted Virginia as she carried a satchel into the bunkhouse. "Go help Wes unload the truck, boy!"

Frank gave one of the cows a quick pat on the head and ran to the back of the truck where Wes was unloading their belongings. Wes tossed the pile of heavy comforters down to Frank, nearly knocking him off his feet. Frank managed to steady himself and carried the heavy bedding into the building dragging part on the ground. Inside, he looked around at the stark, three-room military-style structure, which had nothing more than three cots, a wood stove, and an old wooden table with three chairs. At least he would be able to sit at the table to eat for a change, thought Frank, but then realized it would only put him in close enough range to his ma that she could box his ears more easily. "I'll ring your ears if you don't get back out there!" Virginia pushed past him, almost knocking him down and headed back to the truck as Frank dropped the bedding on one of the cots. Once again as was typical in the south, the structure had no electricity, nor indoor plumbing. It didn't take long for the three to move in their meager belongings and Virginia announced to Frank that she and Wes had to start work right away and she expected him to have the entire bunkhouse clean when they finished work at six. And that included scrubbing all of the floors. It seemed that Virginia had found in Frank exactly what she was looking for—a slave.

Relieved that he had the day to himself Frank grabbed an old, worn broom and started to sweep the filthy room. He opened the cupboard next to the kitchen counter and found several dead mice and a rat, as well as numerous living and deceased spiders, roaches, and ants throughout the room. Frank picked up the carcasses of the rodents and set them on the end of the broom and took them outside and slung them out into the field as hard as he could throw them. He already missed Coleman and Earl and did his best to focus on the job at hand, rather than daydream about playing down by the creek, or up in the hayloft.

At the dairy, Virginia had been assigned the job of milking cows, while Wes did the only job he was skilled enough to do—shovel cow shit from the stalls and pens. The dairy industry had matured enough at the time to employ surge milking machines, which added a tug-and-pull motion to the vacuum of previous contraptions, making milking much faster and more sanitary. Virginia was given the job to hang the strap around the cow and connecting the milkers to the cow's teats. Once started, the milk would flow through the short hose into the galvanized container below the cow. Although the hoses disconnected themselves when milking was finished, it was also her job to cap the canister and move it from under the cow to the cart that Wes would later push to the truck, once the cart was full. She then unstrapped the machine from the cow and another hand would take the cow back out to pasture and a second round of cows would be brought in to start the process all over again, until all breeding cows had been milked. This process happened twice a day, so the days at the dairy were long.

For a cow to provide milk they would be inseminated by their bull and then stayed pregnant approximately two hundred and seventy-five days of the year. Three months after giving birth, they would be bred once again, so they would continually produce milk. The calves were separated from their mothers very early and taught to eat from feeders, which was also part of Virginia's job description—teach the calves to nurse the feeder as opposed to nursing mother's udder. Virginia didn't mind working with the animals, yet she hated the dairy owner and constantly exchanged bitter and often vulgar words with him. It seemed she possessed little control over her outbursts of foul language, or her hair-trigger temper. The only reason, the owner, Mr. Kelly, put up with her scowling attitude was the fact that she seemed to manage the livestock easily and didn't have too many issues when it came to handling them. In fact, if they kicked her she would simply kick them back when the boss wasn't looking, or hit them with a switch she kept handy to keep both the cows and Frank inline.

It seemed that the day that Mack took Virginia for that ride to talk to her, they had gone to Bessy's house so that she might bear witness when Mack forced Virginia to promise never to lay a hand on the boy again. Mack minced no words in convincing her that he would make certain that the cops on his payroll would see to it that she would 'break parole' should she use physical force against the boy in the future and she'd be thrown back into jail to finish her ten year sentence. It was at the end of that visit when Virginia went out to wait for Mack by the car, that Coleman had convinced her to place Frank in second grade, rather than first, so that they would be in the same class together and he could look out for him. Of course, her selfish thought was that it would mean that he would finish school that much sooner and she could put him to work at a paying job, so he could contribute to the household.

So, when the day came for Frank to start school, Virginia walked the long dirt road with him to sign him up for class. When she got to the principal's office she not only lied to the vice principal about his age and birth year, but she signed him in, as she had threatened, as Frank Holliday instead of his real name, Frank Dalton. She also told them they had moved there from out of state so there would be no record of him having attended first grade and that he should be put in second grade. Frank was thrilled to find his uncle Coleman in his classroom, when he was escorted into the room by the vice principal and introduced to the class as Frank Holliday. Colman rode the bus to school, so Frank would wait in front every morning for his bus to arrive. Coleman was confused by Frank's new name and it took several days for even Frank to realize who the teacher was talking about each time she called on 'Frank Holliday.'

Frank and Coleman sat at the back of the class so they could share notes, since pretty much everything the teacher talked about from numbers to letters, to reading was totally foreign to Frank and he felt lost in class. He was unable to keep up with the work the teacher was assigning and every time he was called on he started to panic, finding it hard to speak or answer Miss Green. After all, he didn't know his ABCs yet and couldn't even write his name, not to mention his confusion as to which name to write. It only took two days for Miss Green to separate the two boys since it was obvious that Frank was copying everything that Coleman did.

That first week of class, Frank received three detentions for not doing his homework and was forced to stay in during recess to do the work. The problem was, he still had no idea how to answer the required questions since he didn't know how to read, or even how to count past five pennies.

He looked forward to recess and was very upset whenever he was called to stay in the classroom, while the other boys and girls were outside climbing trees, kicking a can around the yard, or throwing a dodge-ball at the other students. It was very stressful for Frank. Not only was he scholastically challenged, he was quite a bit smaller than the other boys and the girls due to the fact that he was actually a year younger and they teased him about that.

After two weeks of slipping further and further behind the other students, the teacher finally called on the principal, Mr. Cook, to come to the classroom and observe Frank's performance with the assigned work. Frank was put on the spot and embarrassed in front of the other students when Miss Green singled him out and asked him a barrage of questions about reading and arithmetic. It was painfully obvious to everyone that the boy had never attended school before. So, they made the decision to send a note to Frank's mother, which read, "It's as if Frank has never been to school before so we will be moving him back to first grade. He has zero reading and writing skills and it appears to be taking an emotional toll on him as well as distracting the other students."

When Frank handed the sealed envelope to his mother he was scared to death about what it said. What he didn't know, however, was that neither his mother, nor Wes, could read either. Embarrassed, that she couldn't read it, Virginia was forced to take the letter to her boss to have him read it to her. When she returned to the bunkhouse with the letter in hand she was boiling mad. "How dare you embarrass me like this!" she said seething. "I should've known you were too stupid to even make it through two weeks of second grade!" She drew her arm back to slap him upside the head, then caught herself, remembering Mack's warning. "I thought your grandma read books with you?"

"She did….but she didn't teach me how to do it," Frank cowered, expecting to be beaten within an inch of his life.

"All she did was put fool ideas in your head," she accused angrily. "Even I could've done a better job raising you," Virginia said in a huff and went outside where Wes sat smoking a cigarette on the porch. She snatched the lit, filter-less Camel out of his hand and took a long drag of the smoldering tobacco. Wes just looked at her puzzled since he knew that she never smoked. She him gave him no explanation as she strutted down the dirt driveway, puffing away, as the sun dropped rapidly behind the horizon. Even the cigarette, she thought, didn't mask the stench of manure, which permeated the air. She felt she couldn't get the nasty smell out of her nostrils, since even in bed, Wes stunk of cow shit seeing that he shoveled it all day and only washed his clothes and himself once a week.

Virginia cared little about anyone's discomfort other than her own She bitched incessantly about all the wrongs done to her by life and all those who conspired against her. She existed in a world of her own that some would assess as a narcissist—a self-centered person who felt that kindness was a display of weakness and a lack of control. The one person she ruthlessly refused to show any frailty of human kindness to was of course Frank. She complained constantly to him about the burden of ever having conceived him as her son in the first place. What Frank would never know or understand was that the cause Virginia's lack of compassion was her own abusive childhood— perpetrated by her ill-tempered father. Christopher never liked his oldest daughter and she struggled most of her life, seeking his approval. When he was tragically murdered, she felt cheated that she'd been robbed of the chance to win his approval, even though she hadn't managed to accomplish that over the two previous decades as his daughter.

At eighteen, Virginia had been a poor, somewhat disreputable young woman who saw the handsome, young Dalton boy, James Lewis Dalton, as a fine catch, as well as a

good potential provider and she had set out to marry him.
After all, his father and all of the Dalton sons ran a successful trucking company and a filling station. So, Virginia had
set her sights on him early on. Virginia was a somewhat attractive and shapely woman and she knew how to use her
feminine charms with men to her advantage to get what
she wanted. She wasted no time in quickly getting pregnant immediately after the wedding, which took place on
the twenty-second of September 1934. Frank had been
born just ten months later, but by then James Dalton had
already left their nuptial bed. The two had fought like cats
and dogs and often had to have one of James' nieces sleep
between them to keep them from killing each other. It
didn't take James long to realize that Virginia would prove
to be his biggest mistake. Before Frank was even born he
had moved away wanting nothing to do with her and her ill
temper, or his son, whom he would never meet.

Thanks to the roosters on the farm, Frank would be
awakened well before dawn and have a checklist of chores
to do around the dairy before he could walk to school.
Breakfast would be nothing more than milk and Virginia
never packed him a lunch for school. So, on his way there
he would pick an apple or two if they were in season. Most
days, Coleman would bring him a biscuit from Bessy, with
jelly or peanut butter, but for the most part, Frank always
went hungry and was bordering on being malnourished.

The moment he arrived home, he was expected to do
his chores at the house, as well as more miscellaneous jobs
around the dairy until it closed at sunset. Virginia would be
the one to receive his salary and Frank would never see a
penny of his compensation. She would put Frank to work
helping Wes carry and clean buckets used to wash the
cows, because the cows had to be cleaned before each
milking. Then he had to feed the cows ground corn stalks

called fodder, which was mixed with molasses and put into the silo. For every bushel of corn feed to the cows, about eighteen stems could be used to supplement the cow's fodder—preventing anything from going to waste. When full, milk canisters were too heavy for Frank to carry from the milk carts to the truck that would take the milk to be pasteurized. So, Wes struggled and complained about having to lug them, even more than about mucking dung.

Once the milk was taken to the processing plant, it would be heated and pasteurized in order to kill the bacteria. Then the milk could be bottled and delivered daily to people's doors.

On Fridays when the dairy made chocolate milk, Frank was allowed to drink a large glass of the sweet, creamy treat, so he often skipped school that day to be sure he wouldn't miss this special treat. Milk was about the only real nutrition he received since he rarely got fed much for dinner seeing how Virginia refused to cook anything but fried cornpone bread, which she mixed together in one large cast-iron pan before frying. With his lack of nutrition and constant work schedule, Frank became extremely lean, although strong. With Frank's vast list of jobs everyday, it seemed there was never time for him to do homework, which set him back even further with school.

In Europe, a Second World War had begun in September 1939. Few Americans paid much attention due to the fact that the country was still recovering from the worst financial crash in history. However, on December seventh, 1941 Japanese bombers attacked the United States military base at Pearl Harbor, Hawaii. The next day Congress met with President Franklin D. Roosevelt and on December eleventh, America entered the war after Germany declared war on America. It was a long tough winter as the war in

Europe and the Pacific raged on. Most young men in the country were either drafted or joined to go and defend their country's democracy, including Frank's older uncles Ralph, Eliga, and Hank. The oldest, Austin, managed to avoid the draft by claiming that he was Bessy's only provider even though he rarely bothered to even visit her, let alone provide her with financial support. Times were tough in the south and the family was on the brink of starving when Mack stepped in and brought them some much needed provisions. By the end of January 1942 food was being rationed as well as gas at only two gallons per month. The government pushed those who had land to grow crops and can foods, but it was still the dead of winter and supplies began to grow frighteningly lean.

One overcast day that winter, as Frank was walking to school, the clouds were starting to clear only to reveal what appeared to be a giant cigar-shaped rocket floating in the sky. Not knowing about the Navy's 'Lighter Than Air" dirigible squadron, he panicked and ran all of the way to school. When he arrived out of breath to meet Coleman, there was a crowd of children in the front yard looking up at the monstrosity. There was a terrible buzz in the schoolyard about the unknown airship being a secret Nazi weapon. It wasn't until the principal came out and announced that this amazing wonder was called a dirigible airship that the children calmed down. He explained how it was held in the air by means of helium—a gas lighter than air and thus it enabled the giant blimp to actually float in the sky—as a balloon might at the state fair. He explained that since the dirigibles were so quiet, the Navy used them to protect convoys of ships by carrying depth charges to secretly drop on the enemy's ships. The children were in awe and Frank and Coleman were amazed that such a large ship could actually float on the clouds. This incredible vision had set Coleman's mind to dreaming about the possibility of becoming a fighter pilot one day.

As winter set in, Frank noticed that Virginia was getting fatter by the day. She had a big, round belly and he wondered where she was getting fed, since she certainly wasn't sharing any food with him. What he didn't understand was that her burgeoning belly was the result of Wes' wooly booger and it was soon to result in a little half-sister named Carolyn—born nine months after their move to the dairy. The long hot days of summer were upon them and school had let out for the next several months. Frank had somehow managed to make it through first grade but still was unable to read About the only thing he could write at that point was his first name. He was frustrated that Virginia had changed his name since he knew how to write Dalton, but he still struggled with his new surname, Holliday. The school year had taken its toll on him and he felt stupid—as if he were the dumbest kid in the classroom. He often had a hard time comprehending the work the teacher was presenting and the letters and words just didn't look like what she was describing and it confused him terribly. Dyslexia was an undiagnosed learning disorder at that time and he couldn't understand why the letters or numbers looked backwards to him. He also struggled to hear in class since Virginia's habit of 'boxing his ears' was seriously taking its toll on his hearing. That, plus his deficiency in reading and comprehending the teacher's lectures, made him that much more apt to lose interest and he found it hard to keep his attention focused on the classroom. Somehow, they managed to pass him from first grade to second, but all in all, Frank just hoped that second grade would never come and that he wouldn't be forced to return to school at the end of the summer.

With her rapidly mushrooming belly, Virginia's temper was also growing exponentially both at work and at home. One unusually warm day in late May, Virginia was struggling with the heat, as well her huge belly, when the owner gave her an order to stop whipping one of the cows which was acting up. Instead of refraining from her bovine abuse, she turned her switch on the owner. Needless to say, the Holliday family was quickly instructed to pack its belongings and look for new employment, as well as a new place to live. In the process of attacking the owner, Virginia had gotten so agitated her water broke and Wes had to help her back to the bunkhouse before she dropped the baby in the dirt. Wes drove Virginia to Dr. Pepper's farm to give birth—the only birthing doctor in the county. That was the day her precious little girl, Carolyn Holliday, was born.

The owner of the dairy took pity on Frank, who didn't understand anything that was happening, and drove him to Bessy's house. He stayed there for several weeks to play with Coleman and Earl during 'summer break.' Oblivious to the fact he was about to become a half-brother, and an even lower-caste family member in the Holliday household, Frank was in heaven. It was several weeks of a carefree life with his real family and he was thrilled to explore the farm with his uncles and listen to Bessy read his beloved Dalton story. He still wasn't able to read more than a few words of it himself but luckily he Coleman and Earl had traded comic books amongst themselves and they ended up with a collection of popular western comics: Hoot Gibson, Red Ryder, Lone Ranger, and Lash Larue These colorful stories quickly became Frank's classroom of choice and Colman and Bessy became Frank's tutors that summer, helping him to learn to read the exciting graphic novels of the wild wild west, as well as Frank's beloved Dalton.

CHAPTER SIX

The Honeymoon Holdup – The Daltons Turn Outlaw

1889 – A Real Life Outlaw

Bessy sat down with her snuff next to the lantern on her back porch as the boys gathered around excited to listen. They still chattered about the make-believe gunfight they'd had that day.

"Okay boys, let's settle down if you want me to read the Honeymoon Holdup to you," Bessy said sternly loving every minute of their excitement. As the boys got situated in their seats she started...."

"'*There is a strong tendency to do the thing of which one is accused, psychologists insist; the suggestive picture consummating in the act. Undoubtedly something like this was operating in our minds. Who first suggested the Whorton train robbery in the Neutral Strip I do not now recall. But after weeks of dodging and nerve-trying suspense on the borderland between right and wrong we were discussing the thing as a definite plan. For this project Bob had taken George Newcomb and Charley Bryant into his confidence. Both had been with us in New Mexico. They were crack shots and good riders, of a devil-may-care strain. Bryant was suffering from a ravaging disease. It made him doubly reckless...* '"

"You mean they are really going to turn bad?!" Earl exclaimed.

"Yeah, they're going to turn bad because they got blamed for that train holdup in California that they didn't do when the Southern Pacific got robbed! Don't you remember? They just assumed cause Bob and Grat was in

California visiting their brother Bill that it had to be them,"
insisted Frank.

Good memory Frank....shows you pay attention when
you're interested," noted Bessy nodding her head.

"Okay now you boys just hold your horses and you'll see
what happened," insisted Bessy.

Finally the boys settled back into their chairs to listen.

*"'Me, I want to get killed—in on hell-firin' minute of smok-
ing action!" Charley Bryant had said it was we lay in the Salt
Creek ambush with guns trained on the Smith posse. It had
been all Bob could do to restrain him. He had a tiger courage
and a recklessness which had to be curbed even among reckless men; a sort of mocking contempt for life, his own most of
all. This was due no doubt in part to the sickness which whispered in his veins. Charley was to get his moment of smoking
action in due time and to meet it with the verve of a true des-
perado.*

*In the Whorton affair Eugenia Moore, Bob's girl became a
particeps criminal to our activities. Through her knowledge of
telegraphy and one of the local express officers who was related to her she learned that the express company expected a
large shipment of money for one of the Guthrie banks on the
date we had set for the Whorton robbery. Riding a horse
which Bob had given her, she raced to our rendezvous, gave us
explicit information, and returned immediately to the cover of
our friend's house near Guthrie.*

*You will question what manner of woman it was who thus
actually associated herself with our lawless project. How shall
we catalogue any man or woman exactly by our shifting and
expedient standards? Affection, fortunately for some of us,
hasn't much to do with rigid morals. The love which women
bear their men, sons, husbands, or sweethearts, usually trans-
cends infirmities and transgressions, else the lot of the black
sheep would be woeful indeed. I have already indicated that
Eugenia was no tame, spineless creature of soft conventions,
and that the bond between her and Bob had become fixed be-*

fore we stepped over the line. Now she was irrevocably partisan. "Whither thou goest, I go." She was of a kind that leaped without much speculation as to the landing spot.

In this our first train robbery, and in later depredations as well, a surcharged bitterness against express companies was the propelling motive. A blind striking back, if you will, at all corporate interests in any way related to the one that had saddled us with undeserved trouble. Grat was still awaiting trial in California. From report he seemed almost certain of conviction. Bob burned with wrath at the price on his own head. Whorton would be no mere wanton crime. In our disordered minds it had some elements of retributive justice—that "eye for an eye" which has been the frontier code across all the earth. And this feeling, untenable as it may seem to cool consideration, Eugenia shared.

If we made a big haul we would retire far from our old haunts, to South America, perhaps, where we had vaguely contemplated cattle ranching. Bob and his girl had spoken of marriage. Part of the anticipated haul would underwrite the wedding. Whorton, in its conception, was to be a honeymoon holdup. The uppermost thought in the mind of every half-sane outlaw is that some day he will make a big haul and retire to the land of "The Big Rock Candy Mountains."

If, on the other had. Bob was to be backed into a desperate corner, Eugenia would back into it with him. That was the kind of woman she was.... "Out right or wrong." .... Eugenia had merely substituted "my man" for "our country" in paraphrasing that lauded ethic.

On the way to Whorton we initiated a practice we were to follow with slight variation before every subsequent raid or perilous undertaking—an invocation to the gods of chance.

"I for one, will go to the station and force the engineer to run the train down to the stockyard beyond the town," announced Bob. "One of you three will come with me. You can match dollars to see who it will be. Odd man is elected." Newcomb was the odd man.

At about 10 P.M. that night Bob, Bryant, Newcomb, and I rode into Whorton, a little Santa Fe whistle station in the Neutral Strip. We hitched our horses beside the stockyard, half a mile south of town. Bryant and I took our stations beside the track. Bob and Newcomb meandered toward the depot and waited in the shadows. The Texas Express would come thundering in at ten-thirty to make a brief stop. Most of the passengers would be asleep. They were not to be bothered. At no time during their career did the Daltons rob or molest passengers. Sleep had already descended upon the lonely little hamlet. Only the station agent and a few depot loungers were in evidence. One of them was curiously examining a reward poster in the waiting room.

"Feller'd make himself a right smart o' spendin' money if he was to turn in Bob Dalton's gang," he reckoned as his gaze clung to the inciting black type.

"Ain't likely we'll ever get a crack at 'em," laconically replied the station agent. "they wouldn't be over in these parts." He buckled on a revolver and went out to hoist the red stop signal as a whistle roared inquiringly down the northward track. Orders in his hand, the agent went out to meet the express. The loungers followed. They did not observe two men vaulting into the engine cab as the train started rolling toward the stockyards. Bob and Newcomb were commanding the engineer to stop at the designated spot.

"That's queer," said the station agent a minute later. "Train's stopping down by the stockyards. Found a hotbox, maybe." Well, that was none of his business.

"Be funny if the Daltons was jumpin' that train right now," suggested the loquacious lounger.

"Sure would," replied the agent. "She always carries a load o' money." Hearing several shots down the track, the two rushed into the depot and extinguished all the lights.

Bob and Newcomb were at the moment marching the engineer and fireman around the express car. Bryant and I joined them. While he kept the engine crew covered, Bob leaped into the express car and commanded the surprised messenger to shell out. Curious heads popped out of the coach windows and popped in again at the menace of our guns. A man with a big white sombrero and a gun belt shining across his waist stepped out on the smoker platform. I spotted him for an officer. I yelled at him to get his hands up quick and come down where I was. He came down with hands aloft and remained so during the proceedings. Later information led me to believe this man was Ransom Payne, United States Deputy Marshall, who was returning home to Guthrie from the federal court at Wichita, Kansas, where he and a posse man had delivered Territorial prisoners. But I must have been mistaken. Payne himself has been quoted as having retired to a sleeper berth at the time the train reached Whorton. There he heard our intimidating shots and at once concluded it was a holdup by the Daltons, according to his report. Whereupon he ran to the rear sleeper platform, leaped off, and hid in the bushes, "to keep the Daltons from pumping my carcass full of lead." At any rate, he did not get into action.

Meantime Bob was having trouble getting the messenger to open the big through safe. He professed not to know the combination. Word had been circulated by the express company that these through money vaults were always closed and set at Gainesville, Texas, and at Kansas City, and the combination wired to the terminus, so that not even the messenger could open them en route. The same report had been broadcast regarding all trains going through the Indian Territory. It was designated to reach the ears of outlaws and to give messengers greater immunity. Through her access to official circles Miss Moore had learned, however, that this was merely a ruse. And when the obdurate messenger pleaded it as an excuse, Bob in final exasperation fired a stimulating shot close to his feet. The messenger opened the safe with alacrity. Together with the contents from the smaller way safe, he dumped the Guthrie shipment into a sack Bob carried. Simultaneously Newcomb and Bryant had sounded a volley of shots outside, again to warn back the restive train crew and the more inquis-

itive passengers. No resistance had been offered, and no one was injured. The haul amounted to approximately fourteen thousand dollars. Backing away into the shadows as the train got underway we slapped the heavy loot sack on a saddle and drifted. The man in the white sombrero had disappeared into the smoker. Not a shot spurred us on our way.

Regarding the amount of our plunder at Wharton and in later holdups, the newspapers always exaggerated the sum, and the express officials minimized it.

In retiring we cantered within a few yards of where Marshall Payne lay in the shrubbery, according to his version. He had his Colt in hand but did not fire, he said, "for fear that if I winged one, the others would return to kill me." The train he asserted, hauled away without him. Soon the station agent was chattering a wild tale along the wires. The man who scanned the reward poster stood by in shaken awe. Riding west until daylight next morning, we came to a brushy creek where we alternately slept while one of us was hidden back on the trail to act as lookout.

Now we were indeed outlaws. Whorton merely served to confirm the convictions of those who had ascribed the California train robbery to Bob and his associates. The hue and cry for Dalton scalps yelped across the land. Posses, genuine or self-styled sleuths, all the man-hunting ilk, sniffed for our trial. Reward posters blossomed more profusely in public places.

Casting back to recapture the emotions of that time, I cannot say that Bob and I were beset by any disturbing sense of guilt. The bitterness of our "cause" stifled any compunctions. We had rather a feeling of defiant exultation. We had hit back with an insensate revenge. The blood-money brand rested more comfortably on Bob's head. The Whorton adventure had restored his self-respect. "Wrong" as well as "right" may sometimes achieve self-approval, so strangely is the ego constituted.

To be persistently hunted, as we were from now on concentrates the mind sharply and almost exclusively upon the simple problems of survival, food, shelter, safety. Remorse, self-condemnation, these are the fruits of reflection. They come usually on the heels of failure and the prospect of penalty. Remorse is the objective type of man, the man of action, abhors surrender to it, perhaps with profound biological reasons. I have seen very little genuine remorse, either among the lawless legion at large or in the prison where is expiated my crimes and where presumably men are penitent. The mind will not war upon itself. This is unfortunate for the ideals of reform. Obviously, the hard protective faculties, not the softer reflective, are abnormally engaged in the outlaw.

Bob and Eugenia did not take their honeymoon.

The trails just then were too hot to attempt a break through. And the loot which loomed so large when we dragged it from the train dwindled to an insufficient sum when coolly calculated against anticipated needs. Bob's contemplated marriage and our fancied cattle range in an alien land became mere beckoning will-o'-the-wisps dancing on toward other hopeful raids. The vision of safe retirement on forbidden gold is a great delusion. It is the common experience of the lawless that they never get enough money to kiss the game good-bye. Stolen funds are always seen through a magnifying glass.

Two days after Whorton we slipped in to our dugout on the Riley range. We were gaunt from hard riding. The horses were fagged. For a time we holed up in the sod shelter, getting our bearings, charting the future. Pursuit cooled. The tranquil beauty of an Oklahoma spring enveloped us with a sense of security. Bobwhites piped in the hills. Maternal cows bawled anxiously about newborn calves in the grazing herds. The leaves of the cottonwoods rustled fresh along the Canadian. Westerly winds rippled the wild buffalo grass. Familiar, pleasant things about us. Familiar yet suddenly strange; like a cloud shadow on a sunny field. I think I talked a bit loudly and laughed a bit harshly during these days of temporary asylum— whistling in the dark.'"

Bessy closed the book as well as her eyes since the dim light was a strain on her aging vision. She let the message of the last few paragraphs sink in before she spoke to the mesmerized youngsters.

"So boys, what did you learn from that?"

Earl rushed in with, "I want ta be an outlaw!"

Bessy just hung her head. "Seems tomorrow night we'll be reading the Bible. Don't you forget...."Treasures gained by wickedness do not profit."

"Naw Earl, what he's saying is there's no turnin' back....once an outlaw, always an outlaw.'"

Bessy just smiled, put the book away, and headed to bed.

CHAPTER SEVEN

Another Move, Another Child

1942/1889 – 6-Mile Mountain & Mill Hill House

By the time Wes picked up Frank from Bessy's house, the new baby girl they'd named Carolyn was three weeks old and they had moved to a house near 6-Mile Mountain. It was an old, rundown farm with uncut cotton fields, but the house was a slight improvement with the bonus of electricity. However, it was still necessary for Frank to run outside, or behind the barn to shake the dewdrop off his lily. The property was owned by an elderly couple the McChesneys, who needed help to pick up groceries and do work around their farm. Virginia had negotiated a deal to put Wes and Frank to work helping out around the place, until such time that they could find new jobs and would be able to pay them rent. Frank was, of course, offered up as a conscripted worker on the farm and in the smokehouse, where they would butcher the pigs as soon as the weather grew cold. Frank wasn't certain where the hogs had come from, other than it was Wes' brother, JD, who had brought them to the farm, just after they'd moved there. He had however, overheard his mother talking to Wes about the fact that JD had said they were purloin goods. Not knowing what purloin meant, Frank simply assumed that is was a special cut of pork-loin.

In the meantime, Frank was assigned the task of mucking out the pigsty and feeding the pigs with any kind of scraps available in the slop buckets filled from the farm's two kitchens, as well as corn from he barn's large corncrib. The owners of the farm had generously stocked the corncrib with ears of dried corn and it was Frank's job to strip or shell the kernels from the cobs every day to feed to the pigs as well as for his grandmother to make hominy. Wes would pick her up and out in the yard she would boil down

the hard corn in her large cast iron kettle and add Red
Devil Lye to make the hominy swell.

Unfortunately, because Virginia and Wes were unemployed, they were home more than not, making Frank's life
pretty miserable. The only time they were both gone was
when they would go out hunting for paying work, which
they rarely found. Ever since that baby had magically appeared in their lives, Frank thought Virginia was even
meaner to him than before they left the dairy, if that was
possible. Maybe it was because it hurt so much squeezing
that big baby out the way he'd seen the calves and kittens
being born. It seemed that the new child Virginia and Wes
had made together, had turned Frank into a true outcast in
the family. Virginia was also a bear to Wes, yelling and
bitching at the two of them whenever they were within
shouting distance. Wes didn't do much during the day other than sit on the porch and smoke, or lay on the
chesterfield listening to the radio. He left all the chores to
Frank since his stepchild was the prescribed servant
around the house. Other than driving into town for supplies for the McChesneys, Wes was as inert as a wart on
the back of a toad. Even when he went to fetch groceries
he made Frank come along to do the shopping while he
stayed in the car and smoked, watching the young girls
come and go to fetch a soda or an ice cream in their little
summer dresses.

Frank did his best to stay outdoors most of the summer
working with the chickens and the two hogs. He enjoyed
their company, however he knew he was only fattening
them for slaughter come winter, so he did his best not to
get too attached. Once in a while his uncle Marshall, the
next oldest to Coleman, would come for a visit with Mack.
Frank loved Marshall and Mack, as he did Coleman, and
looked up to them both as his mentors. Frank prayed for
those days and hoped that on one of their visits they would
take him away from Virginia. Mack would check on Frank
regularly to ensure that Virginia was no longer serving up

her standard fare—corporal punishment. When Marshall came to visit they would spend their carefree days shooting birds and lizards with a slingshot they had made from a branch and a piece of inner tube.

This house had come with a large, Zenith console radio and they would listen to western radio dramas like the Lone Ranger and Red Ryder, the news, and ads selling chickens and other animals through the U.S. Postal Service, on the local radio station—WCKY. They even ordered a few dozen young chickens, or peeps for layers and it was Frank's job was to keep anything from eating the baby chicks. An array of animals, such raccoons, foxes, and skunks, as well as copperheads would steal the eggs, and the chicks, if given the chance. So he spent his days devising ways to prevent poultry theft from the wildlife. He also had to feed and water the chickens and collect the eggs. When it eventually came time to kill one for dinner, it was also Frank's job to do the dirty work. He hated it, but he'd become quite proficient with his slingshot, which did the unpleasant job quickly and painlessly.

The owners of the farm, who lived in the two-story, white farmhouse down the dirt driveway, were kind to Frank and Mrs. McChesney would bake him oatmeal cookies and her husband would give him apples from the barrel in the smokehouse. When it was time to go to town for groceries for them, Frank would get their list of staples needed, from Mrs. McChesney, and then charge the purchases to their standing account. Unbeknownst to Wes and Virginia, she also allowed Frank to charge a soda and a treat each time he shopped for her on their account. Then Frank would leave it at Mrs. McChesney's house so that Wes and his mother were none the wiser.

One day, Virginia demanded that Frank walk to the local store to pick up a few items for Mrs. McChesney since Wes wasn't feeling well and couldn't drive him. Frank was thrilled to have a short reprieve away from the house, so walked the quarter mile or so up the road to the 6-Mile Market. When he approached the store, Mr. Bruster, the owner, was outside dumping a bushel basket of old fruit and vegetables into the trough for the two new hogs in a pen on the side of the building. It was strange, Frank thought, that they had a single strand of wire around the pen and he was puzzled as to why the pigs wouldn't simply slip out from under the wire. Surely one flimsy piece of wire couldn't possibly contain the two weaners.

"How is it your pigs don't get outta there Mr. Bruster? That little wire can't possibly stop them from going where they want," inquired Frank curiously, as he watched Mr. Bruster step over the wire, giving it a wide berth.

"Well you see it's a new fangled way of fencing....it's an electric fence and them pigs'll get nearly bar-b-qued if they touch that wire you see there. It only takes once and they learn right quick to stay away from it."

"You mean it lights up like the lights in your store?

"Na it don't light up, it only lights up whatever touches it," he explained. "So don't go touching it, you hear!"

"Yes sir" replied Frank fascinated by the thought that that little piece of wire could keep pigs in a pen without the pen.

Mr. Bruster walked back towards the store with his empty basket, since a customer had just driven up. Frank stood there staring at how the wire ran into a box on the side of the building and wondered how he could rig something like that up to keep the raccoons away from his eggs. He looked around to see if anyone was looking and he bent over and touched the wire, forgetting that old saying that 'curiosity killed the cat.' The one hundred-ten volt current shocked Frank so strong that all he could do was scream as electricity surged through his body. Unable to pull himself away, he grabbed it with the other hand attempting to push himself lose. Seeing this Mr. Bruster spun on his heels when he heard Frank's ear-piercing scream and he grabbed Frank by the collar of his shirt and yanked with everything he had to disconnect the child from the current. The two of them flew backwards in the dirt and Frank writhed on the ground having a seizure as Mr. Bruster did his best to hold him still. After a few seconds, the seizure subsided and Frank sat up with his head spinning and his tongue bleeding from having bitten it.

"You okay boy?!" gasped Mr. Bruster, relieved that Frank was still alive.

Frank just looked at him confused and dazed.

"I tol' you not to touch it! Why'd you go and do it anyway?"

"I don't know," answered Frank shrugging his shoulders. "I just wanted to see how it worked."

"Can you stand?" Mr. Bruster offered him a hand to pull him to his feet.

Frank stood there stunned trying to catch his breath and collect his balance, but the world was still spinning as he stumbled a bit towards the store.

"What'd you come for? I'll get it fur ya?" questioned Bruster.

"I....I don't remember," Frank answered, confused and distant as he started walking back down the road weaving a bit between the shoulder and the pavement.

"Don't you think you should sit down for a bit?" Bruster shouted, worried, but Frank just kept on walking.

When he got home Virginia was furious that he'd forgotten the very reason she'd sent him to the store in the first place and sent him straight back out with zero regard to the fact that the boy had just been lit up like a Christmas tree.

"Why is it you always have to create a scene and embarrass me?!" Virginia shouted at him as he walked back out the driveway. "Damn child," she mumbled to herself as she sat down in her easy chair to listen to the radio with Wes.

The next time Bruster saw Wes Holliday in the store, he told him what had happened.

"Stupid kid," answered Wes. "Boy don't got no sense. Tell him not to do somethin' and he'll do it ever' time. He's nothing more than a scatterbrain."

Bruster was surprised to hear the ambivalence in Wes' response to the fact that his stepson had nearly been electrocuted, but he brushed it off as a child's shenanigans. The next time Frank went to the store he saw that the electric fence had wisely been replaced by a traditional pen made of wood.

As much as Frank did his best to steer clear of his mother that summer, she still managed to find the perfect switch in the yard to threaten him with whenever he didn't jump to her aid fast enough, or to her liking. She would command him to pick up his sister when she was screaming at the top of her lungs and the child screamed a lot due to the fact that Virginia totally ignored her and always left her in her makeshift bed—a chifforobe drawer lined with towels. Nights were especially bad. It was always his job to get up and put her in bed for Virginia to nurse, while Wes just slept through the night. Needless to say, he got little or no sleep most nights since he had to wait to put Carolyn back to sleep after nursing and that was never an easy task since she would fall asleep nursing and never seemed to get enough to eat.

Summer waned quickly into fall and before he knew it, Frank was being loaded onto the bus for school in the early mornings. Second grade was even tougher than first since it was based on the principle that you had actually learned something in the first grade. He and Coleman were still in the same school but they only saw each other briefly before and after class, and during recess—assuming Frank wasn't held back for detention. Earl had started first grade that September and he was already reading better than Frank by that Thanksgiving.

It seemed that Virginia's belly was swelling once again and Frank assumed that meant another sibling was on the way. He was already overwhelmed with the work around the farm, as well as his conscription as nanny to Carolyn—all of which left little time for his homework. Due to all of his distractions at home he continued to slip further and further behind in his reading and writing. To his dismay, he was still unable to read his coveted Dalton book and this bothered him more than the fact that he was still receiving failing grades at school.

The weather was starting to grow colder and the time came that Frank had been dreading—slaughtering the two Guinea hogs he'd been raising. He'd gotten pretty attached to them over the months of caring for them. Killing the chickens for food was easier for Frank since he'd never gotten too friendly with the fowl but the hogs were a different story. So, when it came time to kill them, Frank refused to watch the two butchers, Chuck and Jim, who came from town at dawn with a twenty-two-rifle and prepared to shoot and butcher his buddies. Frank was however, fascinated by their rifle since it reminded him of Frank Dalton, the U.S. Marshall. Even though he begged to have a closer look at it, they refused to let him even touch the gun.

The two men had also brought several of their other hogs to butcher, as well as one for the McChesney's. Slaughtering hogs was far too large a job for Wes who certainly didn't have the strength or the know-how to go about draining the blood and carving them up. Since Wes wasn't much needed he and his brother, JD, left to pick up Bessy, Coleman, and Earl to come and help. It was Bessy's job to render the fat to make the lard. Frank was given the order by Virginia to pump the water into buckets and pour it into the large kettle to boil. After hauling the heavy buckets of water, Frank went about finding firewood and kindling and lighting the fire as the men loaded the gun and prepared to shoot the pigs. Frank did his best to busy himself with the firewood so he wouldn't have to see them die. The event had strangely drawn an audience with Mr. and Mrs. McChesney and several other neighbors stopping by to play voyeur to the slaughter. It's was funny, Frank thought, how the letting of blood inspired more interest from the human variety of beasts than did the birth of a new baby calf.

"Now you pay attention Frank, I want you wachin' while they drop them hogs," Virginia insisted as Frank tried to slip away. "I don't need to be raising no sissy boy," Virginia taunted him, embarrassing him in front of the neighbors.

Hesitantly, Frank stopped working on the firewood and looked at the first pig, who stared straight at him as if to say, "Save me," to Frank since he'd been the one to care for them since they'd been on the farm.

Chuck took aim and shot the hog right between the eyes—dropping him in the dirt. Then the two strung the animal upside down from a single tree with a wooden gambrel, rope and pulley and one of them slit its throat to drain the blood. They then set up buckets to catch the blood to be used to make blood sausage.

Wes drove back down the drive just as the pig had been strung up. Colman and Earl jumped out of the truck and ran to help Frank, as Bessy walked over to give Frank a hug. He had tried hard to hide the fact from Virginia and his uncles that he had tears welling in his eyes from watching the pig die, but Bessy saw right through him. Both of them knew that if Virginia saw his glassy red eyes, she would consider Frank as weak and exploit that advantage over him. So Bessy quickly pulled him away, insisting he help her to get the fire set up for the kettles—one for the water and one for the lard.

Once the fire was lit, Virginia ordered Frank, Coleman

and Earl to scrub down the pig to get the dirt off so as not to contaminate the meat, so the boys got to work scrubbing it with buckets of water and old wooden brushes. It was cold out and by the time they were finished the boys were soaking wet and shivering, but instead of letting them change out of their wet clothing, Virginia told them to go dry off by the fire.

Once the blood had drained from the hog, the two men slit the stomach open, from the anus down, and Frank watched in horror as the animal's entrails poured out into a washtub. A few of the organs, such as the liver were saved, but the sight of the men digging through the bloody mess caused Frank lose his breakfast. Embarrassed, he ran into the house followed by Virginia, who grabbed him by the ear and dragged him back outside to watch.

Suddenly, it seemed that the sky started to grow dark for no particular reason—there wasn't a cloud in the sky. The hanging pig now resembled an inverted crucifix suspended in the air with the sun rays shining through between its legs and as they all watched in awe, the moon slowly slid overtop of the sun until it totally consumed the bright solar orb. Cars were stopping on the road as people got out to watch and a sense of awe overcame everyone participating in the slaughter.

"Oh dear God," Mrs. McChesney cried out, becoming hysterical, "It's the end of the world! You took the lives of these poor swine and now God wants revenge. Oh lordy, lordy, save us sinners!" she howled as she folded her hands in prayer and looked up at the darkened sun.

Everyone, even the men from town panicked wondering what evil had befallen them and why the sky had grown dark like the last light of a starless night. They all stared up at the sky where the sun had just been and all they could see was a black orb with the slightest sliver of light slipping from behind it like a halo. Then slowly, the orb slid away revealing shimmering sunlight until gradually the entire sun shown once again in the morning sky. There was an audible sigh of relief from the group and the people on the street gradually wandered back to their cars and went on their way.

"Oh my Lord, God has spared us," exclaimed Mrs. McChesney with a great sigh of relief, as the sky returned to normal and the birds still flew in the sky.

Amongst those present there was an audible sigh of relief as they slowly returned to their assigned duties of butchering the swine and disposing of the waste from the bowels of the beast. Then the two butchers showed Frank and Colman how to cover the pigs in burlap sacs and take buckets of the boiling water and pour it over the pig's tough hide, so they could work on scraping the hair off with the blade of a kitchen knife. It was hard work, but the two boys worked on the head area, while the two men scraped away at the hindquarters of the hog, which was still hanging by his feet.

Once the hair had been scraped from the hide the two butchers set up planks on sawhorses, lowered the carcasses onto them and proceeded to butcher them with bone saws. They turned the animals, who had been alive just an hour earlier, into hams, stew-meat, bacon, grindings, feet, and fat once it was removed from the hide. Even the heads were used for brawn, stock and soup once boiled down, as were the bones for healing bone broth. Pretty much every part of the pig would be used except for the brain, eyes, and ears—even the skin would be cut up and fried into cracklings. Once the meat was cut, it was Colman and Frank's job to salt it and hang it in the smokehouse in sacks. Bessy took the fat as they removed it and rendered it into lard in the large kettle over the outdoor fire. Then they proceeded to do the same with the rest of the hogs until there were five of the beasts being butchered, salted and stored in the smokehouse. By the end of the day Bessy had ten gallons of lard from their two hogs, which she poured into five-gallon containers to store for cooking.

It had been a long, hard day, but Frank had loved working with his uncle and his grandmother, Bessy, while Earl was off playing for most of the day. Wes took the three of them home and returned to a dark house with everyone sleeping. The next morning when Frank was awakened late by the sun's rays shining through the window, he bolted up and looked outside at the smokehouse, which was about fifty feet away from the house. It was strange, he thought that the door to the smokehouse stood open, since he was certain that he closed it and locked it. He jumped up and pulled on his pants and boots and ran outside to the entrance of the smokehouse. He stopped in the doorway and squinted, trying to adjust his vision to the dim light in the darkened building. As things slowly came into focus, Frank could see that the smokehouse was empty—all of the meat was gone—vanished it seemed into thin air.

Frank ran back into the house out of breath shouting, "It's gone....the meat's all gone!" he screamed as he ran into his mother's room.

"What the hell are you yellin' 'bout and wakin' us up?" growled Virginia as the baby started to scream at the top of her lungs.

"I'm tellin' ya it's gone!"

"What's gone?!"

"The meat....all of it!"

With that both Wes and Virginia jumped from the bed pulling on warm clothing and they all ran out to see for themselves. It was true—when they got to the smokehouse and looked in, there was nothing there except for a few scraps dropped on the floor in the rush to steal the lucrative haul. All of that meat was enough food to feed a family of four for a year.

Virginia instantly turned on Frank, fit to be tied, "Didn't you hear anythin' boy!" accused Virginia.

Frank just stood there stunned. He shook his head no, "I was asleep and didn't hear a thing."

"What the hell are you good for around here you no-count, useless child?" Virginia screamed, hysterical while Wes just shook his head. "What are we going to do now? We ain't got no meat for winter," Virginia asked Wes, who, as usual looked like a deer fixed in Virginia's crosshairs.

"Guess we better find some payin' work quick. Damn shame," Wes finally said, shaking his head as he headed back to the house and back to bed.

Virginia quickly got word to her cousin Mack about the swine heist and it didn't take long for him to track down the culprits—some local hoodlums, and to retrieve at least a small portion of the sowbelly through his criminal underground channels.

Soon after the theft of the meat, Wes and Virginia managed to find jobs working at the cotton mill thanks to JD, who worked there as an oiler for the machinery. Virginia was hired to spin the cotton into thread and Wes did the only thing he was trained to do—sweep floors and mop used motor oil on them to keep the dust and lint down. They put in a request for discount employee housing at the mill, but unfortunately, all of the bungalows were occupied. The pay was meager, almost to the point of being less than welfare, but it fed the family and the McChesney's took pity on them, extending their arrangement for housing in exchange for their help around the farm. They did manage to purchase a 1930 Model A Ford pickup to get back and forth to work, however, they couldn't afford a battery for the rust-bucket and they were forced to park on a hill in order to jump-start the thing once it got a rolling start.

Because Virginia and Wes worked the night shift, Frank would be left alone to take care of Carolyn. Frank did his best to keep her calm and get her to sleep, but someone began attempting to break into the house. Frank and Carolyn were scared to death, but Wes and Virginia refused to believe Frank accusing him of trying to get out of the job of caring for the baby. It seemed to happen every other night that Frank and Carolyn were in the house alone and Frank was becoming very afraid to even try to sleep. The two of them took to sleeping in one bed, giving Frank little or no sleep even on the nights that no one rattled the doorknobs and tried to open windows. This continued for several weeks until whoever the culprit was gave up their mission to rob the place, or maybe, Frank thought, they just wanted to frighten them. Was it possible that it was the hoodlums who had robbed the smokehouse—angry that Mack had beaten them so badly for the theft and took most of the loot back? They had never been arrested—Mack had simply taken care of the theft the good old-fashioned way of getting things done.

Just before the end of that school year, Virginia gave birth to a baby boy they named Johnny Holliday. Frank was already struggling between work at school and at home, and now he had one more job on his plate—the care and responsibility of an infant. When Virginia went to Dr. Pepper's farm once again to give birth, Frank and Carolyn were dropped at Bessy's farm for a couple weeks. Frank was forced to miss school, until Virginia and Wes picked him and Carolyn up when Johnny was two weeks old. But Frank didn't mind missing school. He was grateful to spend time with Bessy and his uncles and even more thrilled when Bessy continued their reading from his Dalton book that had been forbidden by Virginia to ever read again.

"'Summer was in the offing. The "Outlaw Moon" was rising. Gradually the old organization had reassembled. Red Rock, a little way station on the Santa Fe line in the Cherokee Strip, was our next objective. It was not far from our old hideout near Whorton. In addition to Bob, Grat, and myself, Doolin, Broadwell, Newcomb, Pierce, and Powers composed the striking force. Again we were lusty in anticipation of the one grand haul. Grat particularly was champing to get a load of angry suppressions off his chest in a burst of action. It was with difficulty that we restrained him to the bounds of caution.

Lightning was signaling along the horizon as we cantered to the edge of town. Red Rock was then in the Otoe Indian reservation, near where the famous 101 Ranch of Oklahoma now spreads. It boasted only a depot, section house, a store, and a few sprawling residences. Never much excitement in Red Rock; the town simply wasn't geared up for explosive deadly ambuscade. The railroad, not the handful of inhabitants, had set the trap.

Confidently we had taken out appointed stations near the depot when the night train rolled in on regular schedule. We were on the verge of going into action.

"Hold on," I cautioned. "Something wrong here. Look at that smoker—it's dark!" We froze in our tracks.

'You're right," said Bob. The station agent is acting queer. He's expecting something to happen."

Nervously peering into the dark and dryly whistling a graveyard tune, the agent had gone to the express car. There he conferred in oblivious agitation with that messenger. So for a space we waited, tensely on guard, while the engine hissed idly. No traveler got on or off. The passenger coaches looked innocent enough: lights dimmed for the night; a few sleepy heads on the reclining chairs; everything apparently regular. But the lightless coach behind the express car. That black smoker—sinister as a vault! Was deadly menace crouching there in rifled readiness, waiting to spit flame at the first sign of trouble? All this had taken us perhaps half a minute to observe and appraise.

"Come on," said Grat impatiently, "we're actin' like a bunch of old women!"

"It's a deadhead," muttered Bob, laying a restraining hand on Grat's rifle arm. "Deadhead, and dangerous as a rattlesnake."

While we waited, undecided, the train pulled out. And now suddenly some of the apparently sleepy passengers came awake and peered intently from the windows as the coaches slid past. Something expected hadn't happened.

"I think we've been buffaloed," said Powers."Yeah," added Doolin, "standin' here like a bunch o' suckers while the money flits away! Gold-bricked again!" Grat exploded as he watched the red taillight vanish down the track. Even I was now inclined to believe that we had let a prize slip away while we stood spellbound by some fantastic apprehension. But not Bob.

"I thought so," he said facing about as a rumble grew in the north. A second section, the regular express, as it proved, came roaring in. Almost it laid its searching headlights upon us before we leaped into the shadows.

"That's her," commented Bob. "she's all lit up. This is the one we want." Doolin, Powers, and Grat looked a bit sheepish. They had a moment's solemn reflection on what we might have stepped into with less caution. We learned later that the railway company had in some way anticipated a probable holdup along the Red Rock section. They had sent through a pilot deadhead loaded with guards. The black smoker had been a rolling ambush, as I had surmised with some intuitive flash.

It was a doubly surprised train crew which lifted its hands aloft when the genuine money train came to halt and we got into action.

A pudgy little Negro porter offered the only diversion. Pompously he had stepped down off the platform to assist possible passengers. Doolin was annoyed at the dusky appari-

tion—but then Doolin was easily annoyed anyway.

"You climb back into that coop," he threatened, "unless you want to shorten your bio-graffey!"

"Yes, sir!" stammered the porter catching the glint of a gun. We saw him racing through the coaches gesticulating wildly to the startled passengers to conceal their valuables.

The robbery was swiftly done, without resistance or injury. Not even a shot had been fired. Red Rock, save for the station agent, hadn't even turned over in its sleep. The proceeds were something short of eleven thousand dollars. The gathering storm enveloped us as we rode away.'"

A year or so later, Virginia was still abstaining from child abuse and forewent the beatings in lieu of emotional and verbal abuse, due to her fear of Mack who came around to check on Frank on a regular basis. She didn't want to leave a physical trace of her anger but she knew that her unkind words would not be evident to the outside world. What was spoken under her roof, stayed privy only to the family's ears. Frank loved Mack's visits and it galled Virginia to see the rich and authentic relationship the two of them had. Mack would take Frank riding in his car sometimes as he collected his marks from gambling or other questionable ventures. Frank was usually in awe and wondered if some of what Mack did wasn't so different than the vocation chosen by the Dalton gang—albeit a little less shoot 'em up,

Although Mack had a beautiful wife named Ruby who owned a successful beauty shop in Anderson, he still managed find his way into another man's wife's bed. It seemed that the husband of the object of his affection had learned about their affair and tracked them down one evening to a restaurant in Anderson, where they were enjoying an amorous dinner in the corner booth. Mack saw the man coming and stood, getting the first shot off wounding him in the shoulder, but not before the man shot Mack point-blank in the stomach. The bullet lodged in his spine—paralyzing him from the waist down for life.

Unfortunately, Frank's hero and savior was no longer able to protect him from Virginia and she quickly resumed beating him every time he underperformed to her expectations. Frank only saw Mack once after that terrible injury, while Frank and Marshall were walking down the road one day. It seemed that Mack's vocation as a gangster had been greatly curtailed by his disability and Marshall had taken up some of the responsibilities for his uncle—handling pickups and deliveries. Marshall met Mack at the gate of a very posh residence with Mack's old partner driving his car. Mack didn't get out since he didn't want Frank to see that he was crippled, but he rolled down the window to speak to him.

"Hey there buddy....how've you been?"

Frank smiled broadly and turned his face to Mack, exposing a black eye and a swollen lip.

"Hey there Mack, are you okay? I heard you got shot and can't use your legs no more. Is that true? Did it hurt?"

"I'm afraid it is, son. And yes it hurt....a lot." He motioned Frank over, "Come here, boy."

Frank stepped close to the passenger window. Mack spun him around and pulled up his shirt to expose his badly welted back.

"Virginia's at it again, I see," Mack said sadly.

Frank turned to him—looked down at the ground as if he were ashamed of the fact that he was beaten regularly. He nodded.

Mack put his hand on the boy's shoulder, "Never be embarrassed by your mom's meanness, Frank. Her meanness is a sickness. It's not your fault....I'm sorry I haven't been around much to protect you. It's just that--"

"--it's okay Mack....I understand. Ma says you're not the man you used to be no more."

"Is that what she says? Well, son....I will do my best to have a talk with her. If I could I'd take you away from her I would, but the law won't let me."

"I understand," Frank said softly.

"Just do the best you can in school and you'll know when it's time to leave this place."

"But where would I go?"

"Go see where your ancestors came from. Go find yourself when you're old enough, Frank. Virginia doesn't own you, even though she thinks she does."

With that, Mack's partner got in the driver's seat and started the car. Mack patted Frank on the shoulder again and smiled. Then the car pulled away from the curb. It was the last time Frank ever saw Mack, but his words stuck with him. In fact, it was something that he would remember for the rest of his life.

Two years passed as Frank struggled with school as well as his domestic charges of child rearing and animal husbandry on the farm. By the time little Johnny was two, Frank had become nothing more than a full-time servant in the Holliday household. Virginia did little around the house and Wes did less. It was totally up to Frank to care for and feed the two children and the chickens, as well as run errands for the McChesney's. When Wes fell sick from his diabetes and Virginia was forced to drive him to the hospital in Greenville, South Carolina, twenty-some miles away, she left the three children alone in the house with zero food or money and no one to care for them. Frank was eight and certainly not able to take care of a two and a three year old alone, especially with no food in the house and no money to buy anything. There were still a few eggs laid a day, but the baby wasn't able to eat so it seemed Johnny never stopped crying. The child needed milk and there was no way for Frank to get any. It was winter and it was all Frank could do to find wood to keep the stove going to keep the house warm.

Frank knew how much Mr. and Mrs. McChesney relied on him so after a day, when Virginia didn't return to the farm and Frank could no longer handle the screaming, hungry children, he knocked on their door to ask for help. Mrs. McChesney was quick to fix him up a basket of biscuits and peanut butter and jelly and she gave him permission to put milk on their account at the store. She even watched the younger children, while Frank walked to the store. With that Frank was able to keep the children's hollering down to a tolerable bawl. Mr. McChesney also took pity on Frank and gave him apples from the smokehouse, from his winter storage bin.

Virginia and Wes were gone for three days before returning late one afternoon to the farm as if it was nothing that she had left her children alone without food. Their absence had left Frank with mixed emotions of fear and relief—torn between the hope of never seeing them again and the thought of having to take care of his half-brother and half-sister all alone.

CHAPTER EIGHT

Alice Hill Community—Mill Hill House

1943 — An Indentured Servant

Frank's hopeful thoughts of never seeing his mother and stepfather again were dashed the day they drove back into the yard in the old Model A.

Virginia brashly shouted orders to Frank, "Get your ass out here, Frank, and help Wes into the house!"

Frank ran out to the car in the snow without his coat or shoes and helped Wes as he hobbled to the door, barely able to walk. "We need food in the house," insisted Virginia as she threw a few dollars at Frank. "Get yourself to the store and buy us somethin' to eat." Then she drove back up the drive to park the car on the hill so it would start without a battery.

Frank donned his only warm clothes and his coat and shoes, and trudged up the driveway in the slippery snow, then headed to the store to buy a few supplies to feed the family. Although somewhat relieved that they had returned, Frank was also frightened to be around Virginia, knowing he no longer had Mack to come to his rescue. Without the threat of Mack turning Virginia into the authorities, Frank was fair game for Virginia's never ending wrath. It seemed that since she'd given birth to Johnny, she had grown even meaner and more short-fused than she had ever been. The dramatic drop in her hormone levels made her the poster child for a malady first recognized in 1926 as postpartum depression. Unfortunately, at that time there was little treatment for the disorder, if it was even diagnosed.

Virginia and Wes were still low in seniority at the mill,

so they continued to work the night shift, leaving Frank alone to care for the two young ones all night. Baby Johnny was a difficult child and always kept Frank from getting enough sleep. The days were also hard since, when he was not in school, he was on call to wait on Virginia, Wes, and the children nonstop. At school Frank was often reprimanded for falling asleep in class and it continued to affect his grades. He did his best to explain to the teacher why he was so tired, but she didn't really want to hear his excuses anymore. Nor did she take much notice whenever Frank came to school with a fat lip, or a black eye from Virginia's beatings. Of course, the welts on his back and arms were concealed by his clothing, so no one really knew how badly he was being abused. Since there were no neighbors close by to hear her screaming and ranting at Frank, Virginia seemed to feel she could do whatever she pleased to him. Maybe she was trying to make up for all the time Mack had prevented her from torturing him so Virginia spent her time at home telling Frank what a 'no-account' he was—'just like his father' and how she was 'fit to be tied because of his uselessness.' Virginia had resumed sending him out to cut his own switches so that she could 'tan his hide,' or 'cut him good,' and Frank always did his best to find the smallest hickory switch. But, she would just send him back out for a bigger one if it wasn't to her liking. Frank thought how ironic it was that he had to provide the very weapon with which she would whip him.

When Virginia and Wes had requested worker's quarters at the Mill Hill houses, all of the bungalows had been occupied, so Frank was relieved to be able to continue going to school with Coleman and Earl. Unfortunately, before spring of that year, one of the mill workers died and that house became available for Wes and Virginia to lease at a discounted price. It was a small three-bedroom, military-style structure with a living room, a kitchen, running water, electricity, and a coal stove for heat. However, there was no heater for the hot water so they simply ran a pipe through the coal stove in order to heat the water. This worked well during the winter months, but come summer, it would be far too hot to light the stove, so they would re-sort to heating it on the cooking stove on the back porch, or in the sun. The back porch also had a toilet, a tub with a faucet, and an icebox—all quite modern and luxurious conveniences for the rural lower class citizens of Pickens County.

Their house was in a row of a number of employee houses—all of which were different sizes. A black man would come once a week in his mule-drawn ice-wagon and chip off a ten to fifteen pound block and put it in their ice-box. The coal hauling truck would come in the fall and dump a load of coal in the yard next to each house, provid-ing them with their winter fuel for heating and cooking. The train track ran only fifty yards from the front of the houses so when the trains went past, it would nearly shake the old stick structures clean off their foundations.

While they moved, Virginia dropped the two youngest off to stay with Bessy on Saturday morning, and took Frank to the new house to clean. She demanded that he get to work moving all the furniture out and scrubbing the floors with a mop and bucket. She insisted that she wanted to move into a clean house, yet she refused to lift a finger to help him move anything, and Wes only helped when it was far too heavy for Frank to move it by himself. So Frank struggled all day until it was cleaned to Virginia's satisfaction or more accurately to her lack of complaints. After Frank had finished washing the floors, she walked through looking in every corner trying to find something he'd missed. When she failed to spot anything he'd forgot-ten to clean she simply turned to him and scoffed, "I guess that's the best you can do so it'll have to be good enough!"

By that point Frank was exhausted, but he still had to drag the furniture back into the house and then ride back to the farm to help pack their belongings. Once again, the

Hollidays loaded their truck and took their meager belongings to the Alice Mill Hill Community, which was known
as the Mill Hill House. By the end of the day, Frank could
barely stand and Virginia hadn't even allowed him to stop
to eat lunch. When they went to pick up the children from
Bessy's, he was then expected to get them settled into the
new house for the night. By this point he was starving and
Virginia hadn't even shopped for food for the house since
Bessy had fed the two youngest. She cooked cornpone for
dinner late that night but Frank was so tired by that point,
he went to bed hungry. That night he was awakened three
times by Johnny, who was frightened by the unfamiliarity
of his new surroundings. Finally, he just put Johnny into
his bed with him so that he could attempt to get a few
hours sleep.

The next day, Virginia took Frank outside behind the
house and showed him where an old wall had once stood,
but was now just a few piles of rocks and rubble. Pointing
at it, "This is the property line and I'll cut you good if I see
you go past this point. And you'd best have the kids fed
and dressed before you leave in the mornings. You understand me?" Virginia growled at Frank.

Frank nodded yes, but kept his eyes trained on the
ground, afraid to look her in the eye.

"I know you get done at three and you'd best get your
behind back here right quick after school to do your
chores. An' if I call your name, you'd best come right
quick!"

Frank could only nod and say, "Yes ma'am." Had he ad-
dressed her in any other way, or with any concerns, he
knew he'd be at the end of one of her firm hickories.
Luckily, looking around he realized there was little growing in the area that could serve as one of Virginia's
correctional weapons.

The next day when Frank got home from school, there
was a tan cow tied outside the house. Confused, Frank

walked in and found Virginia up already with the children screaming. She looked at the clock, "Should've taken you less time to walk here from school, you hear?"

Frank just looked down and nodded. "Sorry, I had to wait for them to hand out new books."

"Ain't no excuse, you hear! I want you home straight after school's out!"

"Okay...." Frank answered uncertainly.

"Now get the kids feed, they ain't had no lunch yet."

Frank busied himself with pouring milk and dishing out cornbread from last night's pan on the top of the stove.

"When you're done with that take that cow out there and stake her 'cross the tracks so she can graze."

"When did we get a cow?" Frank questioned, confused. "And ah....I....I thought I wasn't supposed to cross those tracks," asked Frank smartly, regretting his remarks as soon as he'd uttered them.

Virginia gave him a good slap across the face, "Don't you smart mouth me, you hear?!"

"Yes ma'am, "Frank just looked down at the plates as he set them in front of Johnny and Carolyn at the table.

"Then before dark you bring that cow back here and water and feed it! Feedbag's is on the back porch. In the mornings, you milk her and feed the kids before you head off to school."

"Yes ma'am," answered Frank as he went outside to look at the new cow—the newest job on Frank's daily itinerary.

Frank had had some experience with the cows on the previous farm, as well as at the dairy, but coaxing this one across those busy railroad tracks, with trains coming and going each way all day long, was no easy task. The rumble and loud clatter from the trains had already put the fear of God into that poor beast and it was all Frank could do to drag her out to the field so that she could graze. The only thing that made that track crossing worthwhile to her was the tall green grass that awaited her on the other side. After getting her into the field and staking her, Frank made it back inside to start on his daily chores. He was dreading the trip back across the tracks since he knew there was another train just around sunset.

The only blessing about the new house was that it was close to other neighbors, so Virginia wasn't quite as free to terrorize Frank the way she had at McChesneys' farm. The walls were thin and the neighbors nosey, so she had to mind her p's & q's somewhat—at least where verbal abuse was concerned. The mill was a large company and employed close to a thousand workers, but only a few dozen were able to rent housing on the property. JD had managed to pull some strings, or grease some palms with the foreman in-charge of the housing, and they had managed to secure their place for as long as they were to be employed by the mill.

About the only thing Frank ever had in the way of food was corn flakes and milk for breakfast and corn pone at night. Since Frank had to transfer to Alice Elementary in Easley, he was sad that he would no longer see his best friend, Coleman, every day. It also meant he no longer got a packed lunch from Bessy. Frank could walk to school with the other employees' children and he made a few new friends of those who lived in the mill houses, as well as a few who went to the new school, but Frank really missed seeing his uncles. In school there was a separate room for each grade up to sixth, but he seemed to struggle even more at this school since he couldn't talk to Coleman after class to ask him questions about his homework. The teacher also didn't understand his severe learning disability with his poor reading skills and dyslexia, as well as his increasing hearing loss. So she put him in the back of the classroom where he could hear even less. Although they passed him from grade to grade, he wasn't really learning much. He was reading a little better, thanks to Bessy and Coleman as well as his comic books, but he struggled with it and his reading was slow enough to make him lose interest before he'd finished his assignments. Due to reading his comics—Red Ryder, Little Beaver, Lone Ranger and Tonto, not to mention the stories on Frank Dalton—Frank dreamed someday he'd become a cowboy. And as he figured it, why would a cowboy need to read and do math? That was unless he was going to become an outlaw like the Dalton Gang, then he would surely need to learn to count his money.

Because Wes and Virginia were on the midnight shift, she insisted that Frank stay up until eleven to wake them so they could go to work, even though she had an alarm clock Frank would be totally exhausted from a long day at school and the afternoon and evening chores taking care of the youngsters. Even so, he had no choice but to stay up to be sure they got to work on time, or Virginia would beat him if he didn't abide by her whim.

Frank hated Sunday mornings since Virginia made him go every week to the local Baptist church next to his school. It was his job to dress his half-brother and half-sister in their Sunday best and polish their white shoes, then take them to services. Frank had no fancy Sunday go-to-meeting clothes and only had one pair of lace-up brown shoes from Sears for school. Some Sundays he would even have to go to church barefoot if his shoes were too muddy. He was pressured by the Reverend Ellis to get baptized and to go to revival meetings where they chanted and sang that everyone was going to go to hell who didn't. If that were the case thought Frank, why did it matter whether he was good or bad, since in the end, he was likely to burn in hell anyway?

Eventually, Preacher Ellis, who drove a fancy new Oldsmobile 88, was caught having sex with one of the under-aged parishioners and thrown out of the church, as well as out of town. His wife, who was one of the high school math teachers was humiliated and eventually forced to move in shame to a different county. Frank couldn't understand why it was okay for the preacher to evangelize

Christian ethical behavior—then follow his own wanton ways with women half his age. Eventually, the two got a divorce and the preacher exacerbated his wife's shame by running off with the young girl.

One day, Frank's uncle Marshall, who was about three years older than him, came to visit the Mill Hill House. He was an awkward, lanky, unattractive boy—much larger than Frank and he loved to roughhouse. Frank didn't see him often since Marshall was usually staying with one of his older siblings, instead of with his mother, Bessy. That day they were playing peace officer and outlaw—chasing each other with toy wooden guns that Mack had given them for Christmas that year. Due to the war, metal was high demand and short supply, so most toys were being made from compressed sawdust. Usually, Carolyn and Johnny got toys for the holiday, however the most Frank had ever received was an orange with a straw in it, or a new pair of shoes, so Mack had stepped in to play Father Christmas to the boys.

During their cops and robbers reenactment, Marshall was hot on Frank's heels, prompting Frank to jump over the railing—right off the porch of the house. Unfortunately, he had forgotten that there was a ten-foot drop to the ground with staked tomato plants directly in the landing zone. He touched down smack on top a tomato plant, which was held up by a long pointed, wooden stake. The stake went straight into Frank's backside, skewering him like a Popsicle. He lay on the ground writhing and screaming in pain, while Marshall just stood over him telling him to stop being a sissy and get up. Afraid he'd get into trouble, Marshall took off with Frank lying there in pain for several hours. Eventually, Frank got to his feet and pulled the stake from his derriere. If the extra hole in his bottom wasn't enough, he noticed that the barrel of his toy gun had broken off and had shattered into small pieces. Although he was in agony, he was more upset about the loss of his toy gun than his pierced behind. He was also so afraid that if Virginia found out about his injury, she would beat him just for being stupid. So, for more than a week he managed to hide the fact that he was struggling to walk on that leg. By that point, Virginia was beating him for something almost daily and he was afraid to give her one more thing as an excuse to tan his hide since it was already injured.

Johnny and Carolyn had also adopted the same attitude towards Frank as Virginia and they loved to make up lies to tell on him to intentionally get him into trouble— blaming him for things they had done wrong. It didn't matter that Frank waited on them hand and foot every day, they still thought it was okay to torment him and tattle about his smallest indiscretion.

Around the time that Johnny was about two and a half, Virginia brought a jar of peanut butter home. It was unusual for her to buy anything for the house that might be considered a treat. She gave a little taste to Johnny and Carolyn, but never offered a whiff of it to Frank. She knew Frank loved peanut butter, but intentionally denied him even a taste. In the end she ate most of the jar herself. She then put away the half-eaten jar of peanut butter on the top shelf of the food safe, which had tall wire-screen doors with a latch on the front, so the kids couldn't gain access. That afternoon, while Wes and Virginia were sleeping, Johnny somehow managed to open the cabinet and climb up the shelves reaching the peanut butter. In the process, he pulled the entire safe over on top of himself with a terribly loud crash. Broken dishes, glasses, and jars of canned food shattered all over on the floor, creating a huge mess in the kitchen. Scared to death, Virginia and Wes came running—Virginia screaming, "Oh my God! Oh my God!" assuming the world had come to an end. When she saw the clusterfuck in the middle of her kitchen floor, she immediately slapped Frank across the cheek knocking him down.

"Johnny did it!" exclaimed Frank desperate to defend himself and explain that he had nothing to do with the disaster.

"It don't matter none who did it!" Virginia screamed. "It's all your fault for not stopping him from getting into the cabinet in the first place! It's your job to watch 'em....he could've killed himself" she snarled. "Now go outside and cut me a hickory, boy!" Virginia demanded. When he returned, she proceeded to beat him until he bled. They all helped to clean up the mess, but Virginia made Frank get on his hands and knees and scrub the floor until his knees were covered in bruises and his hands were embedded with slivers of glass.

Frank's great-aunt, Dessie on his mother's side, had a chow dog that was had a penchant to turn mean on people he didn't take a shine to. On one of their visits to her house the dog snapped at Virginia when she leaned down to try to pet the animal. Sorely offended, Virginia grabbed a yardbroom and proceeded to beat the poor dog until it ran away yelping with its tail between his legs.

Dessie said nothing about Virginia's lack of anger management but just turned to her—"You know....I don't think that dog likes you much Virginia.....but then, I don't really blame him."

The poor dog hid under the house from Virginia for the rest of her visit.

Virginia just snarled back at her and turned to another little brown bulldog Dessie owned, named Brownie. Although the dog was a bit leery of Virginia, this one didn't want a piece of her. Maybe, Frank thought, it was because it was afraid she'd be too sour.

Eventually however, the little bulldog warmed up to Virginia, allowing her to scratch him on the head. Then the dog went straight to over to Frank and curled up around his feet. "Well now," said Dessie. "I do believe that dog likes you, Franklin."

Virginia just growled again.

"Yes ma'am," Frank answered Dessie as he squatted on his haunches to give the dog a hug.

"You know Franklin....I've been lookin' to find that dog a good home. You wanna take him home with you?"

Frank looked shocked that Dessie was willing to give him such an enormous gift. He liked the little dog and thought he would make a fine friend. Frank was certain however, that Virginia would never let him keep him. But, oddly, Virginia liked the dog even more, since he hadn't bitten or snarled at her. She allowed Frank have him as his pet, as long as he would take care of him. The dog seemed as happy as Frank to go home with him. He always obeyed Frank and showed him the affection and friendship that he was sorely missing from his mother and family. Virginia even allowed the dog to stay in the house with them most of the time and Brownie made himself right at home at the foot of Frank's bed every night. Even though the dog had really taken to Frank Virginia loved Brownie and would save the best table scraps for him and even brought things from the mill lunchroom. In fact it seemed to Frank, that Brownie was fed better than he was. Virginia even got the dog a collar and a tag with his rabies number on it.

Brownie shadowed Frank and listened to every word he said when he talked to him, which made Virginia a little jealous, since the dog was nowhere near as loyal to her as he was to Frank. Regardless, she did like having Brownie around for protection since on the other side of the train tracks was a Negrotown, and the residents of the Mill Hill were very prejudiced and always nervous about 'them kind of folk' coming to their side of the tracks.

One day when Virginia was sitting on the front porch, a black man walked down the alley on their side of the tracks, which was a very unusual occurrence.

"Morning," said the man in a polite, friendly manner, nodding to Virginia as he walked on down the track. Concerned by the sight of the man so close to the house, she turned to the dog, "Go get him Brownie," she commanded. With that, the dog took off like a rocket after the man. When the poor guy saw the growling bulldog, with teeth bared, coming after him, he ran as fast as he could down the tracks, with Brownie snapping close at his heels. Brownie didn't return for at least thirty minutes, so Frank, who had been watching, wondered if Brownie had chased the man into the next county. Eventually, he returned panting and exhausted and lay down at Virginia's feet as if nothing had happened. She just leaned down and gave him a pat on the head, "Good dog, Brownie."

Come late spring, Virginia made Frank move all of the furniture out of the house to once again scrub the floors. She then locked Brownie out of the house for several days not wanting him to get her clean floors dirty. Denied entry to Frank's bed, Brownie must have figured that he was no longer wanted by the family, so he just up ran away, or was stolen by someone who knew what a good watchdog he was. Virginia however, suspected that he may have been hit by a train, but she never mentioned it to the kids. She was surprisingly upset when the dog didn't return and even posted notices around the mill that he was missing, hoping that someone might find him. Frank searched for his buddy everywhere, to no avail. No one seemed to have seen him. Weeks went by and Brownie never returned. Frank was brokenhearted that his buddy had just up and left him. If it hadn't been for the fact that Virginia was just as upset about the dog's disappearance, Frank would have thought that Virginia had given him away, just to spite Frank.

Late one afternoon while Virginia was taking a bath on the back porch, Frank quietly came in the back door and foolishly decided to play a trick on her. He rattled his belt buckle to make it sound like Brownie's collar and shouted, "Brownie's back."

"Oh I'm so glad!" Virginia effused, happy to hear the good news. When she got out of the tub and dressed and realized that Frank was pulling her leg, she slapped him hard across his face knocking him to the floor.

"Don't you ever try to trick me like that again! You hear me?! Now go out and cut the strongest hickory you can find!" Virginia shouted unafraid of the neighbors hearing her screaming.

CHAPTER NINE

Nothing Like Kin

1944 – '47 – Beaten Within an Inch of His Life

One of Frank's aunts, Jeanette, Virginia's oldest sister, was married to a man named Edward Campbell—they were Frank's favorite relatives. He loved it when they came to visit him. They owned a filling station and grocery store with a restaurant, just south of Anderson and offered the family a discount on fuel and eats. Edward seemed to really like Frank and would sometimes pick him up to stay at their place for a week at a time in the summers. Frank liked Jeanette and especially Edward, who treated him as well he did his own two year old son, Jimmy. Edward seemed to truly like having Frank hang around the station to help him pump gas and clean the customers windshields, and Frank enjoyed every minute of the time he spent there as a gas jockey. Once in a while Edward would even let Frank work as a fry-cook flipping burgers in their restaurant, as well as other odd jobs. Edward would even pay Frank a little whenever he worked with him. It was those weeks of working with automobiles that triggered Frank's love of cars and he couldn't wait until he was old enough to buy one of his own. He studied the people and the cars that patronized the filling station. It didn't take him long to learn every make and model of car on the road.

One day a shiny new Buick Phaeton rolled into the station sporting New York plates and Frank enthusiastically got to work pumping fuel and cleaning all the windows. Just touching that sleek, beautiful car was a thrill. Frank knew it was too fancy to be from around their parts and he was keeping track of the out-of-state license plates that passed through the little town that was barely a tick on the map. He shined the Buick up real good for the driver, who tipped Frank a whole nickel.

"Gee thanks, mister!"

The driver nodded with a slight salute to Frank and pulled back on the road, heading south. Frank was ecstatic when he realized that he could get paid for a little extra effort doing something he really enjoyed—especially for the fancy out-of-town cars that passed through on occasion, since the station was on one of the main state roads. He decided right then and there that he would start saving his money to put toward his own car in the future. As the car cruised on down the highway Frank exclaimed, "Boy, I'm going to buy me a car as soon as I'm old enough to drive."

Edward smiled watching Frank beam, "What kind of car you wanna buy when you get enough tips?" asked Edward.

Frank thought long and hard about it—"Well Uncle Edward, that Buick there that was a pretty smart car....but, I reckon I'll start with a 1930 Model A 30 Ford sedan," he replied, quite seriously as he approached the next car that pulled up to the pump,

"What'll it be mister?" he asked politely, as he got busy pumping gas and washing windows with enthusiasm. Secretly, Frank wished that Jeanette and Edward were his parents and he prayed that they would somehow adopt him, since he realized, for the first time, what it felt like to be part of a normal, loving family.

Virginia's other sister, Geneva, had moved to Jacksonville when her husband, Leroy, was drafted into the Army and sent overseas. Due to a terrible shortage of men in the workforce, women were being drafted and trained to do men's jobs in the factories. The National Service Act of December 1941 had actually legalized the conscription of women and Geneva had been one of them. At first only single women had been called up, but due to dire shortages, they began taking married women with children.

Geneva was trained as a welder and sent to work in the Jacksonville shipyard. When Leroy returned from service a year and a half later, Geneva returned with him to the Anderson area to live and they both went to work for Owens Corning Fiberglass plant. The couple eventually ended up having five children, but Frank never really got to know the older ones well.

Virginia's brother, Austin, had suddenly gotten the idea that he and his siblings, Jeanette, and Geneva should buy Bessy a new farm closer to the sisters in Anderson County, south of the town of Anderson. With Bessy near the home of Jeanette and Edward, as well as Geneva and Leroy, it would relieve Austin of the burden of looking out for her since he wanted to continue living north of Pickens. His reasoning was that Bessy was getting older and as her husband Christopher, his father, was dead, someone needed to be close enough to look after her and he didn't want it to be him. Bessy had been quite content on the old farm with its rolling hills and modest house, but Austin insisted that she move. Since he was the oldest and now the self-proclaimed patron of the family, Bessy finally gave in and allowed him to sell her farm. Of course, there was some sort of financial gain in it for him since he handled the sale of the old property as well as the purchase of the new one. He bought Bessy several hundred farmable acres, with flat pastures, just south of Anderson. Of course, he had other practical, financial reasons in mind with this easily farmable land that he felt would turn a profit. The farm had a nice one-story home with two bedrooms, running water, a fireplace, and electricity. The house was also closer to the main road, which meant it wasn't quite as remote as the other house had been. These conveniences definitely made it easier for Bessy so she agreed that the move did make her life simpler, however it also meant that Coleman and Earl would have to change schools. They would now have to commute by bus to the Anderson school, which didn't make either of them very happy.

Austin was around the new farm a lot, but it seemed that when Frank was there, Austin tended to make himself scarce. He was never very friendly to Frank and always acted as if he was above everyone else. Frank didn't like Austin much because of his air of arrogance, which stemmed from believing that he was more important and smarter than everyone else. Austin had a condescending attitude towards others in the family, especially Frank, since he deemed him a bit of an outcast. When Frank wasn't around, Austin had people plowing the fields and planting crops with their own mules and plows, but he never did any of the work himself. In fact, Austin had rarely worked an honest day in his life and he relied on his wheeling and dealing to get by. No matter, Austin somehow managed to try to make a working farm of it and he had five acres planted, consisting of tomatoes and string beans, and twice as many in corn and cotton. He also put in a small vineyard of concord grapes, hoping to make good money off the crops. Eventually, Leroy financed a huge John Deere tractor and brought it to Bessy's farm since she also had a sizable barn on the property in which to park it. Austin loved driving the tractor so he would come around often to operate it during planting season. When Frank went to visit Bessy during planting season, he got to know Leroy a bit whenever he came to do some of the plowing of the tract for Austin. Frank quickly decided that he liked Leroy and Edward a darn sight better than Austin.

Leroy however had a bad habit of buying things, without putting much thought to, or planning how he would end up paying for them—like the tractor. Eventually, the tractor was repossessed and the planting went back to being done the old fashioned way—with a horse and plow and a lot of backbreaking sweat.

No matter how much Frank disliked Austin, he still loved spending time on the farm with Bessy, so he made an exception to stay with her as often as he could. Besides, being around Austin was a darn sight better than being with Virginia, even though Austin could be almost as mean. Frank and the boys would play in the fields and suck on the sweet grapes Austin had planted, and Frank's favorite thing was to carry a handful of salt into the field and pick, salt, and eat the plump, juicy tomatoes right off the vine.

The three boys would hang out in the three-story barn making things, as well as breaking things, including Frank's foot one night when Coleman decided they were going to have a clandestine meet-up with some neighboring girls. Frank was a little young to be thinking about girls, but Coleman and Marshall had planted the seed of a different crop in his psyche—the female sex. Coleman, Frank, and Earl snuck out of the house barefoot one night, after Bessy had read to them from Frank's book, and gone to bed. The boys ran through the fields to the next farmhouse where a pretty young girl named Lucy lived. She had informed Coleman that her two cousins were visiting and she dared him to meet her after midnight in their barn. The boys, anxious and excited to flirt with some pretty girls, arrived a bit early and no one was in the barn yet. So, Coleman had the bright idea to tap on Lucy's window to see if he could get her attention. He went to the window that he thought was her room and tapped lightly on the glass, but there was no answer. Suddenly the porch light came on and the front door swung open, but it wasn't Lucy coming to rendezvous with the three over-eager boys. Instead it was her irate father standing on the front porch with a loaded shotgun. The boys stood frozen under the window until her dad raised the gun over his head and fired it into the air. Frank took off running like a scared jackrabbit and ran straight off a six-foot high embankment in the dark. He did his best to try not to scream, but he realized that he had most definitely broken his foot. He tried, but he couldn't walk so Coleman ran back to Bessy's get the truck and come back for Frank in order to get him back to the farm. Frank was insistent that he didn't want to see a doctor, or let Virginia know what had happened, so Bessy applied mud poultices on his foot for a week until he was able to get up and hobble around. He spent that week limping around the farm with an old cane of his grandfathers, even though the pain was excruciating. By the time Virginia came to pick Frank up, he forced himself to walk on his foot as normal as possible keeping her none the wiser about his broken bone.

Austin not only disliked, Frank, but he also had a problem getting along with his younger brother, Coleman. Their disdain for each other was mutual and whenever Austin was around, they fought like cats and dogs. He treated Coleman much like Virginia treated Frank—beating him often. One day when Frank was visiting, Coleman got into a terrible fight with Austin who had told him to clean out the barn, but Colman had refused to do it, simply because Austin had told him to.

"You're not the boss around here," Coleman replied sarcastically.

Furious with his brother Austin took the plow line from the tack room and beat Coleman mercilessly—all the while Colman begged him to stop. Frank did his best to pull Austin away, but Austin was a big man—quite overweight for his age. He simply turned on Frank and started to beat him as well. The distraction gave Coleman a chance to run and before Austin even realized it, Coleman was gone. It was at that moment that Frank suddenly realized where his mother had gotten her temper. He had heard that his grandfather, Christopher Alexander, Coleman's father, had believed heavily in corporeal punishment and both Austin and Virginia been raised by this man who had instilled the same vicious streak in them that ran in his blood. Frank vowed at that point not to follow in their footsteps. When the scuffle was finally over between Frank and Austin, Bessy was furious with Austin for beating Coleman again. She insisted that he go and search for Coleman, but Austin flat-out refused.

"Aw he'll be back, he always comes back," he grumbled. "That no-count kid ain't my problem anyways."

But this time Coleman didn't come back. The boy simply vanished and Austin continued to refuse to search for him. Secretly Austin was glad that he hadn't returned. In fact, no one in the family, other than Frank, really tried to search for him. Leroy and Edward made a half-hearted attempt at driving around pretending to look for the boy, but they never found any trace. Coleman was Frank's best friend and he did everything he could to ask everyone if they'd seen Coleman—to no avail. Bessy was terribly distraught and anguished over her next-to-youngest child and continued to beg Austin to do something, but Austin refused to lift a finger to find the child. Bessy begged Virginia and Wes, as well as Jeanette and Geneva, who also made half-hearted attempts, but it seemed that no one had seen the boy. Bessy was such a gentle caring soul and she wondered how she'd given birth to such mean children as Austin and Virginia. How could they perpetrate such corporal punishment on their own flesh and blood she pondered? Eventually, she gave up asking for help and turned to the Lord to protect Coleman and bring him home when he was good and ready.

Right after Coleman ran away, Austin and Bessy decided to take Frank down to his Uncle Edward in Saluda, South Carolina for a week's vacation since he was so upset about Colman's disappearance. It was the first time he'd met his older cousin, Becky, who was quite pretty and very mature for her seventeen years in the world. The second night he was there, sleeping on the floor in her room, Becky came back late at night from a date and seemed to have forgotten that Frank was asleep on the floor next to the bed. She unbuttoned her dress and let it fall to the floor next to Frank, then she pulled a slip over her head. The lights were off, but the porch light shown through the window silhouetting her burgeoning figure and Frank was awestruck with the visage of a real flesh and blood, almost-naked woman standing in front of him. When she slid her panties down and stepped out of them Frank almost fainted. The next thing he knew she walked over to where he lay and pulled the covers off of him and then pulled his pants down and sat on him straddling him. She leaned down and kissed him and then took his willy in her hand and stroked it. Realizing that she had gotten Frank's attention, she situated herself on top of it and Frank's heart nearly stopped. When she started to slide herself up and down on him it took less than a minute to complete the deed. Frank had been so excited by the prospect of having sex for the first time even if he didn't really understand what was involved. Becky was a bit disappointed that he hadn't had time to please her longer, however she was quite proud of the fact that she had been the one to steal his virginity. That night the two of them quite literally became kissing cousins and from that day on she would remain his favorite cousin to boot.

Frank's family was large, with all of those aunts and uncles he could barely keep straight, but most of all, Frank liked Jeanette and Edward the best. Jeanette looked a little too much like his mother, however Jeanette's warm, loving personality endeared her to him. Frank would have been perfectly happy to stay with them indefinitely, but they already had five kids of their own. Unfortunately unbeknownst to Frank, Jeanette and Edward where having very serious marital problems and they eventually ended up getting divorced. Frank was devastated to learn that they were no longer together since it had been the only place that had felt like a normal, loving home to him. It also jaded him about marriage, since they seemed to be the perfect couple. If they couldn't make it how could anyone thought Frank? Now, not only would he no longer be able to go to stay with them, Jeanette moved into the town of Pickens. She could no longer even help out Bessy when she needed it. Surprising everyone in the family, Jeanette quickly remarried another man named, Carl Brazil. Together, they bought a laundromat and dry cleaning business. They called their new establishment The Community Washette a new-fangled 'washeteria,' as they were called at the time. Shortly after, Edward also moved away to Saluda, North Carolina and sadly, Frank never saw him again. On occasion, Frank would see Jeannette in passing, or he'd stop by the washeteria to get Cokes from the vending machine and chat with her, but their relationship was never the same again after she and Edward split. One day when he was visiting, Jeanette was in a serious mood, "You know Frank....if you want to meet your real father, James, here's his address," she offered a piece of paper with an address scribbled on it.

"You mean....James Dalton?

"That's right....James Dalton. He's your real dad, you know."

"Okay...." Frank said hesitantly as he took the note from her. Frank was uncertain whether this man, who was his father in name only, would actually want to meet him. But more importantly, Frank was even more uncertain whether he wanted to meet him. After all, the man had deserted him before he could remember and had made no apparent effort to find him. Frank studied the address and to his shock and surprise, the man lived no more than thirty minutes away in the next county. He thought about the prospect of meeting his biological father for a few weeks and finally got up the nerve to hitchhike to the address on the paper. When he reached the address on the mailbox, he stopped and studied the modest house. Hesitantly, he opened the gate and walked up the steps to the front porch. He could hear children talking through the screen and he started to turn and leave, but he mustered up the courage and hesitantly knocked on the door. A minute or so passed and just as he turned to leave, a young, Hispanic woman came to the door, "Can I help you?" she asked with a heavy accent.

"I'm....Frank Dalton," he said nervously. "I'm looking for my father, James Lewis Dalton."

The woman looked quite shocked and disturbed and suddenly blurted, "Sorry, I can't help you. No one by that name lives here."

Although Frank wasn't certain he believed her, he turned and left the porch, heading back out to the street to hitchhike home. His fleeting thoughts of finding his real father, who might actually be happy to meet him, were instantly dashed. Now Frank wished that Jeanette had never given him the address. At least it didn't feel quite so painful when he thought his father was far away, not right on his doorstep. Unbeknownst to Frank, the Dalton family picked up and moved from the county the very next day.

Virginia's other brother Lee was married to an attractive woman named, Carol—they had two children close to Frank's age—Nancy and Jerry. They also had a two-year-old baby named Jesse. Lee was a drunken gambler and was gone a lot. He would go to the woods to gamble in illegal stills and play cards and dice with extremely questionable sorts then return to the house totally snookered to beat up on poor Carol. Due to his total lack of luck he was constantly running to his mother, Bessy, to borrow money to buy more whiskey, or to pay off his many gambling debts.

Frank had heard tell years before that Hank and Carol had actually lost a son, Roy, who'd been killed one summer day when Hank was drinking heavily and driving his pickup with the three oldest in the back. He lost control of the truck and flipped it into the creek, pinning their Roy under the truck and crushing him. His insides had been washed down the creek and Hank was too drunk to do a thing to save him. As fate would have it, Jerry and Nancy were thrown clear of the truck and landed in the water un-harmed. The boy's name was never spoken of in the family. Frank had never heard his name mentioned until he'd heard the story from his young uncle Coleman.

Virginia and Wes would occasionally take the family and go over to Hank's to visit and check on Carol and the kids. Hank was a smart man, who worked as an electrician and was also skilled in many aspects of building. He was in the process of building a new house next to the one they lived in so there was a lot of lumber and other building ma-terials stacked next to their home. On one of their visits, when Hank was home and drunk out of his mind, he and Carol were in the midst of one of their knockdown, drag-out fights. As Virginia and Wes pulled into the drive, Hank grabbed a two-by-four and chased Carol around the yard hitting her over the head and across her back with it. Vir-ginia and Wes jumped from the car and restrained him, but Hank continued to try and get at her. Virginia yanked the two-by-four out of Hank's hands and threatened to swing it at him.

"Hank, if you don't stop I swear I'll beat you myself, just like I beat those five boys that day saving your lousy ass!" she screamed.

"You wouldn't dare hit your own brother, now would ya?"

"Hell, I'd as soon kill ya just like that guy, Hendrix, that shot pa!" she screamed still waving the two-by-four as she aimed it at Hank's head.

Hank froze for a second knowing Virginia well. He had no doubt that she wouldn't hesitate to clobber him if given the chance. He remembered it well when five of his class-mates had pinned him down on the ground at school and Virginia came to his rescue, beating the five boys bloody with a fence post that she'd wrenched from the ground. She had saved Hank that day, but now Hank had no doubt she'd do the same to him if he gave her half the chance. Frank and the kids just stayed in the car watching the entire spectacle unfold until Hank finally backed down. The boys thought the spectacle was better than the shoot-out at the OK Corral. Frank had heard rumors at school about his mom shooting that guy that had killed his grandpa, but until that moment, he'd thought it to be nothing more than hogwash. Now, he suddenly realized that given the chance, Virginia just might kill him someday with that temper of hers and her unrestrained superwoman strength when she got mad.

Poor Aunt Carol was badly hurt, with a split head bleeding all over, as well as a broken rib, but she refused to go to the doctor for her injuries. She was afraid that Hank would only retaliate later if she reported the attack.

On one of the future visits they made to visit Hank and Carol, their kids, Jerry and Nancy, asked Virginia if Frank could spend the night to play with them. It was Saturday and they were off work for the whole weekend, so to Frank's surprise, Virginia agreed to let him stay over. Frank was thrilled that he would actually have the night off from tending to the children and would just be able hang out and play with his cousins like a normal kid.

That night when Frank and Jerry were playing sheriff and bank robber from the old west, Nancy came out of Carol's bedroom with a gold ladies watch and handed it to Frank. "Look what I've got. I got gold," Nancy preened showing off the watch to Frank.

"Wow, is it real gold?" Frank asked.

"Of course it is," Nancy smiled. "Do you want it?" she asked casually. "You can have it if you let me play with you two."

"Okay," said Frank, looking at Jerry who shrugged. "Are you sure I can have it?" Frank questioned.

"Sure....it don't work no way....mama don't want it."

"Okay," answered Frank hesitantly, studying the watch. Then he stuffed it in his pants pocket, "Thanks," replied Frank to Nancy, "So who you wanna be....the saloon girl or the storekeeper?" Frank questioned.

"I wanna be the bank teller," she answered matter-of-factly.

"But girls can't be bank tellers," insisted Frank.

"And why not? If you don't let me be the bank teller then I want the watch back," Nancy demanded.

Frank hesitated a moment, shoving his hand in his pocket feeling the watch, then relented, "Oh okay....you can be the teller I guess."

Frank spent the night there that night and took the watch home with him the next morning, forgetting it was in his pocket. That afternoon, Carol called Virginia and told her that Nancy said Frank had stolen her gold wristwatch. Virginia hung up the phone and shouted, "Frank you get in here this minute!" she demanded.

Frank came in from his bedroom recognizing the tone of her voice—he knew he was in some kind of trouble.

"Did you steal Aunt Carol's watch?"

Frank just stood there like a deer in the headlights with his hand in his pocket fingering the gold band.

"Well....did ya?"

Frank just shook his head no, "I don't know what you're talking about," he said nervously.

"Cause Carol says Nancy told her you stole it from her dresser."

Once again, Frank denied even knowing about the watch. He was starting to panic—knowing this was going to end badly for him. He desperately wanted to run, but Virginia was between him and the door. He was scared to confess that he had the watch, even though he was told that he could have it by Nancy. It seemed that his cousin had set him up and thrown him under the bus, and now he was going to get it good from his mother who was already steaming mad—not certain whether to believe Frank or Carol.

Carol continued to call over and over again insisting to Virginia that Frank had the watch. So every time she asked and he said, "No," she slapped him in the face with an open hand. After the third call she started punching him in the face with her fist. "I'm not asking again! Did you steal that watch?!"

Frank continued to deny having the watch, but when Carol called and argued with Virginia several more times that night, Frank finally confessed that Nancy had given him the watch. "Nancy gave it to me," he screamed as Virginia held him in a headlock and punched him in the face. "She said it didn't work and her mama didn't want it no more!"

At that point Virginia lost it and really started to whale on him, as she continued to punch him in the face until it was bloody and swollen and he could barely open his eyes. "Get out there and cut me the thickest switch you can find. And you know damn well I'll send you back if you bring back a feeble one!"

Frank knew he was in trouble and he contemplated the consequences of running, but he knew that it would only make things worse if he did. Where would he go? To Bessy's? But he knew Virginia would find him and then she'd likely kill him and come up with a justifiable reason to the sheriff as to why she did it. When he finally returned with the strongest hickory he could find, she was even angrier that it took him so long. She pushed him into a corner and mercilessly switched him across his back until he was bleeding so badly his shirt was soaked with blood. All the while she hollered, "I'm going to kill you! I'll cut the blood right out of you!" She kept screaming, not worrying about what the neighbors could hear.

Frank begged and pleaded for her to stop, but she kept right on, whip after whip after whip. "Pleeeeease....stop, please...." he begged.

But she was like a madwoman with a deranged look in her eyes as if she was enjoying it. It seemed that sheer violence got her off somehow. When she finally stopped and saw what she'd done, she screamed for Wes to drive Frank to Bessy's house. "Get him outta my sight," she yelled at Wes. "I outta kill you....I should've killed you when you was born!"

By the time they reached Bessy's house an hour away, the blood on Frank's back had dried and his shirt was imbedded in his wounds. His grandmother was shocked to see what torture Virginia had inflicted on her grandson this time and she went to work trying to ease the boy's pain. Bessy had to soak Frank's back with a warm, wet cloth to soften the scabs in order to pull the shirt away from the scabs and dried blood. Frank screamed in agony while she worked on him for several hours. Then she cleaned and dressed his wounds and put him to bed, but it would be months before he could sleep on his back. Frank's face was also black and blue so she chipped some ice to try and take the swelling down on his cheeks and around his eyes and lips. She sat down next to him and read to him from his beloved Dalton book....

"'The summer of our doom year was coming to full flush. Yellow ripe ran the wild grass to the rippling winds. Cattle sought the shade and switched interminably at the flies. Frogs croaked in the pools after thundershowers. Buzzards hung high in the blue, searching, searching. Ravaging 'coons left the bleaching bones of fish along the creeks. In the weeds the mating call and battle cry of the lesser creatures thrummed incessantly upon the ear. In the shabby eaves of our sod shanty there was mourning. A pair of wrens had brought fledglings into a bright and sunny world, only to have them destroyed by a butcher-bird—a little paradise in an outlaw's roof suddenly turned into desolation....Life and death in the wild incitements of July. And in our bones too, a fever.

July, The "Outlaw's Moon," as the author of the astrologer's zodiac might well have named a midsummer sign, was rising. Brightly agitating, it gleamed upon the red rivers of the old Indian lands and beckoned through the portholes of our dugout. But black were the shadows it cast in the little prairie town of Woodward where Eugenia Moore watched its growth with troubled eyes, night by night, from the window of a friendly shelter. For Eugenia Moore and Bob Dalton this silver blaze in the sky was to be the last lover's moon, and she seemed to have some fore-knowledge of its portent.

Two dreads lay close together in Eugenia's heart. One was the ever present worry about Bob's safety. The other was about herself, for Eugenia, like Bob was a refugee. Her Nemesis was an encroaching malady; it was harder to shake off than hounding posses. These two shadows had dimmed her hope of marriage. It just wasn't in the cards, but Eugenia was gambler enough to make no complaint at the deal. Like a good gambler she masked her ill luck with a smiling shrug. Only the good folk with whom she lived in the little Woodward house could see that autumn leaves were already falling in her dark eyes while yet summer tossed the green and vital outside. They thought she might feel better out in New Mexico and suggested that she go....'

'....The moon was sinking toward No Man's Land when again they stood beside his horse at the picket fence.

"I've been thinking about going back to New Mexico," said the girl, ever so casually. "I like that country—where you and I first met, Bob. You couldn't come along, could you?

"Like to," said Bob, but I've got a little job to 'tend to first—something the boys and I have been sort of speculating about."

"You mean—that kind of business?" she asked significantly.

Bob admitted it. The Dalton gang had already planned another raid. Bob was loath to give it up for mere sentimental consideration. I'm sure he did not then know how rapidly Eugenia's illness had progressed....If the girl felt a pang in the fact of the inevitable, she hid it well.

"You go along out to Silver City," he said. "I know you feel

better there. I'll be joining you soon—if I live." He gave her money for the trip. *"Take care of yourself, little girl, there's not much else in this world I care about."* She watched him ride away....*The marigolds were dark in the shadow along the garden walk.'"*

It seemed to Frank that it was also the summer of his doom. He stayed with Bessy for the rest of the week and then another, and although Bessy did her best to stop Virginia from taking him back, she insisted that Frank come home with them, back to the Mill Hill House.

Frank was unable to go outside, or go to school for weeks due to his battered face, but Virginia made up a lie that he had the mumps and couldn't return to school. Bessy berated Virginia about the beating, as did other family members, but everyone was just a bit afraid of her wrath. It seemed that not much could be done to reason with her insane assaults on the boy now that Mack was no longer a serious threat to her. She had been raised on Proverbs 13:24 by her father—"He that spareth his rod hateth his son: but he that loveth him chasteneth him betimes," a quote that Christopher would rant when he was beating Austin and Virginia, his two oldest. By the time his last came along he was tired and just didn't seem to care anymore if his offspring ran wild. Virginia also knew that should a family member turn her into the police for 'child abuse,' punishment for such a deed would consist of negligible action since excessive corporal punishment was not considered a crime in the state of South Carolina. The court would likely only order that the person's name be entered in the central registry, 'if' there was a preponderance of evidence. But what did she care? After all, she'd already spent time in prison for attempted murder. What would her name on some additional county record do to tarnish her reputation?

Eventually, Frank went back to school, and gradually the scars started to heal—at least the physical ones. The emotional ones would remain so embedded that Frank would do everything he could to bury them deep behind the steel trap door in his mind. He kept his distance from Virginia as she did with him and she spoke little to him after that day of the beating. For Frank, it was perfectly okay that she acted much of the time as if he were invisible. Christmas came and went and Johnny and Carolyn got lots of toys and other presents. As far as Frank's Christmas presents went, he only received whatever article of clothing he needed for school that year—a sweater from Sears and Roebuck and nothing more. It seemed that Frank was totally pushed aside—no longer a member of the family. Wes said little as Virginia now vocalized her frustration berating him, instead of Frank—calling him stupid and useless. It seemed that everything that was wrong in her life was either Wes' or Frank's fault. Wes would simply sit smoking and drinking a Coca-Cola with a BC powder on the side and stare into space as if he were totally tuning her out.

Luckily, a few of Frank's aunts and uncles would give him comic books since it did seem to help his reading skills and also helped him to retreat into his fantasy world. Whenever he was able to go to stay with his grandmother, she helped him to read the Dalton book where he was able to escape to into his wild west world—the life of a gunslinger in the Old West.

CHAPTER TEN

A Reckoning

1948 / 1888 — Dead or Alive?

It was the end of summer 1948, however fall had yet to make an appearance with the long hot Indian summer still scorching the earth. Frank's physical scars had healed for the most part but his emotional ones felt much like the scars left in the dirt after the harvest—stalks lay on the ground and vines shriveled in the sun. Frank's spirit had been broken by Virginia and he did his best just to get out of bed in the mornings to get Carolyn and Johnny ready for school.

Ever since the world war had ended there was a hope that had awakened in the residents of Pickens County. Even the bankers held a positive outlook for the future. Somehow with Austin's wheeling and dealings with the bank, Wes and Virginia were able to buy a farm five or six miles southeast of Easley, which would allow Frank to continue going to the same school. However, he would have to walk several miles to catch the bus, which meant he had to get up that much earlier. Johnny and Carolyn attended a one-classroom school for all grades and Frank would have to walk them to school on his way to catch his bus and then walk them home when he returned in the afternoons.

Frank tried cutting across the neighboring fields to shorten his walk to one mile, however it seemed that the farmer's bull was not up for having anyone trespassing on his turf. The first time Frank slipped over the fence and started his stroll across the frozen remains of a cornfield, he was feeling quite smart that he would make it to his bus stop in half the time. That was until good old Ferdinand got a whiff of his scent upwind and started pawing the ground and snorting. This quickly caught Frank's attention and he realized he was in serious trouble when he saw the bull glaring at him—shaking his head. When the bull turned to show him his side, Frank knew he was in imminent danger. He took off running as fast as he could towards the fence, making it only seconds before the giant animal rammed into the wooden slats, shattering them to pieces as Frank fell to the ground and rolled under the fence in time to avoid becoming a shish kebab. A week or so later he was foolish enough to attempt taking that short-cut once more, only to decide as he climbed over the fence that he shouldn't temp fate when it came to learning one of life's lessons. Indeed, one round with that bull was enough and he determined that walking that extra mile was much better for his health, since he didn't really want any holes bored into his body by a two thousand pound bovine.

At that point, Frank was so far behind in school that they simply kept him in the back of the classroom so he didn't interfere with the other students' progress. Due to his 'dunce' status in class, most of the kids teased him and called him dumb. Frank heard it so often he started to believe they were right—maybe he was dumb. Most of the time he did his best to ignore them and kept to himself. It was a rare day that he was ever allowed to go out during recess since he was usually busy catching up on homework from the day before. The days were long and boring and Frank struggled to make himself attend class every day. Some days, he simply cut school and hung out in the pasture—Virginia and Wes being none the wiser.

When they moved to the farm, Frank got a reprieve from his usual hard labor. Strangely, Virginia didn't force him to help with the move. Instead, they dropped him off at Bessy's farm, while they transported everything to their new home. Frank was thrilled to have a few days with his uncles and grandmother, not to mention the fact that he avoided cleaning the new house and hauling their furniture on and off the truck. Best of all, he was thrilled to have any amount of time away from Virginia.

The farm had a modest two-bedroom house with a kitchen, dining room, living room, and electricity. Unfortunately, they had digressed in conveniences and lost the indoor plumbing that the Mill Hill house had afforded them. This house was old style with an outhouse and a well and pump in the backyard and it even lacked an icebox to store milk and food. To keep the milk fresh and cool it required straining it through cheesecloth and lowering the bucket into the well water to keep it fresh. The best part of the farm other than the expansive pasture and the solitude, as far as Frank was concerned, was the huge creosote barn, which contained a complete blacksmith shop. Frank loved to fire up the farrier's pit and heat metal and pound on it, making nothing, but it succeeded in expelling his pent up frustrations. He even thought that one day he might learn to be a blacksmith. After all, it would come in handy if he became a cowboy or an outlaw since he'd be able to shoe his own horses.

About fifty yards from the house flowed a wide, clean stream—well stocked with large fish, but Frank had little time to catch them. There was also a June apple tree that promised some amazing yellow and red apples.

Since this house had a radio, he was able to listen every evening to the Lone Ranger on WCKY, while cleaning up after the children and the dinner dishes. Frank loved to listen to the radio stories, however he tried hard not to show how much he enjoyed it since he knew that to spite him, Virginia would deprive him of anything he truly cared about. As usual, not much had changed in the cuisine department in the Holliday household since cornbread or cornpone was still about the only thing Virginia could cook. Once in a while they would have some ham or eggs from their chickens, but Virginia felt that after a long day at work, she shouldn't have to cook dinner.

Frank wasn't exactly knowledgeable in the kitchen, even though Bessy had taught him a few things like fried green tomatoes and fried squash and okra, so once in a while he would prepare a dish or two for himself if someone gave him the vegetables, or he stole them from a neighboring farm. But he never gave up the secret that he could cook when Virginia was around. In fact, he stayed out of the house whenever she was home. He chose to keep things a secret from her for the most part, since he was certain he'd be forced to do one more job in the household—chief cook. After all, he was already the bottle washer and nanny of the house.

Of course, with the new farm came many new expectations of Frank's indentured servitude to the family. Aside from his already assigned duties with the care of the children, Frank was now expected to do all the chores on the farm such as milking the cows, cleaning the stalls, feeding and watering the animals as well as turning them out to pasture and returning them to the stable when it was too cold, or time for them to eat. Their livestock now included dozens of chickens, five cows, a goat and a mule, as well as a wild flock of guinea hens. On Saturdays, Frank was expected to work on the farm from sunup to sundown doing chores, but since there was no church close by, Frank did get some time to himself on Sundays, since he didn't have to dress and take the children to bible school. Luckily, Wes and Virginia were now working day shifts at the mill, so Frank had time to himself in the afternoons without them around. Some days after finishing his chores he would just wander out into the fields and sit for a while thinking— wondering for what reason he'd been born. Was it just so that Virginia would have someone to torment? Or, did God have a greater purpose for him? It was a burning question that he was unable to find the answer to.

After that terrible beating at the Mill Hill house, Frank had fallen into a deep depression. It may not have killed his body, but it had done irreparable damage to his spirit. There were days he truly felt as if he didn't want to go on living. What good was his life, he wondered? He'd learned about slavery in the south in school—a reality not so many years before he'd been born—likely right there on that very farm. To most of his classmates, it was an inconceivable notion to live life as a slave, but Frank understood how those indentured servants must have felt. He realized that his life wasn't truly that different from theirs, except for the fact that other than Bessy, Colman, and Earl, Frank felt loved by no one. Even the kids at school made him feel stupid and worthless. Aside from Coleman and Earl, Frank truly had no friends. He fell into such a dark place, those early days on the farm, as the scars on his back healed from the brutal lashings at Virginia's hand. It was such a dark place that he decided one day that he, and everyone around him, would be better off if he was dead.

One Sunday when Wes and Virginia had taken the kids to town for ice cream, Frank loaded Wes' shotgun and walked deep into the cornfield to end it all—all of his pain and loneliness. It was still cold and the ground crunched under his feet when he walked across the frozen soil and he felt a cold chill run up his spine as he gripped the stock of the gun. The cornstalks still on the ground lay as dead as his soul as he stretched out on the cold hard earth next to the stream and watched as the carefree clouds rolled past. Soon it would be spring—time to plow the earth and plant crops—but Frank decided he didn't want to be around to be Virginia's slave this time. He would show her that ultimately, he held power over her since she couldn't control his decision to leave. Maybe it would just be better to run away like Coleman had, but he had no idea where he'd go. He felt he wasn't smart enough to make it on his own and he knew little about the world since the farthest he'd ever been from home was Anderson. He'd never even traveled out of South Carolina, or even out of the county, let alone to a big city. He propped the shotgun under his chin and reached for the trigger. How easy it would be to end his suffering. But then he thought of how Bessy would feel when she heard the news of what he'd done. He lay there for a while watching a skywriting plane write the letters Coca and then he thought about the day Mack had bought him a Moon Pie and Coca-Cola and he realized that there was indeed one more person in his world that truly loved him. He thought of what had happened to Mack and how life as he knew it was over—Mack would never walk again. Then Frank felt his legs and realized how lucky he was to be able to walk and run whenever he wanted—but Mack— Mack would be bound to that wheelchair for the rest of his life. He'd also heard that Mack's manhood was taken from him the day that jealous husband had emptied his gun into Mack's belly and paralyzed him for life. Then Frank thought how could he be so ungrateful about his own life? After all, he was still whole and had his entire life ahead of him. He didn't know what it would be, but he vowed that day that it would be different. Maybe he'd be a lawman like Frank Dalton. Maybe he'd be an outlaw like Frank's brothers, but whatever it was, he decided that he would be sure that it would be his decision, not someone else's. It was then that Frank decided that he would find a way to get away from Virginia as soon as he could.

It was Frank's job to milk the five cows every day and due to his poor cattle-handling skills the cow would often end up kicking the pail of milk over, or sticking her hoof covered in manure into the bucket. After milking he would go to the stream to wash the manure from his shoes and face and any other place the cow had flung it with her tail. Then he'd strain the cow dung from the milk with the cheesecloth, pour it into a jug, and lower the bucket into the well to keep it cool. Of course, he didn't tell the family about the questionable sanitary properties of the milk, but he did avoid drinking it himself. To say the least, milking was not his favorite chore on the farm—not that any of them were. One thing was for sure—Frank did not aspire to being a farmer or anything that involved dirt.

His favorite part of animal husbandry was caring for the flock of sixty or so guinea hens, which had nested in the brush instead of in the barn. They were great egg producers as well as watchdogs since they were so noisy they would either scare off predators, or alert Frank whenever a fox or coyote was on the prowl for his chickens. Come spring however, Frank's newest job was to plow the fields with their mule so that Wes could plant his watermelon patch and Austin could plant corn. Plowing was a back-breaking job, and particularly difficult with their ornery mule, Balkin—aptly named since he balked every time they tried to get him to do anything. The first day that Austin instructed Frank to plow the field for him, he showed him how to harness up the difficult animal and plow the rows for the seeds to be planted. After an hour or so of struggling to make Balkin go, Austin insisted he whip him to make him behave. To show him how to do it properly, Austin took the whip from the barn and wailed on the poor animal, making him that much more obstinate. Frank was horrified since he knew how it felt to be whipped mercilessly. Finally, Austin beat the mule so hard he simply bolted, pulling Frank halfway across the field—dragging him behind the plow. After a hundred yards or so the harness broke and Balkin took off for the next county.

It took Austin and Frank most of the day driving around the area searching for their missing jackass.

"Why is it they call a mule a jackass?" Frank inquired quite seriously.

"Well you see....it's a cross between a female horse and a jack."

"What's a jack?"

"A male donkey, don't you know that boy?"

Frank thought about it a bit, "So what's it called when it's a male horse and a female donkey?"

"It don't work that way you fool, " Austin belittled him, laughing, "Ain't no jenny gonna give birth to a mule twice her size and a mule can't reproduce. This damn mule ain't never been gelded that's why he's so damn stubborn."

Frank knew what gelding was, but he was confused by the concept of a female mule not being able to reproduce. He kept quiet however, since he didn't want Austin to make him feel anymore stupid than he already did. It took them hours to find the animal and when they did, he was indeed half way to the next county. Problem was, the only way to get him back to the farm, since they had no trailer, was for Frank to ride him home. It was well after dark when he finally got Balkin back to the stable. The next day Frank tried again, coaxing him with some sugar cubes he stole from the kitchen cabinet. Miracle of miracles it worked and by the time Austin showed up that afternoon, Frank had the entire field plowed.

"See what happens when you do it right," preened Austin. "You just gotta show'em who's boss."

Frank just smiled and shook his head, wondering what was going to happen when Virginia realized so much of her sugar was missing. It goes to show you, he thought, how one could get so much more accomplished with a little cube of sugar than with a gallon and vinegar.

Eventually, Wes got his watermelon patch planted and Austin put in his cornfield. Spring slowly rolled into a wet, hot summer making the corn reach for the sun and the watermelon vines stretch across the mounds of earth as they sprouted tiny bulbous melons, which were culled down to three per plant so as to make them sweet and juicy. Wes' mouth was just watering at the thought of his tasty Cucurbitaceae fruit come summer. He could hardly wait for them to mature and ripen unfortunately, neither could Frank's, uncle Marshall, who came to visit for a few weeks in the middle of summer when Leroy dropped him off at the farm. One day when Wes and Virginia were at work Marshall got the bright idea to plug the melons to test to see which ones were ripe and ready to eat. Frank tried to tell him that they weren't ready yet, but Marshall was determined that he was gonna eat him some August ham, as he called it, before he left the farm in late July. Marshall took a knife from the kitchen and plugged two out of three of the largest melons trying to find a ripe one that was sweet and juicy enough to eat.

"I don't think this is such a good idea," Frank said nervously to Marshall as he forced Frank to taste test each and every one of them, to no avail. They were all still quite green. By the end of the day, Frank had the worst stomachache and pretty much the entire melon patch was deer, possum, and rabbit food. The shit hit the fan when Wes arrived home and went to the field to inspect his prize watermelon patch that he'd been bragging about at work for weeks. Virginia, of course, blamed Frank for letting her younger brother, Marshall, do such a stupid thing. Thank goodness Wes was not a proponent of corporal punishment, but they promised they would find a way to make Frank pay for his lack of judgment in the future. The only thing that saved him from one of her whippings was that Virginia knew her brother, Marshall well and knew that he wasn't the sharpest tool in the shed. But, no matter, she still insisted that Frank should have done something to stop him. There was also a small part of Virginia's meanness that made her happy that 'good for nothin' Wes had been deprived of his favorite treat.

After a few days had passed Marshall and Frank somehow managed to slip out of the house to go to the local Bijou Theater in Easley to see a double feature—"Billy the Kid Outlawed" and "The Mummy." Frank was thrilled at the thought of seeing both features in one night. Marshall manned up enough to admit that he was sorry he'd gotten Frank in trouble since he knew how mean his sister could be, so he paid the thirty-five cents for Frank to get in and even sprang for popcorn.

The minute Marshall went back to Leroy's house, Virginia sent Frank out to cut her the 'toughest hickory he could find.'

"But it wasn't me, it was Marshall that had the idea to plug the watermelons!" Frank howled.

"Yeah, but you let him do it, didn't you?!"

"I swear, I tried to stop him but he wouldn't listen," Frank pleaded to no avail. The beating came anyway, as it always did and there was not a thing he could do to stop it. Virginia had been certain however, to wait until her brother had left the farm so there were no witnesses to another one of her whippin's.

When she was finished she commanded Wes to make Frank plow under the watermelon patch even before the last remaining melons were ripe. As far as she was concerned, no one should have any of them including her 'dumbass' husband. Luckily, Austin had talked Wes into trading Balkin for a new, much larger mule. The handsome, new mule, Bongo, did just was he was supposed to do—work like a mule. So, Frank didn't mind so much having to go out in the hot sun and plow the field with Bongo, who obeyed his every command.

"And when you're done plowin', you be sure to clean out the stalls, and I mean clean you hear!" Virginia screamed after him.

"Yes ma'am," Frank answered as he slammed the screen door behind him. Frank plowed all day only stopping occasionally for a cup of water from the well and an apple from their June apple tree. It was dark when he finally walked Bongo back to the barn to feed and water him and clean out the stalls. Before putting Bongo into his stall, he poured corn into the wooden trough and shoveled all of the manure into the wheel barrow. Then he climbed the ladder to the hayloft to spread hay down below. As he reached the top and stepped onto the floor the board covering a large hole slid and Frank fell straight through the hole, landing flat on his back. Luckily, the pitchfork flew in the opposite direction of Frank, or he might have been skewered on its five metal tines of the hayfork. As he dropped to the ground he nearly hit the mule who panicked with fright and nearly stomped Frank to death. Frank did his best to roll away from Bongo's thrashing feet, but it was all he could do to curl into a ball to protect himself, because of his aching back. Frank lay there, with the wind totally knocked out of him, struggling to breathe for nearly an hour. He was certain he had broken his back and he panicked, thinking that he would end up like his uncle Mack—unable to walk for the rest of his life. In the time it took him to recover his breathing, his new friend, Bongo, calmed down and nudged him and whinnied nearby with concern. By the time he was able to stand and walk back to the house it was after bedtime and neither Wes nor Virginia had come to check to see what happened to him. That was typical—Frank knew no one really cared if he were dead or alive. Although he had not finished cleaning out the stalls, he realized that he was in no condition to continue and he figured he'd just do it at the crack of dawn, before Virginia was awake.

Of course, the best laid plan didn't lay out so well since Frank didn't wake up before Virginia and Wes and they realized that he hadn't finished mucking out the barn as ordered. Not only was he in hot water for his screwup, he could barely get out of bed due to the fall from the hayloft, but of course he didn't want to tell them what really happened. Virginia went on one of her rampages and came up with a whole new list of chores for Frank to do, which included her famous spring cleaning, even though it was the dead of summer. As always, she made Frank drag all of the furniture out of the house and scrub the floors down on his hands and knees to get it 'clean enough to eat off' she kept insisting. What Frank couldn't figure out is why anyone, other than a dog, would want to eat off the floor.

As the summer wore on, Frank did his best to steer clear of Virginia whenever she was on the farm and because of it she was starting to get fed up with Frank's habit of disappearing. The minute Wes and Virginia left to go to work in the morning, Frank quickly did his chores, fed Carolyn and Johnny and took off to his spot on the far side of the farm under his apple tree by the stream. He would use a seining sack to catch a catfish or a horneyhead, clean it, and build a small fire to cook his lunch. Once in a while he'd bring the shotgun with him and shoot a rabbit, skin it, and put it on the spit, but he preferred watching the rabbits run around gathering food to eating them and he stuck mostly with the fish and apples for his lunchtime feast. It was, he thought, the best he'd eaten in his life; since he was so sick of corn-pone and cornbread he hoped he'd never have to eat them again. He could live like this in the wilderness he thought— maybe he should just run away like Coleman did and live in the woods and be totally self-sufficient. He didn't really need anyone now that he was getting older.

Maybe he'd find himself a horse and go out west to live on the range like the Dalton boys did. They were totally self-sufficient when they were running from the law—but then they did have each other, so they weren't totally alone. Frank thought about it—maybe he could convince Earl to be his posse and together they'd go find Coleman. He'd always wanted to ride with a posse. In fact, so far that and hanging a horse thief were really the only things he could think of to put on his bucket list. That, and getting as far away from Virginia as he could, but he wasn't sure he had the guts and the guile it would take to be a real Dalton. Maybe, he thought, he just needed to get a bigger bucket, as well as a big horse. That day he brought his book with him and did his best to struggle through the pages reading more about his wild west ancestors.

"'THE FIGHT AT ADAIR

This was the "business" project of which Bob Dalton had given his girl some hint as they said farewell in the garden at Woodward. From our western lair we had skirted in to bivouac on the Neosho River, a few miles beyond Pryor Creek station on the K. & T. Railway—Bob, Grat, Powers, Broadwell, Pierce, Newcomb, Doolin, and myself. For two days we lay in the brush waiting. Our plan was to hold up the "Katy" express at Pryor Creek, a town of some fifteen hundred inhabitants, south of Adair, Indian Territory.

Before every serious undertaking it was our custom to put a stamp of fate upon the proceedings, to draw cards or flip a coin in fixing the various assignments of the raid. This was done to equalize the chances, to relieve Bob, our chief, from any possible cry of favoritism, and to shift any possible "jinx." I usually carried the fateful and much thumbed deck. Forcing the express car was regarded the most ticklish part of a train holdup; messengers were always armed, and some of them had plenty of fighting nerve. Boarding the engine was only a little less hazardous. Next came the intimidation of the train crew and possible fractious passengers. There was, of course, always the unknown factor—no tow forays were ever quite alike—which might shift the dangerous emphasis here of there. The gamble gave us a sharp preliminary thrill.

On the morning of the holdup I produced the cards. We knelt about a saddle blanket. Grat caught the deal. Up flashed the first card—the ace of diamonds—going to Powers. By prearrangement this meant that he and another member of his choice would take the express car. Powers selected Bob. The cards flipped around. Doolin caught the cock-eyed jack. He named Newcomb and Broadwell as his aids to cover trainmen and passengers. The king of spades came up for Grat. He picked me as his comrade to mount the locomotive cab. Finally the deuce, symbol of the horse guard, fell to Pierce.

"Liveryman again!" snorted Pierce in disgust. "If I was drawing for a stock ranch I'd probably get the goat!"

Bob toyed a moment reflectively with the ace of diamonds. Broadwell looked at him with enviable admiration.

"You lucky son of a gun, Bob, you always catch the top card. If you don't draw it yourself, somebody's sure to hand you the benefits of it!"

"Yeah," replied Bob sardonically, "I'm a bear-cat for luck!" I knew he was pondering life's erratic deal, his mind for the moment far away.

"Speakin' about luck," interrupted Powers suddenly, pointing off, "what would you call that?"

We all looked around. A man was coming across a little clearing. He halted and gaped with curious surprise, I could see him eyeing our rifles.

"Campin'?" he inquired politely.

"Just passin' through," someone answered.

"You ain't seen nothin' of any stray shotes?" asked the farmer. "They busted the fence right after sloppin' time this mornin', and I can't find hair nor hide of 'em." He angled off across the clearing, peering back once of twice, puzzled.

"Looks to me like a black cat crossin' our path," said Grat. We all did some sober thinking.

A few hours later the alert station agent at Pryor Creek had correct information as to our whereabouts and our number, if not our identity. But so sure was he that we were the Daltons, and so sure that Pryor Creek was our objective, that he frantically flashed the word to Muskogee. The hog farmer had undoubtedly carried the warning as fast as he could get to town. This gave the railway and express companies a chance to organize a counter surprise—an opportunity they had been praying for.'"

Frank decided then and there to put his stamp of fate upon his future and he flipped a penny to seal that fate. Heads, California—tails, South Carolina. He flipped the coin into the air and caught it in his right palm, then slapped it onto the back of his left. He lifted his right hand and his fate stared him right in the face—heads.

CHAPTER ELEVEN

Another Move

1948 – '49 – Austin's Wheelings and Dealings

When school started that September for Frank, he was starting into the ninth grade. He had a new science teacher that taught chemistry. It was the first time he'd studied science and he quickly decided that he actually liked going to Miss Pitts' class and learning all about mixing stuff together to get a chemical reaction. For the first time, Frank actually started paying attention in class and he really wanted to learn what she was teaching—maybe he'd finally found his calling—he would be a scientist. That is, if he didn't become a cowboy out west first. However, when he took his first science test and scored 100 percent, his teacher was certain he'd cheated since his previous grades to date had been so poor. For the first time he was proud of his grade and when she made him take the test over again, he was very upset. The teacher made him stay after school to retake the test alone and she watched him every minute, making certain he wasn't cheating. When he was finished, she graded it on the spot and lo and behold, once again, he answered all the questions right. Miss Pitts took her glasses off and walked around the desk to confront him. "So Frank, I don't know how you're doing this, but I still believe you're cheating."

"No ma'am, Miss Pitts....I just really like your class and I think I want to be a scientist."

"Do you expect me to believe that after eight years of failing pretty much every test you've ever taken, you're suddenly a straight 'A' student?"

"I, I....I don't know, ma'am.....I just like studying about chemistry and such. You know, I like makin' things and figuring out how they work."

"You do, do you? Well then, maybe you should be in trade school instead of wasting my time and the other serious students time here in school."

Nothing Frank said made her believe he'd actually scored a perfect grade on his own. Frank had been proud of the fact that he had received an 'A' for the first time in his life and he was crushed when they refused to believe that he'd actually earned a passing grade on his own. After that, he figured what was the use of trying and he simply gave up and refused to go back to school. Frank would walk that way in the mornings, then circle back to the farm every day, leaving Virginia and Wes none the wiser.

It was about that time that Virginia announced that Austin had sold the farm for them for a big profit and they were moving into town to a new house that Austin built, on McVey Ave in Easley. It seemed to Frank that their newest move was the result of Austin's wheeling and dealing and Frank was upset that they would have to move away from his newfound safe haven. He had finally found a place where he felt at home—not so much in the house with Virginia, Wes and the kids, but on the land. It had become his only solace and comfort and being in a small space with them full-time didn't seem like a good situation for him. Nonetheless, the move was happening and there was nothing he could do to stop it. He begged Virginia to allow him to go to live with Bessy on her farm, but Virginia wouldn't hear of it.

The McVey house was a small ranch style house with three bedrooms and an indoor bath. It had almost every modern convenience, including a fancy electric stove and oven and a modern refrigerator with a freezer. Most kids Frank's age would have been thrilled with the step up for the family, however Frank was feeling as if he really wasn't part of that family. The kids were now old enough that he didn't have to wipe their bottoms and watch over them every minute, so Frank decided it was time to start making some money of his own. Virginia and Wes assumed he was going to school every day, since he'd walk toward school with his books, but then he'd spend the day taking odd jobs to make money. He was enrolled in the Easley high school, but rarely showed up for class. He'd made a plan that simply didn't include school at the moment—to escape Virginia's reach and get out of the state as soon as he was old enough and had enough money stashed away. The only good thing about moving into town was that, within a few months, Frank had a paper route for the Greenville News comprising over one hundred daily papers at thirty-five cents a week per customer. Within a few weeks of the commencement of his first job, Frank had put together enough money to fix up an old bike he'd found in a drain by an old house. A little paint and some new tires and he and was in business and his new transportation allowed him to expand his route to two hundred twenty households. Frank realized that the delivering of the papers was the easy part, even though it took a lot of time. It was the collections from the customers that was challenging. Many would not be home when he stopped by on Saturday to collect, or they made some excuse about not having the money and telling him to come back later or next week. He was also taking odd delivery jobs for stores in town and before Frank knew it he was rolling in money, at least as far as he was concerned. Within a few months he'd managed to scrape up seventy-five dollars to buy a 1930 Model A Ford sedan from the old man who ran the junkyard. He figured if he had a car he could deliver papers to another 200 customers. The car was a little banged up, and Frank was too young for a drivers permit, but in time Frank figured he'd fix it up and sell it to buy something better. Although he was still too young to legally drive a car, he drove it home and parked it in front of the house. The minute Virginia laid eyes on it she threw a hissy fit.

"Where the hell did you steal that from?" she screamed as Frank walked in the door after his Sunday collection attempts.

"I bought it with the money I made from my paper route."

"You're too young to own, or drive a car!" Virginia screeched, waking Wes from his stupor on the chesterfield.

Wes stood up and shuffled to the door and looked out. "Well," he said, "I can fix that. Where the hell'd you get that boy?"

"I bought it from Doc Wade over at the junkyard....runs great....jus' needs a little fixin'," Frank answered proud of his purchase.

"I'll tell you what....I'll take her off of your hands and drive her to work 'til you're old enough. You can work on it on the weekends."

"But it's my car...." Frank insisted, "....and I need it for my paper route."

"Don't matter....you're too young and that's that," Virginia insisted and took the key away from Frank and handed it to Wes.

Frank was crushed. He was so proud of the fact that'd he'd made the money to buy his first car and had negotiated such a good deal with Doc Wade. In fact, part of his deal was delivering parts for him with the car and now he would have to explain to him that he would have to renege on his arrangement. He figured he would just have to find another means of getting around quickly. Luckily, when he told Doc about his dilemma, Doc took pity on him and showed him an old motorbike he had for sale. He told him if he could come up with thirty dollars, he'd help him fix it up. Frank, realizing he had to up his game on the job front, quit his paper route and went to work as a carhop at The Grill, the local diner, in order to buy a new, more efficient means of transportation than his bicycle. Frank worked hard at the diner and made good tips, however the owner, Bill Gillard, liked Frank a lot and that made his own son, Bobby, jealous. In return, the boy took to stealing Frank's tips off the dirty trays before he'd had a chance to clean them. Bobby was a bully and quite a bit larger in stature than Frank, so Frank was actually a little scared of the kid. He was also afraid that if he said something to his father he would believe his son over him. After a month or so of skipping school and working pretty much everyday, Frank had enough money saved to buy the used motorized Schwinn bicycle with a Whizzer gas powered, air-cooled engine. The bike was surprisingly fast and it allowed him to make all sorts of deliveries with the makeshift basket's he'd fashioned from found-wood scraps for the handlebars and the back seat. The bike was much cheaper than the Model A to drive since it took so little gas and Frank figured Wes had actually done him a favor. However, he sure did wish he had his seventy-five dollars back that he'd paid for the car. But, he realized he'd never see that again, nor use of the car.

It was about that time that Virginia started accusing Wes of having a girlfriend since he would disappear after work to go to the local filling station to have a Coca-Cola with his brother and friends. Up until that point Wes had never really pursued a social life. In fact, most of the time he sat like a toad in front of the radio listening to his shows when he wasn't at the mill sweeping floors. Frank thought the concept of any woman wanting to be Wes' girlfriend was pretty funny, since the man had the personality of a wet blanket. Not only did he sweat profusely, he rarely bathed, or washed his clothes. However, Frank had seen him standing on the corner of the station flirting with the woman who worked at the poultry farm as a chicken plucker and beak trimmer, so he figured maybe Virginia was right. But then, who could blame him when he had to live with Virginia every day. Frank just hoped she didn't kick Wes out—then he'd be stuck with taking care of her all the time.

Frank's little charade of pretending he was still going to school lasted almost a school year before Virginia got wise to his routine. She was furious when she found out that he hadn't been going to class and had been making money for the last year and giving her none. Virginia had gone to the high school to enroll him in tenth grade only to find out he had quit early on in ninth grade. Then she heard from her sister's husband, Leroy, that he'd seen Frank working at The Grill in town. As far as Virginia was concerned, if he wasn't learning, then he'd better start earning money for the household, or her.

Virginia told Austin when he showed up at the house around the end of September, about Frank's dropping out and making money behind her back. Austin managed to convince Virginia that he could straighten Frank out if she'd let him go live with him. He didn't need to be in school, Austin said. He would simply put Frank to work for him, picking cotton and then he'd take him to work at his sawmill. Most of all, Virginia liked the sound of her brother's offer to pay her Frank's wages. She was also kind of worried that next time she lit into Frank's hide, she might actually kill him, so she agreed to let Austin take him to live in the mountains with him and his family. He wasn't learning anything of value anyways, so at least she could make a little money off him.

"Okay, you take that boy and beat some sense into him," Virginia commanded Austin. Then she negotiated that half of his gross for every pound of cotton the boy picked would go to her. Grumbling, Austin agreed with a handshake. Frank had become nothing more than a business deal between Virginia and her eldest brother. It was harvest season and Frank went to live with him and work for him every day. Austin had leased acres of farmland from several landowners to grow cotton and it was time to pick it and sell it to the Alice Manufacturing Company.

Austin moved Frank to the makeshift house he'd built in a very isolated area in the Reese Mountains, north of Pickens. The house was rough, but had electricity, running water, and septic, so the place was comfortable, but very far away from everyone and everything. The nearest neighbors were a mile away and the nearest paved road over ten miles away.

Frank felt very isolated, however he was thrilled to be away from Virginia, but Austin wasn't a darn site better than her when it came to temperament. Austin didn't like Frank much and he showed it, but at least he didn't beat him like Virginia did. So Frank counted his blessings that he had a safe bed to lay his head on at night after an exhausting day of work under the hot sun. It was one of the hottest Octobers he could remember and Frank got lean, hard, and tanned by the Indian summer sun.

Austin would drop Frank off at the cotton field everyday with his mother's sister-in-law, his aunt Carol, who had thrown him under the bus for the watch theft, as well as another older woman and her husband, whose names Frank never knew. Frank did his best to ignore the fact that Carol had caused him so much pain—both physically and emotionally—he just kept his focus on those white fluffy wads of cotton everyday minding his own beeswax, as Bessy would put it. They would gather the cotton in canvas tote sacks and weigh it—then they'd take it to the barn and empty it onto the floor that was covered in canvas. Once it was all gathered into individual sacks Austin would deliver it to the mill and sell it to them by the pound.

Once the mill received the raw fiber they would run it through their cotton gin machine, or cotton engine—an invention of Eli Whitney from 1794, which would separate the seed from the fibers quickly and cleanly. The fiber would then be spun into thread and the seed ground into cottonseed oil. The revolutionary invention of the cotton gin had rapidly elevated the growth of slavery in the south, since the cotton industry suddenly became a profitable enterprise. No one had invented a machine to pick the cotton in the late eighteenth and early nineteenth centuries, so it was necessary to find human labor to do the picking. Thus, the gin was indirectly blamed for the outbreak of the Civil War over the Thirteenth Amendment, which was adopted into the U.S. Constitution in 1865, "....neither slavery nor involuntary servitude... shall exist within the United States, or any other place subject to their jurisdiction.'

This new amendment, of course, caused the northern and southern states to suddenly be in conflict over the abolition of slavery and the south was determined to fight for its way of life and its livelihood. Doing away with slavery would mean that the southern plantations would have to pay wages to laborers that they still owed contracts on, since each slave had been bought and financed through slave-traders who would find a way to collect on the debts no matter what. Southerners' very life-style was about to come to an end, since cotton was considered to be the foundation of the Confederacy. In the south, cotton was king since Britain, as well as much of the world, depended on the southern states of America to supply them with the textile. Many of those, in all aspects of the cotton trade in Britain, supported the south during the war with the north, since the cotton trade had been an integral part of Britain's manufacturing and import industry. The cotton trade had been threatened once for Brittan, when they lost the revolutionary war and America gained its independence. Britain, although claiming a neutral status during the war between the states, did everything in its power to support the southern states due to the fact that they were Britain's primary resource for cotton and the British ultimately believed that the south would win the war.

Frank remembered the day the teacher had taught her class about the ultimate cause of the Civil War. He heard her read The Thirteenth Amendment out loud and he wondered why that law didn't apply to his involuntary servitude under Virginia's rule. And now he was living under Austin's reign, which wasn't much better since he certainly didn't treat him right. At least he did feed him right, or Austin's wife, Claudia, whose life was about cooking, made him a feast for breakfast every day. She would cook up eggs and ham with biscuits and gravy, not to mention cakes and pies, but Frank would be up at five and hurried out of the house by Austin, so Claudia would put together a box of leftovers for the two of them to eat for their lunch every day. It was quite obvious why Austin carried a few extra sacks of potatoes around his middle and Claudia seemed to be working hard to also fatten up Frank.

Come dinnertime, when they staggered in from a long day's work, she would lay out a spread of chicken, fish, ham, peas, lima beans, squash, and fresh tomatoes. They weren't always home in time for dinner of course, since they had to give the workers a ride in back of pickup with a canvas roof. But, no matter how late they would make it home they would always find dinner waiting for them, warming on the stove.

"I could eat the north end of a southbound polecat," Austin would often say, slamming the door as he entered the house especially if they should happen to get home a little early due to rain and Claudia didn't quite have dinner on the stove yet. He'd smack her on the ass just a tad bit harder than a love tap and grab her cheek as if to show Frank that he owned it and would be certain to dip into some of that sweet poontang later. Then he'd kiss her on the back of the neck, "Looking forward to churning the butter with that honeypot of yourn's later," Austin would tell her for Frank's benefit, so as to sound like a big man.

Claudia was a good woman and a good wife to Austin,

even if he lost his patience with her every now and again and knocked her around a bit. But, somehow, even if he left her with a shiner she'd always find a smile for Frank, whom she called Precious, which in the south was usually a sarcastic nicety, however Frank somehow knew that Claudia really meant it when she said it and it made him feel special.

Austin and Claudia had two younger children, Prissila and Wallace, but Frank was quite certain that between the two of them, they only had one oar in the water. He figured they must have gotten their lack of smarts from Claudia's side, since Austin was anything but stupid. The man knew how to work any sort of deal to his advantage. He could sell ice to an Eskimo or fire to the devil himself. Frank didn't really get along with the kids, so he steered his own rowboat to the far shore and avoided as much interaction with them as possible. Frank often pissed off Austin, but Frank knew better than to argue with him so he just gave in and did whatever he said, even if he knew it wasn't right.

A man named Thomas Reese owned the property Austin had built his house on, as well as all the surrounding acreage for nearly a mile. Austin also leased most of the cotton fields from Reese, as well as much of the timbered acres where they jointly ran their sawmill business. The two men worked together every day and they would move the sawmill whenever they finished felling a stand of timber. It usually took them about a month's time to cut a new stand.

Reese's family lived there on the land also and Mr. Reese just happened to have a son about Frank's age named, Charles. Frank liked him and would walk the three miles of dirt road to his house to hang out with him, whenever Austin was engaged in family business—mostly, churning butter and dipping into Claudia's honey-pot. Most of the time Frank and Charles would shoot buzzards and wild goats up on the granite mountain. Charles was

Frank's only friend since Coleman left and he was unable to spend time at Bessy's with Earl. The two didn't have much else in common, other than the fact that Charles didn't go to school either. He'd been homeschooled by his mother, but he hadn't learned too much as far as Frank was concerned. He didn't even know who the Dalton Gang was or even about western comic books.

Thomas' brother, Henry Reese was in the business of illegitimate spirit production—he was a bootleg whiskey distiller to be direct—in the hills north of Thomas' house. Any random whiskey bottle was fair game if found along the road, discarded by a local drunk. He'd just pick it up, clean it, and reuse liquor bottles to sell his whiskey. The only thing he would have to buy were the corks. He figured that his rotgut was so potent that no germ could survive in the bottle, so he really didn't even bother to clean them out so good.

Austin would make the going rate a pound on the cotton he sold to the mill and he'd give a few cents of that to his pickers. However, Frank got nothing in exchange for his efforts, since he served as Virginia's loaned out slave, since Austin had been instructed to give her all of his money. Frank and the others were expected to pick at least one hundred pounds of cotton a day, each, which made for very long days. It took over four weeks with the four of them picking every day to empty the fields of all viable cotton. Frank figured that Austin must have made a pretty penny on their hard labor in the end. He also figured that Virginia was likely making more off his hard work and sweat than she actually made working at the mill.

CHAPTER TWELVE

The Sawmill

1949 – Austin's Indentured Servant

After the harvest was over, Austin took Frank up to his sawmill in east Pickens County, or wherever there was a stand of timber to cut. Frank worked every day with, Bill, the sawyer, who ran the massive saw which cut the logs into slabs—usually four per tree. Austin just dropped him to work with the other men and after everything was running smoothly, he would leave to go take care of his many other dealings. Frank's job was dragging off and bearing the heavy slabs from the cut logs to the edger, Ralph, who would trim the bark from the slabs as Roy turned them. Then they were set on a metal incline so they'd slide down to John to put them on the carriage for the slabs to be cut into lumber by Roy.

It was heavy work and Frank was getting tall and strong, but it was well into the winter months and Frank wasn't really equipped with winter clothing, so he had to keep moving to stay warm. He had no gloves and his hands got especially cold and torn up by the jagged wood, and cracked by the pine resin that got into his pores. But Austin didn't give a good god-darn about Frank's discomfort, or his hands, so Frank just kept his complaints to himself and did his assigned job.

Once the wood was cut into lumber, they would load it onto a truck, and then Reese and Austin would sell it to the Pickens Lumber Company. The two men, it seemed, where inseparable when it came to business and they would ride around together all day—Reese in his neat bib overalls chewing his tobacco and Austin in his torn and unbuttoned overalls, due to his huge belly. He knew he was overweight and needed to curb his over-eating, but he'd stop nonetheless to graze at every eating establishment they passed. Austin was still a young man, but he was working on an early case of diabetes, heart disease, and an early demise.

Frank had been struggling for the last year or so with a severe case of acne thanks to his teenage development and his poor hygiene, since no one ever took more than one bath a week unless something unusual was in the wind like a wedding or getting the business end of a skunk. So, Aunt Geneva took pity on Frank and took him to town one Saturday to Betty's salon in Anderson that Mack had opened for his wife. Betty was a beautician as well as an esthetician, so she applied some awful smelling ointment on his face and gave him a batch to take home. He put it on for a few days, but Austin's kids teased him so badly about the smell and the fact he had some brown goo on his face that he threw it out. Needless to say, it didn't clear up his acne. But as luck would have it, he was working at a new location for the sawmill a week later when they hit a nest of yellow-jackets in the ground at the base of the pine tree they were cutting. Frank was swarmed real good around his head— leaving him with dozens of wasp stings on his face and hands. His face turned beet red and his whole head swole up like a pumpkin. He quickly packed snow on his face to deaden the sting, but nothing seemed to relieve the severe pain he was suffering. Yellowjackets, although they look like a harmless honeybee, are the most aggressive of the stinging variety of insects. Not only can they sting numerous times, leaving fresh venom with each sting, they also bite if they feel they're in danger— and there was no doubt they had seen Frank as imminent danger. It was getting hard for Frank to breathe, so he started to panic. The men onsite quickly mixed up a local concoction of mud and spread it all over his face and Ole Bill whipped out his bottle of moonshine and stuck it in front of Frank "Drink up boy, it'll ease the pain!" Bill commanded and Frank did his best to comply through his strained breaths to choke back as many swigs of the rotgut whiskey as he could and still keep breathing. Frank sat in the truck, sweating, until the end of the day as the puss from the stings rolled down his face. He was in sheer agony and there was little other than snow and moonshine to relieve his pain.

When he returned home with Austin that night, Frank was a little lit. Claudia took one look at him and took immediate pity on Frank, "What on earth got you boy?" she cried when she saw his pathetic, swollen face and heard his irregular breathing.

"Boy done got himself in a nest of yellar jackets," Austin announced, "Done tole him to be careful of them devils. They love buildin' hives at the base of old pine trees."

"Oh my, my, you poor thing," Claudia crooned as she studied his face. "You just sit right down there at the table and let me get those stingers out."

"Forget the damn stingers and get me my dinner woman!" Austin replied angrily. He hated that she was giving Frank more attention than him and he wasn't about to let her touch Frank's face until he'd finished eating.

"Alright, alright," she said as she busied herself putting dinner on the table. "But would you at least chip some ice for the boy, while I finish up here Austin?"

Grumbling, he went to the refrigerator and came back in with a chunk of ice—shoved it at Frank. Claudia took it from him and wrapped it in the dishtowel from her shoulder and handed it back to Frank. "Here you go, dear."

"Thank you ma'am," Frank said attempting a smile turned grimace, since it was far too painful to do anything but grit his teeth. Frank pressed his face into the ice and did his best to settle his breathing. He didn't feel much like eating that night and once the dinner dishes were cleared, Claudia mixed up a batch of salt and baking soda paste and got out a butter knife. For several hours she gently scraped at his face to slide the stingers out, which were causing him continued pain. Then she smeared the concoction on his face and gave him a large glass of whiskey to help him sleep. As far as Frank could reckon, it was the first time he could remember getting drunk. He sort of liked the warm feeling of the whiskey going down and how it felt as that warmth spread throughout his body. When the liquor started to take effect he did indeed feel less pain and more relaxed and he suddenly understood how some of the old local drunks got that way, and how his Uncle Hank had turned into a drunkard. Frank decided that night that he'd have to be careful not to get to liking that sensation too much cause he could see how easy it'd be for a man to slip right over the edge into a vat of homemade moonshine.

The next morning when Frank came down to breakfast, Claudia had a black eye that she'd obviously tried to cover with powder, but she just smiled at Frank and said nothing. Frank felt bad that he had been the cause of her pain and Austin's abuse and wondered why a grown woman would allow herself to be beat on like that. His beatings were one thing since he was just a kid with no place to go, but he knew Claudia had family. But, he reckoned that having kids made it tougher for a woman to protect herself from that sort of quandary. One thing was for sure Frank realized; Austin was certainly a devil's concoction made up of the same vile stuff as his mother. That morning Austin took no mercy on Frank and made him go to work no matter how bad he looked and felt. As he was walking out the door with his full lunchbox, Frank turned to Claudia, "Thank you ma'am for fixin' my face....and I'm....I'm sorry."

Claudia just smiled touching her face and nodded, then looked down in embarrassment. Austin drove Frank to a new stand of timber that morning and the other men were already there, setting up the saws and slides. Thomas Reese had been feeling under the weather so Austin had scouted out the property the day before based on Reese's directions. Austin stayed to oversee the operation long enough for them to fell their first tree and then left for more pressing business—some other property transaction that he was putting together. They worked the stand for a month, cutting most of the trees on the five acres of land. Then one day an old man drove up in a Ford pickup and got out screaming at the men and waving his arms, "What on God's green earth do you think you're doin'! That's my land and my trees you're cuttin' down!"

Frank just froze and Bill stopped the saw and approached the irate man—spit a wad of tobacco out of the side of his mouth and waited until the man stopped yelling. "What you mean this is your lands, I do believe it belongs to Thomas Reese."

"Ain't his land, gosh darn-it!" The man spun around, pointing, "Over yonder's his land 'cross the street," he said with a flourish of his hand. "How the hell did this happen! And where's Reese?"

"Well sir, I believe he's a mite under the weather and told his partner Austin Alexander where to cut."

"Well, either he don't remember what the hell I sold him or Alexander can't tell his north from his south. He owns the south side of the road....I own the north. I should have known that good-for-nothin' Alexander boy had somethin' ta do with it," he said shaking his head.

"I'm sorry sir I jus' do what I'm told ta do," explained Bill.

"Well that ain't no good reason to strip a man's land down to kindlin'. You tell Reese, John Jones is gonna sue him for everthin' he's got!" By that point he was swinging his arms around and raising a ruckus as he walked back to his truck. "Now you folks better be getting' off my land and you best leave that timber right there where you found it!"

That night when they got home Austin was in a foul mood after the news about them cutting someone else's timber. Frank and Claudia, it seemed, were directly in the path of a tornado riding on the back of a category five hurricane as Austin ranted and raved, blaming Frank for the screw up. Of course, Austin never admitted to Reese or anybody else that he had screwed up his north and his south and cut the wrong timber. Reese was livid when he found out after Austin drove up to give him the bad news.

"Not only did you cut the wrong timber, but you cost me a month's worth of wages and then left the boards on the property, as well as the equipment! You can bet your bottom dollar you ain't getting' paid for this month," Austin screamed at Frank.

"Well....I don't get paid nohow," Frank retorted, making Austin that much madder.

Austin was so angry he started throwing stuff around the house and both Frank and Claudia were the recipients of flying tableware. A flying saucer even split Claudia's lip and chipped one of her front teeth. Frank received a few new bruises, but luckily Austin didn't draw blood from any of his wounds. Of course, Frank's face was still hideous from the yellow-jacket stings and you likely wouldn't have noticed any new contusions even if Austin had made a direct hit.

By the next day, both Reese and Austin were slapped with a lawsuit by Mr. Jones, and he seized the sawmill equipment. Reese was madder than a wet hen and fully blamed Austin for the fuckup. It didn't take long before the judge had handed down a verdict in Jones' favor, but he never was able to collect from the two men who had no intention of owning up to the mistake. He did, however, keep the sawmill equipment, which in effect put them out of the timbering business entirely.

It took several weeks for the swelling on Frank's face to go down from the wasp stings and with it went his acne.

Evidently, yellowjacket venom was a sure cure for teenage acne, or so it seemed, but of course Betty took all the credit for her famous cure and her secret ointment that had magically made his pimples vanish. Overnight, Frank had turned from a gangly awkward looking boy into a handsome young man.

Frank's year with Austin came to an abrupt end over the timber fiasco and Austin dropped him at Leroy's house screaming that he'd given up on the boy and he was washing his hands of him. It felt to Frank as if Austin were dumping a load of refuse from his truck, as he tossed Franks meager belongings from the back of the pickup into his front yard. Leroy took pity on Frank and drove him and his motorbike to Bessy's. Frank was mighty relieved and thrilled to be back with his grandmother. That was, until he found out that Bessy was about to lose the farm. Bessy was truly the only person in Frank's life he trusted. He knew she loved him even more than her own sons and it nearly killed him when he learned what Uncle Hank had done to cheat her out of her home.

CHAPTER THIRTEEN

The Adair Holdup

1892/1950 – Time Spent with Bessy

Frank was thrilled to see his grandmother when Leroy dropped him off at her farm. Bessy welcomed Frank with open arms, however she seemed tense and distant to him—not the happy woman he'd seen the last time he was home. He knew something was up, but Bessy wasn't talking when Frank asked what was troubling her. She just sat quietly saying the Lord's Prayer before they broke bread. But in the first few days spent at her dinner table it seemed she was praying a lot more than usual. It was only she and Earl at home now, but Marshall would come home now and again when he needed a place to crash and check in with his mother. Marshall didn't drink or smoke and he was the smartest of the Alexander siblings. Marshall was a type A personality and didn't get along with many of his brothers and sisters, however he and Frank had always been pals. So whenever he showed up at the farm, he and Frank would hang out together. They still loved going to the Bijou Theater to see Zane Grey westerns, or movies with Roy Rogers and Hoot Gibson. They even saw a big new movie called *The Grapes of Wrath*. It had reminded him of his poor beginnings and how he had high hopes of heading out west to find his fortune. The family in the movie had not found what they expected California to be and he hoped that he would have better luck than the Joad family.

Frank's reading had improved immensely thanks to his Dalton book and the comic books he loved to read. When Bessy sat down to read the second night he was home, Frank made the effort to read from the Dalton book to Bessy, instead of her reading to him, for a change. Since he'd read this chapter on his own a few times he started....

"'On the evening of July 14, 1892, the wires chattered with unusual intensity. So....something was in the wind...."

His reading was slow and Bessy had to help him with a word every now and again, but she was proud of the fact that he seemed to be a bit better than the last time she'd seen him.

"...Dispatchers along the line pricked attentive ears or transmitted code talk with flying fingers. What startling news the agent at Adair might have imparted to the depot idlers, the spooning couples, the waiting passengers—if dispatchers were not paid to hold their tongues. The Dalton gang was coming up to raid Pryor Creek, just a few miles down the track. They would run into a crashing surprise. Probably be wiped out to a man. News to thrill the entire Southwest!

But we had changed our minds at the last moment. We had anticipated the tip-off by the pig farmer. It was Adair into which the Daltons were riding. Even now we were disposing our horses in a little draw at the western edge of town.

Mind you, we had no way of knowing about the officers in the approaching train. They were indeed a surprise to us. It was the citizens of Pryor Creek we had figured on in making the last moment switch to Adai. The folks of Pryor Creek had had previous experience with train robbers; they had acquired a certain technique of resistance. We knew they would have given us a hot reception, forewarned as they had been.

Adair was familiar territory to Grat, Bob, and me. Bob and Grat had Marshalled in the district. Only thirty miles away lay Vinita, our former home. More than once on peaceful mission we had tromped along the depot platform and had boarded the "Katy" express as passengers. The streets were known. Now the scattered elms made deep pools of shadow along the dusty ways as we padded into town afoot. Over yonder was the station. Quite a few people about. At the last moment Bob had decided to let Charley Pierce go into action with us. Pierce was elated. He thumbed his nose at the horses.

"Ten o'clock," said Bob.

"Looks like we're going to have an audience," commented Powers, indicating the depot loiterers.

"They won't be around long," added Doolin.

Somewhere a banjo was playing, as we sauntered along. A child squawked: colic, likely. Lights burned dim and homely in the scattered dwellings. Far off a long blast quavered in the stillness.

"There she comes now," I said, "a little behind time."

"Five minutes late," said Bob.

That delayed arrival of the express might have seemed significant, short as it was, had we had the slightest inkling of what was to come. But it had only served to whet our tension.

A longer stop than usual at Pryor Creek had accounted for the lost time. As the Katy approached Pryor Creek, scene of the expected trouble, the window blinds on the smoker had been pulled down. Engine and train crew naturally knew what was in the wind. So did some of the passengers. The hastily picked deputies had become very quiet. No boastful blatting now. Behind the trio of seasoned officers the men hovered a moment at the doors. Cautiously they piled out as the train slid to a stop. As nothing happened the posse men again took heart. They began to strut again, importantly, handling their weapons pretentiously before the few hardy citizens who had remained at the railway station.

"False alarm," they chattered—with obvious relief, so the Pryor Creek folk later averred.

"The Daltons must got word that we were on the train," proclaimed a white-faced deputy loudly.

"High-tailed it to the tall timber, like them kind o' rannies always does when it comes to facin' the real thing," piped his six-foot-two companion theatrically.

"Yeah, they didn't have the guts!" declared a rough shooting-gallery proprietor from Muskogee.

"Well, we was fixed to give 'em quite a reception our-

selves," said the embattled citizens of Pryor Creek more mod-
estly, "and we aimed to stand by all night in case they had
something besides the express car in mind."

Thus the five extra minutes had dragged along. The Pryor
Creek station agent was wiring a message of relief as the train
pulled out.

"We'll make up the time before we hit Vinita," said the engineer to his coal-shoveling fireman, "unless we happen to get
a long stop at Adair."

The curtains in the smoker were lifted again. Marshall
Johnson, Kinney, and La Flore looked relieved. They grinned a
little sardonically as their henchmen piled boast upon boast as
to what they would have done had the Daltons appeared.

"We got a much braver lot o' deputies than I suspected,"
drawled Johnson.

"They seem right disappointed at missing a scrap," agreed
Kinney.

The express was stepping along. She whistled a strident call
for the way signal at Adair....

We had taken our appointed stand. Bob saw the semaphore
light flash on the depot in answer to the engineer's inquiring
blast. He was a bit dubious as to the signal. The loungers at
the depot and the station agent worried him too. He had Newcomb, rifles in hand, strode rapidly up the platform. In a
moment they had covered the startled group. Newcomb herded them into a compact roundup.

"Is that signal throwed for a stop?" Bob demanded of the
agent. The man nodded. "It better be," emphasized Bob, still
suspicious, "if you ever expect to throw another!"

"You can see that she's slowin' for the station," replied the
agent. Satisfied, Bob motioned him over under Newcomb's
vigilant rifle with the others. They huddled there in fearful curiosity of what was to happen.

Precisely we went into action. Grat and I swung aboard the
cab and covered the engine crew. Bob Broadwell, and Powers
were beside the now halted train, at the express car. Its doors
were closed. The messenger, too, had known what was to-

ward; he had locked himself down beyond Pryor Creek, prudently. Farther down the platform Doolin and Pierce ranged watchfully to cow any possible interference from train crew and passengers.

There was a peculiar reserve in the eyes of the engineer and the fireman after the first startled instant, as they faced Grat and me. A novice at stud poker displays it sometimes when he has an ace in the hole. We noted it and set it down to cool nerve. Engineers are selected from a kind not easily rattled, not even by an outlaw's "Hands up!" They know how to face risks and sudden emergencies. In none of our holdups did the engine crew ever show a lack of sand. They were wondering now, these two, when the firing would begin from the smoking-car arsenal. It ought to start any instant.

Inside the smoker the veteran officers suddenly had become aware of the singular quiet at the station. They peered out. Got a flash of Doolin and Pierce alongside the train with glinting rifles. Saw the strangely huddled and inert group in the depot shadow. Realized in an instant what portended.

"Well, here they are boys—the Daltons!" said Marshall Johnson. La Flore and Kinney grabbed their rifles and made for the platform with the Marshall.

"You're jokin', ain't you, Sid?" gasped one of the deputies.

"Hell, no!" rasped Johnson. Swiftly he issued orders. Tried to allay the surprise. Roused the men from sudden stupor. But as the trio of veterans disappeared, panic seized the deputies. Some stood transfixed. Others cast aside their weapons and concealed their badges, as passengers later reported. A few did muster sufficient courage to follow their leaders from the coach to the smoker platform.

Grat and I had taken the engine crew from the cab on the side opposite the depot. We got a flash of three figures scuttling from the smoker into the shadow of a coal shed close to *the track. Frightened passengers we thought. Too dark to see plainly....The trio were Johnson, Kinney, and La Flore.*

"We expected you fellers at Pryor Creek," remarked the grizzled old locomotive pilot.

"Well, we didn't like to disappoint you—and here we are," retorted Grat.

"Expected?" I exclaimed, instantly alive to what the engineer's unguarded words implied.

Rifles crashed from behind the dark coal shed. Bullets whacked against the engine, all around us. Johnson, Kinney, and La Flore had gone into action. The four of us—the locomotive crew and Grat and I—stood sharply outlined in the light from the firebox. Why were we not dropped at that first surprise volley, delivered from a distance of not more than twenty yards, is inexplicable unless the three officers were afraid of hitting the engineer and fireman.

Instantly Grat and I began pumping lead into the coal bin, returning two shots to their one; firing blindly because we could not exactly locate the officers. And even as we began shooting Grat yelled to the engineer and fireman, "Lay down on the ground or you're liable to get killed!" The two flattened to the earth. A bullet kicked a coal shovel off the tender behind me. Another ricocheted from a drive wheel with a high snarl. And still we stood unscathed. The engine panted lazily like some great immune observer, breathing jets of steam about us. For perhaps twenty seconds there was this sharp exchange of shots. The flashes came no more from behind the coal shed.

Either in this first half minute of battle, or later, when the shooting became general, Marshall Johnson, Kinney, and La Flore all were so badly wounded that they were out of the fight. These three of all the posse alone showed any sustained courage.

Ordering the engineer and fireman off the ground Grat and I forced them around to the far side of the train, where we joined Bob and the others. Echoing our own guns, we had heard broken shooting on the far side of the coaches. At the opening shots a few of the thirteen deputies had stepped out on the smoker platform with a wild flurry of brandished weapons and shouts. But they had scurried back with even greater celerity when Bob and the rest of the bank called their vociferous bluff with threatening guns. Not one of these vaunted fighting men received a scratch. They became the scoff of the passengers who had listened to their braggadocio and expected them to annihilate the Daltons. Some of them took refuge back in the coaches among the noncombatant passengers in expectation that we might come rampaging through the train.

Bob, Broadwell, and Powers had already forced open the express car. The shooting had ceased. Messenger Williams had shown no resistance. But he had opened the big through safe only after considerable delay, protesting that he didn't know the combination. Bo had just fired a shot close to the messenger's head when he heard an agonizing groan. He whirled around with a tingling shock. From behind a large box protruded the biggest pair of booted feet he had ever seen.

"What you doing here?" demanded Bob, chilled at realization that the man might have killed him.

"Just takin' a ride," stammered the fellow. "I come along with my friend Williams. Recon I must sort o' dropped off to sleep. What's all the excitement?"

Bob took his gun. Together with the revolver and the Winchester of the messenger, he hurled it out of the car.

"Sorry to bust in on your dreams this way, stranger," jeered Bob. "But we won't keep you awake much longer if your Mr. Williams will kindly oblige by filling this sack quickly." The tall fellow, we later learned was a boasted bad man from Texas. He had been placed in the express car for added protection. Powers kept him covered while Bob speeded the messenger in filling the sack with loot. Broadwell watched the door.

As the three of them leaped from the car, Grat and I were ordering the engine crew back into the cab.

"Get goin'!" commanded Grat, at a waved signal from Bob.

"This engine," retorted the old pilot, "is a mighty quick starter—I'm kinda proud of her that-a-way." His calm was still unruffled. In a jiffy he had the drive wheels spinning.

As we backed away down the darkened street, there was sporadic firing from various sources. The three wounded officers had managed to get aboard the smoker. The train gathered speed. The red lights of the rear coach glared at us balefully from the dark.

We counted heads. All present. All unharmed.

The town huddled still and lampless as we strode to the horses. Practically every light in Adair had been extinguished when the shooting started. But we sensed frightened, hostile faces watching us from those darkened dwellings as we passed. It seemed odd that the colicky child should still be whimpering. An age seemed to have passed since we had come in under the elms. The fight had lasted perhaps five minutes. WE were mounted again in less than ten. The telegraph ticker began to chatter in a frenzy as our horses thundered away.

This was the first time we had encountered anything that amounted to real resistance. Again I had heard the close sigh of deadly lead. The whole thing had been like a jumbled kaleidoscopic picture; flashes of fire, shoutings, running figures, bullets booming like bullbats in my ears; the haunting sense that my own weapon had perhaps taken some kind of toll in the darkness. It clung to me with nightmare persistence as we careered northwestward toward temporary shelter in the Dog Creek hills. I brooded the miracle that I was alive after that rifle crash from behind the coal shed. "Born lucky," I thought.'"

CHAPTER FOURTEEN

The Showdown with Virginia

1951 – Hank's Gambling Sickness

Bessy worried about Frank more than any of her own brood. Since Frank had been so badly abused by Virginia, Bessy feared that he would never have the self-assurance needed to make it on his own in the world. He had always been a sensitive boy and Bessy worried that Virginia had done irreparable damage to his self-esteem. But somehow, Frank seemed to be growing more confident by the day, now that he was no longer under Virginia's or Austin's thumb. He carried the Dalton book around with him pretty much everywhere he went, and somehow took his strength from just knowing that those proud, brave brothers lived in his blood somehow.

Frank was resourceful and found odd jobs around the county with his motorbike to help his grandmother with food money. He also helped Leroy plant some of the fields that spring when he brought his big John Deere tractor out of the barn to hoe the rows of dirt to plant corn, cotton, and string beans. He never had made any payments on the tractor and the dealer was still searching the county for it to repossess the machine. It eventually disappeared from the barn and Frank assumed the bank had finally come to take it back. Frank took it upon himself to plant a small patch of tomatoes, okra, bell peppers, lima beans, and watermelon for Bessy since he knew they were her favorites come summer.

Hank would stop by every other week to try and weasel money out of Bessy, but she didn't have much to give him other than maybe enough to buy a bottle of moonshine or two. She knew she was enabling him, but she'd never been able to say no to her children. Earl was a perfect example of her spoiling. Although he still lived with Bessy, he didn't hang around much, which was just as well, since he and Frank didn't get on the way they used to. Since Coleman, who was always the boss, had left, Earl had taken on the role of man of the house. He seemed to think he was smarter than everyone else and he talked down to others, especially Frank. Maybe he was threatened by Frank's homecoming, since Frank was his elder by a whole year and he worried that Frank just might want to usurp Earl's power in the final say as boss around the house. In the time that Frank had been gone, Earl had not only grown belligerent, he had become downright mean and his temper was beginning to shimmer as a reflection of Virginia's and Austin's uncontrollable outbursts. Maybe it was simply a mean gene that ran through the Alexander bloodline, but Frank sure hoped that since he had Dalton blood, he'd never turn that way.

So, needless to say, Frank didn't hang out with his younger uncle, Earl, anymore. Frank didn't like the boy that Earl had turned into and he didn't want to follow in his footsteps. Now that Earl was fifteen he thought he was old enough to drink so he would go to the bars in downtown Anderson and fight with anyone who crossed him or he'd just pick a fight for good sport. Nine out of ten times he'd end up in jail and Bessy would have to send Leroy into town to bail him out. This was a kid who'd had a pretty easy upbringing under Bessy's wing and Frank wondered if he'd have been better off being coddled by Bessy his whole life. Or, had Virginia's and Austin's wrath molded and hardened him into a stronger young man?

Frank was on the edge of seventeen and even though his ego was still in tatters from Virginia's and Austin's domination, he was bordering on manhood. Overall though, Frank felt me might not ever emotionally recover from Virginia's last beating. There's something that breaks in a child's heart when his mother turns on him and his father never even claims him as his son. But Frank kept that pain locked deep inside and did his best to act as if it didn't bother him. He had Bessy in his life, thank God, and she had molded his early childhood into one worth remembering. He recalled something she'd told him right after that awful beating he took from Virginia—"Sometimes it's necessary to wade through the darkness Franklin, my boy, in order to find the light." And now he was starting to feel as if could see the light at the end of that long dark tunnel that had been his short life so far. Frank had yet to run into Virginia and Wes since he'd returned and he was hoping that he might just keep it that way.

One day when Bessy was at the market with Leroy, and Frank was just finishing up in the field with the last of the planting, a sheriff's car pulled into the yard and stopped in front of the house. Wiping the dirt from his hands onto his jeans, Frank ran to the car thinking that just maybe they'd found his cousin Coleman and were coming to tell them where he was. He hoped the news was good and that the man in the brown sheriff's uniform wasn't bringing bad news about his best friend.

The sheriff got out and walked around to the front of the car to meet Frank.

"Hey there, Sam, how've you been?" Frank asked the man he'd known all his life.

"Hey Franklin....good to see you boy," the sheriff said, patting him on the back. "You've sure grown up since I last saw you," he said as he shook Frank's hand.

"Is it Coleman....? Did you find him?" Frank asked hopefully.

"I wish it was about Coleman son. I'm here to see your grandmother. Is Bessy home?"

"Naw she's gone to the market with Leroy. What you need her for?"

"Well I'm sorry to say the bank's foreclosing on the farm," he said handing the foreclosure notice to Frank.

Frank was stunned. He had no idea that Bessy was in

trouble. Had he known, he'd have found a way to get a good paying job and help her keep her home and her land. When Bessy returned it broke his heart to give her the bad news as he handed her the foreclosure notice. Bessy just bowed her head and closed her eyes tight, squeezing back her tears, wanting to be strong in front of Frank.

She spit a wad of snuff on the ground, "Knew it was just a matter of time....I'd hoped he'd live up to his word and was making the payments, but I should have known."

"But, who's he....how did this happen Ma?"

"Well....you see....your uncle Hank got into some financial trouble a ways back and I took out a loan on the farm to keep some very bad men from killing him."

"You mean he ran up gambling debts with those men in Pickens?" Frank insisted. He'd heard stories around the dinner table at Austin's about Hank's gambling sickness and the bad men that he was beholding to. Frank figured that by now, even though Bessy had bailed him out of his mess, he was likely in debt all over again and unable to help Bessy thanks to his bad judgment as well as bad luck—not to mention his sheer stupidity.

Frank knew he had to do more to help Bessy, since she'd done so much for him over the years. Leroy and Geneva had moved just down the road from his grandmother in Anderson when Leroy was released from the Army and they were both working at the Owens Corning plant nearby. So, Frank went straight to Leroy and asked if he could get him a job at the plant. Luckily enough, they were in need of some part-time laborers and hired Frank right on the spot when he went into work one morning with Leroy.

"Leroy's one of my best workers, so any relative of his would be a good addition to the plant," said Leroy's boss, Stanley Smith, as he patted Frank on the back. "Only thing is you'll need to bring in your birth certificate so's we can get you one of them social security numbers you need so you can get paid. You can start right away on a trial basis under Leroy for ninety cents an hour, but I'll need that number no later than thirty days from now."

"No problem Mr. Smith, thank you replied Leroy, delighted. I'll make sure to train him myself and we'll get you what you need," he continued leading a confused Frank away.

"But Leroy, I don't have no birth certificate. What does that mean anyway, and how am I going to get that security number he says I need?"

Patting him on the back, "Don't you worry none boy....I'll talk to your mama about it. She's bound to have it somewhere."

"Yeah but, she's gonna want whatever I make for herself and I need the money to help Bessy keep the farm."

"What do you mean keep the farm? questioned Leroy. "She owns that free and clear."

"Not no more she don't. Seems the bank owns it."

Frank told Leroy all about the foreclosure notice Bessy had received and Leroy was hopping mad when he found out what Hank had done.

"I'm going to kick his ass for going to her to bail his ass out again. She's always had a soft spot in her heart for that boy and he's done nothing but take advantage of the whole family! Between his drinking, his gambling, and his wife beatin', he's a sinner in the eyes of the Lord if there ever was one. And now he's gone and stole Bessy's home from her!"

"Please don't tell him I'm the one who told you and don't talk to ma about my birth certificate....I'll find a way to get it."

Frank went to work that day as a slava handler, working the two-thousand-degree melted sand as it came down from the hopper through a grate as it turned into liquid glass, creating several hundred tiny strings of glass thread. The trick to keep from getting burned was to keep his hands wet in order to pull the fine strands down for Leroy, the winder below him, who put it on a wheel and wound it onto a spool as if it were thread. He had to maneuver it quickly or it would bead up into a small ball of fire if he hesitated for an instant. Frank worked hard making sure to keep up with the winder since he didn't want his work to reflect badly on Leroy. This was his first job in a factory so he had to get used to relying on others to do their work and, in kind, he had to make certain that he did what was expected of him by the next man down the line. Frank had watched his mother work at the mill and although it was a very different material he was working with, it was a similar concept. Instead of making thread from cotton, they were actually making it from sand, or molten glass. Who would have thought it possible to make thread from glass, Frank wondered to himself.

Word, it seemed, got around quick in the Alexander family and when Carol found out what Hank had done with Bessy's farm she damn near killed him, since she was the one, this time, to swing a two-by-four at his head. She didn't kill him but she did take the kids to her family for a bit, until Hank came around begging her forgiveness and swearing to give up drinking and gambling. But, like a politician who makes promises to his constituents that he'll never keep, Hank got sucked right up his own bullhorn when, no more than a month later, he was back in that sawdust strewn shanty playing cards and rolling dice, not to mention sucking on a bottle of moonshine.

After the first week at the factory, Leroy saw how well Frank was doing and suggested finding him an alternate means of transportation than the little Whizzer motorbike. So, Leroy took Frank to a used car and motorcycle lot to look for a real bike. Right out in front a red and white Harley immediately caught his attention. It was a 1945, F 74 power-glide motorcycle and the minute he saw it, he knew he had to find a way to buy it. After a little finagling, Leroy, a keen negotiator, had talked the salesman into taking Frank's Whizzer bike as a down payment and the rest on credit now that Frank was gainfully employed at the plant. Leroy signed the note for Frank and within thirty minutes, Frank was the proud new owner of that Harley. The salesman was a little concerned since Frank had never ridden a full-size bike before, but after a few turns around the car lot without hitting anything, Frank rode off down the road smiling like Alice's Cheshire cat. When he pulled up in front of Bessy's house, she walked out on the porch shaking her head and drying her hands on a well-worn dishtowel slung over her shoulder. "What on earth you got there, now boy?" she asked then spit out some snuff—her teeth black from the juice.

"Like it?" Frank preened. "Leroy got me a deal to pay for it from my earnin's at the plant," he explained. "Hop on....I'll give you a ride."

Bessy just laughed, hiked up her skirt, and climbed on the back, hanging onto Frank for dear life as he drove down the road past Geneva and her kids driving in the opposite direction. Geneva looked stunned and confused as Bessy waved at them. Frank rode about three miles, made a u-turn, and then headed back to the farm, where Geneva and the kids were waiting worried to death. Bessy disembarked giggling like a school girl."

"Are you crazy Ma?! I thought that was you," Geneva exclaimed shocked when they pulled in.

Bessy spit her tobacco on the ground, "Well you can slap my head and call me silly, but that was the most fun I've had since I was knee-high to a grasshopper!" Bessy effused sporting the biggest brown smile they'd ever seen on her.

"How about you Aunt Geneva, would you like a ride on my new bike?

Geneva exclaimed horrified, "Not on your life would you get me on that thing!"

All the while her kids were jumping up and down squealing, "Take me, take me!"

"You don't know what you're missing," Bessy exclaimed shaking her head. "I don't know 'bout you, but I'm going to have myself some Kool Aid."

Suddenly, the kids were distracted by the mention of that sugary drink, invented by Edwin Perkins in the 1920s, and they quickly forgot about the motorcycle and raced to follow Bessy into the house.

Geneva turned to Frank, "If I ever catch you with one of my children on the back of that bike, Frank Dalton, your ma will be the least of your worries!" She then turned and followed her brood into the house.

One day while Frank was at the filing station he ran into a pretty brunette with big brown eyes, about his age. She was just coming out of the store with her sack of purchases when he pulled in and the attendant started filling his tank. Unfortunately, Frank was so shy, he couldn't bring himself to speak with the girl, but luckily, she was more outgoing than Frank in the flirtation department, and she walked right over to his bike, studying it with admiration.

"That's an awful nice bike you got there," she said as she ran her finger over the handlebars.

Frank beamed proudly, but was speechless–totally uncertain how to handle talking to a girl who obviously seemed to be flirting with him.

"You know I've always wanted to ride one of these things."

"Well....I....I could give you a ride back home."

"But my mama told me not to ride with strangers."

Putting his hand out, "Well then....my name's Frank Dalton. I work at the Owens Corning plant."

"Judith Maxwell," she said taking his hand to shake it, "But you can call me Judy. So now we're not strangers, so I guess I could take you up on your offer," she smiled at him coyly.

Frank quickly paid the attendant and started the bike. Judith jumped on the back with her groceries and wrapped her free arm around Frank's waist making him smile. He liked the feel of having her lean her firm young breasts against his body. It made him think of the night his cousin decided to teach him the facts of life. "Where do you live?" he asked.

"Just up around Hobbs Corners. I'm visiting my grandmother. I'm up from Saluda," she said gesturing to the south as they pulled out of the filing station.

That Saturday night Frank borrowed Leroy's 1948 metallic, maroon Pontiac to impress Judith. Frank had a few dollars in his pocket from the factory so he took her to eat at the diner he had worked at in town. Of course, everyone knew him by name and welcomed him back, which impressed Judith even more than the Pontiac. On the way home, he pulled onto an old dirt road near the farm, where he grew up, for a little 'parking.' He'd gotten a quick lesson from Leroy about how to conduct a first date and he wanted to do his best to impress Judith with his worldly knowledge, hoping she wouldn't figure out that it was in truth his first date, and that entire world as he knew it, was Pickens County. Instead it was her impression that he must be from means and importance since everyone in the town of Pickens seemed to know him. In fact, the thoughts running through Judith's mind were marriage, two kids, and a little house in Saluda near mom and dad, so she was determined to leave an indelible impression on him too.

Once they were parked, Frank just sat there afraid to make the first move, but Judith had no reservations in that department. She quickly took matters into her own hands and simply leaned over and kissed him gently on the lips, then grabbed his face and laid one on him, giving Frank the confidence to take it from there. This girl, it seemed, meant business and the next thing Frank knew, she had placed his hand under her sweater where Frank could feel her brassiere covering her firm round breast. He had often perused Austin's girly magazines and for only the second time Frank was getting the opportunity to explore the female anatomy in the flesh, instead of on the page. The loss of his virginity with his cousin had only been a quick interlude—not much more than a 'wham-bam thank you sir for your service' and Frank had not had the opportunity to really go exploring, or spelunking for that matter. As luck would have it, Judith seemed to be the more experienced of the two teenagers and as his tour guide, she led him through the most thorough tour she could muster, with Frank an eager and willing tourist. It was a tour, which even included a little cavern spelunking with his near-virgin Lilly Willy. It was the first and last date Frank would have with Judith, since she returned to her parents' home in Saluda the following week, due to the fact that her grandmother felt she was too wild and, she was unable to control her in Anderson.

It took Frank another week or so to get up the courage to go see Virginia at the mill. Since he got off work before her, he figured that seeing her at the mill might be a safe place to ask her for his birth certificate, so she wouldn't be able to wail on him or scream at him while on the job. She had heard that Austin had dropped him off at Bessy's, however she was still unaware that Leroy had gotten the boy a job at the plant.

"Ma, I just came to ask you for my birth certificate. I need it to get a job to help Bessy keep the farm....need something called a social security number so they can pay me."

"Yeah, I heard 'bout them repossessing the farm." Virginia continued pulling the thread through the spinner.

"What kind of job you talking about that you need that for?"

"Well Leroy got me a job at the plant. I kinda like it. It makes me feel like I'm part of something."

Virginia laughed, "What little bit you could earn ain't gonna help Bessy keep that farm. And I could care less what you like boy, you're too young to work a real job."

"I'm sixteen Ma and besides, it's not for me....Bessy needs help.."

"Hummph....that dumb son-of-a-bitch, Hank, gone and gotten himself and the family all deep into his gambling sickness. I tole him he would find nothing' but a gambler's ruin in that sawdust joint he plays poker in and drinks moonshine."

She thought for a minute. "No what matter he done or what ma needs, you ain't going ta work in that sort of job. You can work for the family, but nohow you're gonna be put on the books of some payroll. And besides....I ain't got your birth certificate anyways. You were born at home and you never got one."

"Then how do I go about gettin' one?"

"I don't know and I don't care. If'n you wanna stay with Bessy then it's your problem. Now I gotta get back to work."

Frank left the mill angry and frustrated wondering how he could go about getting himself a birth certificate. When he asked Bessy how to do it she was confused, "Now why on earth would you have to get a birth certificate, you've got one?"

"But Ma says I was born at home and she didn't have it."

"Child, I was there when you were born and the mid-wife, Miss Tina, wrote one for you. In fact, you were born in my house. I'm sure Virginia has it somewhere, unless she lost it moving around so much," insisted Bessy. If not, maybe the county would have record of it. We recorded it a few days after you were born."

Frank thought about why Virginia would intentionally keep him from having his birth certificate. Maybe she didn't want proof that he really was a Dalton. Or maybe she just wanted to keep him from running off like Coleman did. In fact, Frank had recently been thinking about heading out west, like the Dalton boys, to California and making some real money to send home to Bessy. He wasn't planning on robbing any banks, but maybe he'd find gold there, or maybe he'd become a cowboy on a ranch somewhere, or even start a ranch of his own. He wasn't sure—all he knew was that it was closing in on the time that he might be able to actually escape the noose Virginia had had round his neck for the last eleven years of his life—ever since she'd returned from prison and turned his world upside down.

Frank worked hard over the next few weeks at the factory trying to make a good impression on his uncle and his supervisor— hoping they'd keep him on after his probationary period. But the thing that worried him most was what he'd do when it came time to give them his social security number, something Franklin D. Roosevelt had implemented in 1935, the year Frank was born. He didn't really understand what it was, but it was certainly affecting his life at the moment. Two days before his thirty-day period was up, Frank rode back to the mill on his Harley to confront Virginia again. When he arrived she knew what he was looking for and she walked outside for a showdown.

"Ma says you did get a birth certificate when I was born. I need it, or they won't let me stay at the plant."

"Like I told ya before....you don't have one. Now I don't want to hear no more about it! Do you understand?"

For the first time Frank was feeling strong enough to not back down from Virginia. After all, he was a Dalton and the Dalton boys had backbone, guts, and guile, "I know you got it and you're keeping it from me so you can still control my life."

"I don't give a goddarn about your life, Frank. You just go on and do whatever it is you want! You always do!" she said, getting angrier by the minute—her voice getting louder and louder was starting to draw a crowd from the other workers as they poked their heads out of the door to see what kind of drama was on the airwaves today.

"I know you got it and I'm going to figure out a way ta get it....one way or the other."

"You don't talk to me that way damn it!" she screamed as she drew back her hand to slap him—stopping as she realized she had an audience of voyeurs lining up for one of Virginia's beat-downs they'd heard about. She lowered her arm and took a step back.

"Just do whatever the hell you want. I'm sick and tired of dealin' with you. I regret the day you were conceived. I've hated you since the moment I saw your Dalton face. It's cause of you he left me you know? Your real father, I mean. You think he wanted anything ta do with you?" she laughed. "His very words before you were born were, "I hope you and the baby die in childbirth." Virginia laughs sarcastically, "In fact, the day after you went to his place trying to see him a while back, he upped and moved his whole family out of the county to Columbia, South Carolina. That's the kinda man a Dalton is....spineless."

"Honestly....I don't blame him for running if it means having any sort of ties to you," Frank stated matter-of-factly and turned and walked away. It was the first time he'd summoned the guts to stand up to his mother and it felt good in the pit of his stomach—like the warm feeling of Bessy's Sunday dinners of roast chicken and fried green tomatoes in his belly. Not to mention just dessert—hot apple pie.

Frank got on his Harley, started it up and drove straight to the McVey house. He knew that Virginia kept important things in an old chest she'd dragged from one house to the other, so Frank figured that if she did indeed have his birth certificate, he would find it there. He even knew where she kept the key—in an old sewing box on her dresser. She thought it was a secret, but Frank had seen her hide it there many times over the years. When he arrived the back door was unlocked and he let himself into the kitchen. It had been over a year since he'd been under Virginia's roof and he didn't like the feel of it much at all. He wanted to get in and get out in case she decided to follow him back. He found the key in the sewing basket and quickly opened the old chest. Inside he found old clothes, photos, trinkets, keepsakes, and some yellowed documents. Quickly, he rifled through them trying to find his birth certificate. It was at the bottom of the pile of papers. He opened it to find his real name—Carl Franklin Dalton— date of live birth, August 14, 1935. He expected to find the Franklin Dalton part, but he'd never heard the name Carl before. He quickly folded the paper and stuck it in his pocket, then replaced the keys and went straight to his motorcycle. As he rode away he took what he knew would be one last look at the Holliday household and drove directly to the social security office to file for his number.

Frank had made his decision before he left Virginia at the mill that day, that there was no way he could stay in the county and work with Leroy. He knew in his gut that Virginia would never let him be. She would always be chained to her if he stayed there within her scope of meanness in Pickens.

He decided then and there that he had found his ticket to freedom and that he was going to follow the path of his forefathers—the Dalton brothers and head west. He'd heard that there were plenty of well paying jobs in California and now that he was legal to work he knew he could do most any job and get by. He'd just lie about his age and tell them he was seventeen. After all, he'd be sixteen in a few days and he knew he was tall enough to pass for a man. Frank had seen the Fox motion picture the, *The Grapes of Wrath*, at the Bijou Theater with Marshall and he liked the idea of moving west—leaving the poverty and the pain behind. Starting over with a whole new life. There he could make more money to send back to Bessy, to help her keep her farm, than he could if he stayed in South Carolina. It was 1951 and the economy was recovering in California after the war, but South Carolina was still living two decades behind the times economically and in every other way possible. On the west coast life was getting back to normal—people were getting good paying jobs, marrying, having babies and buying homes. The GI bill was allowing many of those who'd returned from the war to go to college and now they were entering the workforce and creating new commerce.

Bessy was not pleased when he told her of his plan to head to California and make enough money to send her what she needed to save her farm. "But, you have to promise me to keep it a secret, Ma....I don't want no one to know where I'm going"

"Frank, it's too late to save the farm and it's not your responsibility, anyways."

But, Frank wouldn't listen. He'd made up his mind for the first time in his life, since everyone else had been making it up for him up 'til then. Now he was free to do and go where he wanted.

Bessy plugged a dip of snuff between her gum and cheek from the tin she always carried in her pocket. "As much as I don't want you to leave....I know it's for the best. She'll never give you any peace if you stay here. You go on and find yourself boy. Find your fortune where your heart takes you." She gave him a hug a mother would give her son as he left her hearth for the world, knowing well that as with Coleman, it could be the last time she'd ever see him.

Frank had saved maybe thirty dollars, which he had stashed in his jeans pocket. He stuffed a few clothes and his Dalton book, his birth certificate, and a few comics in a brown satchel and left his bike with a note for Leroy, thanking him for trusting him with the job and the bike, but explaining that he couldn't stay. With the little cash he had, Frank figured he could hitchhike across the country for free along Route 66. He'd heard stories from friends who knew someone, who knew someone, who'd done it. First, however Frank wanted to see Atlanta and then he'd ride on his thumb, pretty much the same trail the Dalton boys had ridden on horseback—starting in Oklahoma City—all the way to the Pacific Ocean.

Frank set out that evening with his sack, walking the four miles to highway twenty-nine from Greenville, which led south to Georgia. He smiled to himself and sighed a breath of relief to finally get away from his family, even though he regretted having to leave Bessy. When the first car stopped to pick him up on the side of the road the salesman from Tulsa asked him, "Where you going son?"

"Atlanta....Atlanta, Georgia," Frank answered with certainty. He figured he work there a week or two and put a tad bit more cash in his pocket before setting out on the road, west.

"Hop in....going just outside the city myself. Good jobs to be had in Atlanta, lots of industry."

"Oh, yeah?" Frank questioned, eager to hear more. "Got any suggestions?" he asked eagerly.

It was still daylight when the man passed the Atlanta City Limits sign on the outskirts of town and pulled over. "Sorry kid....this is as far as I go. Heading to the eastside so I'll have to drop you here. It ain't too much farther into the city. You can walk it 'fore dark."

Frank got out with his pack and waved at the man. "Thanks mister....really appreciate the lift," Frank called out as the man pulled away and turned left at the County Road. Frank looked around and figured that this was as good a place as any to spend the night, so he found himself a spot in the weeds off the side of the road under a street lamp, where he figured he'd be safe. He stretched out tucking his satchel under the back of his head and before the sun was down, Frank was asleep. He rose the next morning to birds chirping and the sun high in the sky. In the morning light, he could see the city blooming ahead of him as the buildings seemed to grow taller and closer the farther he looked.

Frank was petrified being in a big city on his own after living under Virginia's thumb for so long, but he knew he had Dalton blood running in his veins and as far as he was concerned, fear was not an option. He was determined to make it on his own. And to make it to California and the land of milk'n honey, movie stars, and the good like. They didn't even need to put the tops up on their convertibles and one day Frank planned to be driving one of those fancy cars down Hollywood and Sunset Boulevards.

CHAPTER FIFTEEN

The Big City

1952 – Atlanta – A Plan Derailed

Frank's next ride into the city was with an old farmer and his wife from Saluda, South Carolina and Frank made the mistake of asking if they happened to know Judith Maxwell. When they said they knew her well, but she had moved to Anderson to live with her grandmother, he thought better of saying anymore. After all, he was running away from home and didn't really want word to get back to them of his whereabouts.

"Do you know her well?" asked the wife who was quite chatty with gossip about most of her neighbors.

"Naw....just met her once at the filling station in Anderson's all," answered Frank nonchalantly.

The couple dropped Frank near the outskirts of downtown and he walked from there to get a bite to eat at a diner—one not so different than The Grill he'd worked at for a while in Pickens. He ate a hearty breakfast and thought it was the best meal he'd ever eaten, since it was also the first meal he'd ever eaten in a big city, or for that matter in another state. Frank knew he needed more cash in his pocket to make it to California, so he asked the pretty waitress with a nametag that read Kathy Jean, where he could go to find work—he'd seen a bunch of guys standing outside of a building down the street and wondered if they might be there looking for jobs.

"Yeah go on down to the Georgia Employment Office hon....they always have work," offered Kathy Jean, jotting directions down on her order pad. She ripped it off and laid it on the table.

"Mind if I ask where you're from?"

"Pickens originally....been living in Anderson recently."

"So you planning on staying in Atlanta?"

"Actually, I'm headed to California," Frank said confidently "But, I'd like to get a few extra dollars in my pocket first."

"I can appreciate that. I hear California is an expensive place to live. Good pay, but expensive. Good luck to you now, hon," she said as she took her coffee pot to the next table to top off their caffeine.

After Frank had paid his check and left a generous tip for the service and the information, he headed out to find the employment office. Even though he was lean on cash he swore to himself that he'd always be fair with others who lived on tips, since he'd worked as a carhop. When he checked the note in his hand and looked up to find the sign he was looking for, he noted that the line stretched out the door and down about a half a block.

Frank approached an amicable looking fellow in line, "Is this where I can get work?"

"Yes sir, this is the place. Just stand in line....shouldn't take too long. They'll find you something," the man answered with the confidence born of experience.

"Gee thanks," Frank replied and headed to the back of the line. The line moved into the building at about the speed of a tortoise crossing a country intersection, however the men leaving the building appeared to be satisfied with the results as they studied the worksheet they'd obtained from the job service. An hour or so later, Frank stepped up to a middle-aged woman at one of the windows—her nametag read Miss Reynolds.

"What's your name handsome?" the woman asked.

"Frank paused a moment taken aback by her descriptor, and then said....Frank....Frank Dalton ma'am."

"What like the U.S. Marshal?" she laughed.

"Well yes ma'am, just like him. We're related," Frank boasted proudly.

"Well then," the woman said, impressed, "Just what are

you looking for? You know the police department is taking new recruits, but I'm afraid you look a little young."

"I'm seventeen, ma'am, "Frank insisted.

"Well you've got to be eighteen to become an officer of the law....maybe next year you can follow in your forefather's footsteps. So, just what are your qualifications?" She slid her glasses down her nose to look over the top rim at him, putting him on the spot.

"Well ma'am, I just need to make some money. And....I....I.... don't know? What do you mean by qualifications?" Frank seemed confused as the question tumbled from his lips making him feel stupid and wondering if he was truly qualified to do any of the things on her list.

"Well, you know....what kind of work have you done in the past, son?"

"Oh, well I done lots of things, ma'am," his confidence growing. I was recently working in Anderson at the Owens Corning plant. Before that....I worked at a sawmill, picked some cotton, worked as a carhop at the diner, delivered papers and other stuff."

The woman pushed her glasses back up to study her clipboard of job postings. "Got a place to live yet?"

"No ma'am....I was hoping to find a boarding house, maybe."

The woman took one of the sheets from the stack that he'd seen other guys carrying as they left and she wrote on it for a while, filling out the lines. Then she jotted two addresses at the bottom of the page and abruptly passed it to him. "I'm sending you to Merita Bakery."

Taken back a bit, "Well I know how to cook a bit ma'am, but only eggs, catfish, and fried green tomatoes."

Mrs. Reynolds chuckled, "Well that's something....most men can't boil water without burning the pan. Don't worry none, they won't be asking you to cook anything....just grease pans."

"Oh....," Frank studied the paper a moment. "I can do that. And they pay for that sort of thing?"

"They sure do Mr. Dalton. Ninety-nine cents an hour is the pay. Does that suit you?"

"Sure Miss Reynolds....thank you, ma'am," Frank smiled as he backed away from the window wondering if she was going to change her mind.

"Oh son....I put the name and address down of a boarding house right around the corner so you can walk to work."

"Thank you again ma'am," Frank added relieved she hadn't changed her mind. As he turned to leave the next boy stepped up to the window.

As Frank left the building he thought about what Miss Reynolds had said suggested—following in his forefather's footsteps and becoming an officer of the law. Maybe when he got to California he'd become a policeman. But Frank still didn't have a clue what fate and destiny had in store for him once he reached his destination if he indeed ever would. After all, the world is round for a reason—to prevent us from seeing too far down the road. But, he would soon find out about the detours that God, or maybe it was the devil, had in store for him.

If nothing else, one thing Frank had learned for sure from Virginia was to be polite. And Bessy had always insisted that one could attract more bees with honey than with vinegar. He'd always wondered why then Virginia only served up vinegar, when she insisted on receiving honey in return. If he hadn't been polite around Virginia, he knew she would have whooped the tar right out of his hide, not to mention blood. Maybe she had simply been trying to let that Dalton blood out of his veins, he thought. Maybe for her that helped to get rid of the memory of his father. But whatever the reason, Frank knew the things she'd done to him were not right and wondered if he could ever stand to see her again. Frank stepped outside to get his bearings and asked one of the fellows in line how to get to the bakery and the boarding house.

Frank stopped first at the boarding house next to the headquarters for the Sears and Roebuck mail-order house. He rented a room with a bath in the hallway for ten dollars a week with kitchen privileges, from a nice old lady named Mrs. McGovern. Frank assumed Mr. McGovern was deceased, since her tiny bed-sitting-room showed no signs of a man in residence, other than a framed photo on the counter of a man dressed in his Army uniform. She showed Frank to his room on the top floor, which was even smaller than her place, however it did have two bunk beds, so he asked if it was possible for him to take a roommate. The old lady agreed as long as she met them first and he quickly paid her a third of his life's savings and stashed his satchel under the bed. His remaining money he kept secured in his dungarees pocket.

Frank took his paper from the employment office and walked to the bakery, about a block away. Within fifteen minutes of arriving, Frank was working the assembly line, greasing bread pans with another young guy and two girls. He was relieved to find his duties to be pretty simple, however boring they were, but he convinced himself that every penny made there would help to fund his dream of getting to California. He figured he'd work three to four weeks and then head on to Oklahoma—the starting point of the infamous Dalton boys reign—his kin. The Dalton family had settled there in 1882 before the government had opened their newly purchased land from the Indians. Maybe Frank could find the old home they'd lived in, or even some of the banks they'd robbed. Frank worked hard all day trying to outdo the speed of the other greasers since he wanted to make a good impression on the foreman. Maybe they'd give him a raise, or a more interesting and challenging position, like the one he had at Owens.

Frank was afraid to look at people too long afraid they might find something wrong with him, as Virginia often did. His years of living under Virginia's rule instilled a fear in him against speaking his mind. He finished his day at the bakery, punched his time card, and left without speaking hardly a word to the other workers. The two girls spent their day chatterboxing and the guy working with them kept trying to make inroads with Frank. But Frank responded with only the minimum, so as to be polite and ask the necessary questions regarding his duties. In fact, unlike his co-workers, Frank was quite stingy with conversation for sake of hearing oneself talk.

The second morning around ten, a young, overweight, redheaded boy named Glen was introduced to the pan greasing line and placed next to Frank. The two spoke a few cordial words between them and drank a Coke together on break, but as usual, Frank was not forthcoming with small talk. Glen however, loved trivial discourse, even if it was a one-sided conversation. At the end of the day, Glen turned to Frank, "Hey buddy....how about we buy some Cokes and go down to Grant Park to see this thing called a cyclorama."

"What on earth is a cyclorama?" questioned Frank.

"I don't know exactly....I just heard tell by some of the guys in line at the employment office that it was this huge painting of the Civil War. The Battle of Atlanta I think."

"Sure....I guess....I ain't got no place I need to be later," answered Frank. "I wasn't very good at history in school, but the Civil War sounds interestin' to me."

The two boys walked from the bakery to the park just in time to take the last walk-through of the cyclorama.

The round building housed a three hundred-sixty degree painting of the Battle of Atlanta, along with a zoo, which had been gifted to the park by G.V. Gress. The painting had been painted by seventeen German artists, who were commissioned to paint the depiction of the Northern victory of the battle, for a debut in Minneapolis in 1886. It was later moved to Grant Park in 1892 and modified to suit the Confederate sympathizers of the South to depict a Southern victory. By the time the boys saw the exhibit, the Atlanta modifications had been reversed back to the original painting depicting the Union Army's actual victory, with General Sherman taking the city.

The boys were awed by the scale of the scenic depiction of the battle, however they were far more entertained by the pissed off gorilla in the zoo, who retaliated at the children who threw chewing gum and trash at him, by slinging his dung through his bars and chasing them away screaming.

After two Cokes and a lot of shared laughter, Glen had managed to pull Frank out of his shell and the two were chatting away like two girls on a Sunday picnic. Glen openly admitted that he'd run away from his home in New Jersey and that he was only sixteen, entrusting Frank with his secret. Then Frank alluded to the fact that he was hiding the same furtive past.

"Ahh....okay....we have to stick together, then. Make sure no one finds out. We'll be coconspirators," Glen chuckled.

"What's that?"

"Well you know....it means we share a secret pact....like outlaws," Glen bragged.

"I like the sound of that," Frank preened at the thought. "You know I'm related to US Marshal, Frank Dalton and the Dalton Gang?" He said trying to top Glen's boast.

"You mean the bank robbers?" Glen asked, impressed.

"Yep....they're the ones."

Awed, "Wow....I never met anyone related to someone famous in books and all."

"I even got a book about them," Frank bragged.

"Wow can I see it?"

"Sure....hey....you got a place to live yet?" Frank asked. "Cause if not, I got a room I could share for five dollars a week at the boarding house next to the Sears and Roebuck mail-order house. It comes with kitchen privileges. Only thing is, you have to meet the landlady first."

"Naw....I just figured on sleeping in the park down the

way. I've only got five dollars to my name," the boy admitted, pulling three bills and a handful of change out of his pocket.

Frank thought for a minute. Feeling comfortable with a guy that was in the exact same predicament him, "Tell you what. I guess I can spot you for a few days. I'm already paid up for the week. How 'bout you pay me at the end of the week when we get our first check? We can be roommates."

"Wow, thanks Frank, that's mighty nice of ya."

"After all we're both outlaws," Frank smiled. "We can call ourselves the Dalton Gang just like in the old west."

"Now I like the sound of that."

Glen raised his Coke to it and the boys shook on it—outlaws and runaways—together they could conquer the world. Frank thought maybe this boy could help replace the friend he'd lost when his uncle, Coleman, ran away and never returned.

Later that night, once Mrs. McGovern had given the okay for Glen to stay, Glen moved his meager belongings into Frank's room and took the bottom bunk. The two talked 'til the wee hours of the morning about their plans. Frank's plan was to travel Route 66 from Oklahoma out to California—some of the same miles traversed a half–century earlier by his blood kin. It was somewhere in the middle of the night that they decided that robbing banks was likely not the best way to fund their trip, so they decided they'd work long enough at the bakery to bankroll their journey west.

After three weeks of working in the bakery, Glen came back to the room one evening all excited about a man he'd met in front of the job service office that afternoon. He told Frank all about the Marine Corps recruiter who'd convinced him that going to California on the Marine's dime was far better than hoofing it alone.

"He tole me that after just twelve weeks of basic training, we'd be sent to southern California on a big airplane.
Can you imagine flying to California and getting paid for
it?"

Frank liked the sound of it, but thought about it for a bit.
"But the bad thing about that is, then we don't get to see
the country between here and there."

"Yeah but after that we might even get stationed in the
Hawaiian Islands," Glen continued, hyping the possibilities
that came with becoming a Marine.

"Where's the Hawaiian Islands?"

"I don't know....somewhere's in the Pacific Ocean," he
said, "....but I think it's part of America."

"How can it be part of America if it's out in the Pacific
Ocean?" Frank asked, perplexed by the concept.

"No matter....he said to come down to see him tomorrow morning since we ain't working and talk to him about
it. Look here he gave me this," Glen handed him a slick
pamphlet resembling some sort of fancy travel brochure.

Frank took the pamphlet and looked it over, struggling
to read the description. "Well the pictures look good."
Frank thought about it, "Well....I don't see any harm in going to listen to what he has to say."

"Only problem is you have to be seventeen to join, so
we have to lie about our age and tell him we're already
seventeen," Glen added.

"But, do we need to show our birth certificate?"

"Naw....he didn't say nothin' 'bout that."

The next morning the boys got up early and grabbed
two slices of bread from Mrs. McGovern's kitchen for
breakfast, then walked to the recruiting office and got in
line outside the building. The door was still closed and a
short line had already formed out front. About an hour lat-

er Frank and Glen were called over to sit at the desk with the recruiting officer, who gave a very enticing spiel extolling the provocative reasons for joining the Marines. By the end of his sales pitch the recruiter had Frank and Glen practically begging to sign on the dotted line. He didn't even push the issue about their age when they both said they were seventeen. When they walked out the door, it seemed the two boys had suddenly become the property of the U.S. government and they were told to report the next day out front at seven am to meet the bus that would take them to Parris Island.

"Wow," exclaimed Frank, "we get to go to an island right away!"

"Then to California! I told you it was a good idea to join. Now we get to go see the world on their dime," declared Glen, grinning from ear to ear. "Let's go quit our jobs and give Mrs. McGovern notice we're leaving. Maybe she'll even give us our ten dollars back for next week."

The next morning the boys lined up by a chartered bus with a group of ten others, who carried their worldly belongings in canvas sacks. A man in plain clothes asked their names as they stepped up to board and took their enlistment papers. Glen and Frank grabbed a seat far back on the right side so they could watch the scenery and stashed their packs on the rack above. Once all the boys were onboard, the bus pulled out and made its way through Atlanta to US Route 12.

"Looks like we're headed north. I thought we was goin' to an island on the coast."

"I don't know, maybe it's an island in Paris," Glen said hopefully.

"How far is Paris?"

"It's a long ways I think. Maybe even across the ocean."

"Then how can we get there on a bus?" Frank asked.

Confused, yet intrigued Frank sat thoughtfully on the bus next to the window watching the roads signs pass by.

The other boys on the bus started singing songs they knew. When they passed a pet store one started a chorus of, "How much is that doggie in the window...," as the other boys howled along.

When Frank spotted the 'Welcome to South Carolina' sign he let out a loud groan.

"What's the matter?"

"We're headed back to South Carolina. You know how long it took me to get out of that state?" Frank protested.

"Well maybe we're just driving through it," Glen offered, hoping he was right.

The boy across from them with a thick Arkansas accent piped in, "Naw that's where they're taking us. Parris Island is on the coast of South Carolina. Didn't you know that?"

Frank just moaned—worried that he might run into someone he knew from home and then word would get back to his family where he was. He rode the rest of the way in silence wondering if he'd gotten himself into something he was going to regret. Suddenly, he went from excited about their new adventure to a deep depression. Like the one he'd felt the day he'd walked into that field with his gun planning to end it all. There was a sinking feeling in the pit of his stomach. He thought he never should have listened to his new friend, Glen, who had gotten him into this mess. He should have stuck to his original plan to hitchhike cross-country to California and see the trail of his kin—alone.

CHAPTER SIXTEEN

Dashed Dreams

1952 – Boot Camp – Parris Island

They drove the boys to Charleston where they stopped in front of an old hotel and unloaded the bus—the plain-clothed man assigning them each a room of their own. That night in his room Frank lay in bed staring at a flashing reflection on the dirty ceiling from the hotel's red neon sign. He listened as sailors on leave laughed and joked in the streets, soaking up every minute of liberty by imbibing as many libations and girls as they could afford on their meager pay. As he listened to their jovial mood he felt all the more heartbroken—his well laid plans had changed. They'd been dashed by the stroke of a pen when he signed those enlistment papers. A dark cloud had come over him as if he'd walked into a dark room and he couldn't find his way out. How could he have screwed up his life so quickly? He hadn't been gone a month and Frank had already made the wrong decision and ended up committed to something he didn't know how to get out of. He could run of course, but he'd heard the boys talking about what they'd do to you if you just up and disappeared. After all, he'd signed his name to a contract and now his life was no longer his own, for the next three years of active duty and five years in the reserves. Of course he thought, his first sixteen years hadn't been his own either—they had belonged to Virginia. Now he'd simply substituted one servitude for another.

Dawn came early with a heavy knock on the door and a strong voice, "Time to go Marine! Be downstairs at O-six-hundred, not a minute later!" Frank looked at the clock and it was already five-forty-five. He jumped out of bed and pulled on his dungarees, laced up his boots, and grabbed his shirt from the chair. He threw some cold water on his face and ran his fingers through his long hair. He was overdue a haircut, but he hadn't wanted to spend the money on something so unimportant. He figured the Marines would take care of that. He grabbed his satchel and ran from the room still buttoning his shirt.

When he got downstairs a few wisps of orange light were cast across the far wall, but it was still pretty dark outside. In the lobby there were now twenty-five or so young men assembled with their duffels. Dry bologna sandwiches were laid out in the lobby table for the men and Frank grabbed one and wolfed it down. The man in plain clothes calmly and quietly organized the boys in a holding area off the lobby and then checked them in one-by-one to be sure they were all there, as he loaded them back onto the bus where the driver waited. Once on, the man took the front seat, the bus started up and pulled out of the parking lot.

As the bus drew closer to the camp the chatter amongst the boys died off and the quiet almost amplified Frank's dread. When they finally arrived at Parris Island, Frank watched the other Marines hoofing it around the base doing drills in the sweltering temperatures. They passed the Iwo Jima statue of Marines planting the American flag at Mount Suribachi and it made Frank feel proud for a fleeting moment. When the bus stopped in front of an old wooden WWI building with a brick entry at the staging area for the Marine Recruiting Depot, the boys were quickly herded off.

"GET OFF THE BUS!" shouted the uniformed officer who stepped on after the man in plain clothes got off. "And stand at attention on the yellow line!" he screamed in their faces.

The plain clothed man had spoken to them civilly and kindly, but now that they were through the gates of hell Frank thought, all bets were off and the induction officers were ruthless with their orders. The boys were instantly thrust into a stressful whirlwind of in processing, and from that moment on, every command was screamed at them.

After a rather sharp welcoming to Parris Island, the boys were quickly looked over in line. A few of the smaller, fatter, or skinny ones were pulled aside and the rest of the boys were herded into a large shower-like area where they were told to strip off all of their clothes and put them into a large bag with all of their belongings. Frank panicked about his book, but he was promptly yelled at by the induction officer and told to do it. Reluctantly, Frank relinquished possession of his things and stood there naked at attention.

One by one their heads were shaved and they were herded into a shower and lined up sideways against the wall. "Assholes to elbows!" shouted the induction officer. They were sprayed with disinfectant then told to wash well, while the officers watched. They were then given a number and sent to stand on that number to wait, naked. Frank watched as the officers continued to stand around surveying them. He had never been naked in front of strangers before and he felt humiliated even if his physique was far better than most of the boys in line. What he didn't know was that the officers were watching the naked, vulnerable boys to see if there were signs of 'queers' in the group. They wanted to observe them to see if any of the boys seemed overly interested in looking too closely at the other boys' current condition of undress or showed any other homosexual tendencies. Frank searched for his friend Glen, but with his head shaved he wasn't sure which of the larger boys was his buddy. All the long dark combovers had disappeared and been replaced with ripe, shiny, summer melons. Now they all looked pretty much the same with no real distinguishing feature other than build.

Frank searched for the bags they had put their things in, but they were gone and again he started to panic about his book, "Sir," he timidly said to the officer, "my book, will I get my book back?" He asked the man with a crew cut and a sour look on his face.

"SHUT UP! You and your precious book are government property now, asshole, "Do you understand?"

Frank just looked down at the floor and nodded, mimicking his usual response to Virginia whenever she called him out or chastised him. Now he knew he'd made a mistake by signing that paper committing himself to eight years of what didn't seem all that different to Virginia's treatment, except for the fact that here, he had company— a lot of company.

The boys were called one by one for their physicals. A few were immediately sent home, but unfortunately Frank passed the quick cursory inspection with flying colors and was sent ahead. After their physicals were complete the boys were sent back to stand on their assigned numbers once again. After they were all lined up, the officer stood in front of them, "Anxious to get your clothes on, are you?"

Pretty much every boy standing answered affirmatively.

"Then line up by number at that first window to get your 'new' clothes!" Before he could finish getting the words out of his mouth the boys ran to the window anxiously awaiting their new attire. When each boy got to the first window he was given six skivvies with T-shirts and six pairs of socks. At the next window the Private sized them up, pulled clothing from the shelves behind him, and shoved the clothes at the boys, who gratefully took them and quickly dressed in their new uniforms for the first time. They were given two sets of dungarees with solid green fatigue jackets sporting the Marine Corps emblem on the pocket, canvas leggings, lace-up shoes, and one flat V-shaped hat, with an emblem on the front left—known as the 'piss-cutter." With the hat they were given explicit instructions about cover regulations and etiquette. The piss-cutter was to be worn two fingers above brow line–straight front to back. If one was caught wearing their cutter sideways, they considered it to be 'attitude' and they would be punished with verbal abuse until their cover was put cover on correctly. One was never to wear one's hat into a building and without your hat you could not salute. However, you were to never be caught outside without your cover and you were to always salute an equal or higher ranking officer when wearing one's hat. So to be clear—saluting outside, not inside was the rule of thumb.

So, with the boys dressed and holding their remaining garments, they were then taken to their wooden barracks and assigned to their racks. There were two boys per rack, or metal bunk beds with springs—one guy up, one down. Unfortunately, Frank got the bottom and he didn't know the tough looking guy assigned to sleep above him. They were also instructed that they must sleep head to foot. It seemed that most of the guys there were in their teens, like Frank. However, many of them had been given the option to join or go to jail for petty crimes, so needless to say, it was kind of a tough, intimidating crowd.

They were then issued a bucket, a bar of sandsoap, a scrub brush, a toothbrush with toothpaste, a safety razor, a bedroll or mattress and a footlocker at the foot of their beds. They were then quickly instructed how to dress and how to store things in that footlocker. There was a very specific way in which one had to fold and store one's undergarments and outer attire and that was drilled into the boys relentlessly. Following their dress rehearsal they were taught how to pack their backpacks. They were instructed to always have extra socks in their pack and should they get wet, to wring them out and change into a dry pair—clipping their wet socks to their pack to dry. They were then shown how to wear the leggings laced up the side over their shoes with the strap under the sole and their pants tucked inside the legging. All the while the drill instructor, Sergeant McVey an NCO (Non-Commissioned Officer), and his 'Leaders,' who were also new recruits, would come around and inspect how they were folding and packing everything and giving screaming commands to do it the correct, or regulation way. Luckily, Frank was at the end of the barracks so by the time they got all the way down the line, they weren't quite so picky. As well as the fact, they were starting to get hoarse. The men were also issued a blanket and two sheets and a pillow with pillow-case, and then the drill sergeant showed them how to make up their rack according to protocol.

That first night when Frank lay in the bed in his regulation-made bunk, in the sweltering heat, listening to the springs creak from his bunkmate on the top rack rolling around above him all night, he wondered how he was going to get himself out of this mess. He was so tired from the long stressful day that he should have been able to sleep anywhere, but he still tossed and turned thinking about his grandmother back home. The guilt of leaving her homeless gnawed at the pit of his stomach. Maybe he should have never left, he thought. He had a pretty good job at the Owens Corning plant and he already missed his Harley. Most of all, he wondered if his dreams of seeing California were a nothing more than pie in the sky fantasies that had gone up in a puff of smoke when he got on that bus back in Atlanta.

The next morning Frank officially met his bunkmate, a guy of about twenty named Donahue, a steelworker from Pennsylvania, since the recruits were bunked in alphabetical order. Donahue was built like a tough wrestler or boxer and he impressed Frank as someone not to be messed with. More importantly, this was a man Frank was certain he'd make friends with, since he figured he might need a friend like him in the future. He looked around, searching for his buddy Glen, but he couldn't recognize him, even though he knew he was somewhere in the barrack.

Drill Instructor McVey took himself very seriously and

carried a swagger stick with a fifty-caliber shell on one end—a projectile bullet and a shell casing on the other end. As he walked the hall he slapped his palm with the stick, and if he was addressing someone, he would point it threateningly at them to make his point.

Since they were not allowed to converse while the drill instructor was inspecting and correcting them on the proper way to fold a 'hospital corner' on their blankets, Frank wisely kept his mouth shut. As the sergeant strutted through the barrack, he stopped in front of Frank's and Donahue's bunk and announced, "Some of you will get pissed off at me and make threats. If anyone wants to take me on no charges will be filed....it's between you and me, do you understand?" Something suddenly caught his eye as Donahue puffed up looking as though he wanted to be the first to volunteer for McVey's open invitation to kick his ass.

"What's wrong with you pansies, haven't you ever made your beds properly before!" he screamed in Donahue's face, leaning over Frank.

Donahue bristled and stood up straight to face him, "I don't do housework....SIR!" he exclaimed sarcastically.

"So you think keeping a neat rack is for pussies, do you?" The Sergeant screamed as he got in the private's face. "Well around here we do housework and you'll be scrubbing floors for the next twelve weeks, do you understand, private?!" McVey poked Donahue with the point of his swagger stick.

"Yes," Donahue answered arrogantly to the angry man with a uni-brow who was practically nose-to-nose with him.

"IT'S SIR, YES SIR, PRIVATE!" the sergeant shouted as spittle hit Donahue in the face.

Donahue stepped back making fists as if he was about to clock the sergeant and the officer stepped forward to back him down while poking him again with the stick. "If you think you can take me on then go ahead," he said inviting Donahue to hit him.

A second later Donahue took a swing at the Sergeant and it only took one reciprocating right hook from McVey before Donahue was out cold on the concrete floor.

"Get your bucket, Dalton and get some cold water to revive this idiot!" the sergeant hollered at Frank, looking down at the unconscious man.

Frank scrambled to get his bucket from the hook and quickly emptied its contents on the floor, then fled to the sink to fill it—returning to stand at attention in front of the drill instructor.

"Throw it in his face, YOU IDIOT!"

Frank's eyes grew wide and he dumped the bucket's contents over the prone man's head. Donahue shot up, sputtering and shaking the water from him like a dog who's just had a bath he didn't want.

"NOW GET UP AND MAKE THAT RACK THE WAY I SHOWED YOU, DONAHUE!"

Embarrassed, but aware that this man meant business, Donahue scrambled to remake the bunk. Frank just kept his eyes on his own bed and made some minor adjustments to the blanket tucked under the mattress, knowing that this man was not one to fuck with under any circumstances.

The next few weeks were a blur for Frank—up at five a.m.—thirty minutes to make his bunk and dress. Every day there were bunk inspections as the men stood at the foot of their racks at attention, and Frank wondered how a neatly made bunk could help win a war. They would then fall out with one hundred twelve guys trying to get through the four-foot-wide door at once to get their morning meal in only thirty minutes time. They'd line up at attention to wait to get their mess, and many mornings, Frank either didn't have enough time to finish his breakfast, or he had indigestion the rest of the morning after inhaling his mess. In the evenings they'd shower and stand at the foot of their bunk in their skivvies, while the drill instructor came around to be sure the men were actually changing their skivvies, not just turning them inside out. The officers still stood watch while the boys were in the shower to prevent any sort of homosexual activities from developing, but no one ever seemed to be inclined to that proclivity.

During the second week they were all issued their M1C Garand sniper rifle, fitted with a telescopic site—the most exciting part of becoming a Marine. The men looked at their weapon in awe, actually getting to hold this new piece of hardware in their hands. The leader commanded the men to remember their rifle number—no matter what one must know that number at all times. They were instructed on how to disassemble their weapon and clean it, but most importantly, they were never to call their weapon a gun—they could be punished for using that three-letter-word. If anyone was caught with a dirty weapon they were forced to sleep with it in their rack. There was a weapons rack in the barrack for every man's rifle and when not in use, the rifle was to be placed into its assigned holder. Then the men were taken to the firing range to practice firing their newly acquired weapon. From that moment on, they spent many days on the rifle range learning to become good marksmen. It seemed to Frank at this point, that every minute of his life was accounted for from reveille at oh-six-hundred to hitting the sack and lights out at twenty-one hundred.

They were issued a cord to hang their wet clothes on, after they'd scrubbed their salty garb in the two rows of big metal troughs for sinks where the water drained straight to the ground outside. Someone would be chosen to stand watch on four-hour shifts, or Firewatches, both day and night, to keep people from stealing their clothes. Even on the base there were thieves about, as well as pranksters, who wanted to screw with new recruits. Scrubbing floors was a foregone conclusion for punishment, using a scrub brush and sandsoap. Sometimes they weren't even told why they were ordered to do it or what they were being punished for. Sergeant McVey most definitely kept his promise and had Donahue scrubbing floors every day for the next twelve weeks unless of course they were outside doing drills.

A week and a half after they arrived the men were ordered to stand at the foot of their racks while Drill Instructor McVey unceremoniously drummed out one of the men who was required to put fabric on his head and carry his footlocker on top of it as he walked past all the men standing at attention. As he passed Frank he looked at him as if to say, "Be careful, you'll be next." Suddenly, Frank drew in a quick breath realizing that it was none other than his friend Glen, who had gotten him into this mess in the first place. He was never to learn why his buddy had been escorted out of basic training, but he suspected they had discovered his real age. Frank was worried about his own secret—would it get him in trouble, or would it actually be his way out? He even considered 'fessing up to Sergeant McVey that he was in fact, only sixteen, in hopes they'd kick him out also.

After the man left the barracks the Leaders walked around dumping the men's footlockers upside down, kicking their clothing and toiletries all over, mixing everything into a big heap in the middle of the room. Then Drill Instructor McVey shouted, "NOW! PICK UP YOUR THINGS AND HAVE THEM FOLDED AND BACK IN YOUR FOOTLOCKERS IN ONE MINUTE!!!"

The men scrambled trying to identify and retrieve their things and fold them properly back into their footlockers— a hopeless task since they were still searching when he called one minute. Then he punished them with washing everything in their footlockers and cleaning the entire barrack.

McVey would make the squad stand at attention with their rifles on their shoulders for long periods of time. Then when he shouted, "Present arms," the men had to hold their rifles out in both hands and the drill inspector would come around to inspect them. He would leave the men standing in that position for more than thirty minutes at a time—checking his watch all the while. When he reached Frank, after thirty minutes of struggling to hold the heavy rifle his arms were so tired they were shaking and he was grimacing—almost to the point of crying.

"Dalton why are you grinning....you think this is funny?"

"Sir, no sir....I'm not grinning, sir."

The drill instructor took the rifle from him commanded McVey, "Hold out your arms palms down!" He then placed the rifle across the backs of Frank's hands and made him hold it there—a position even tougher than the previous one Frank was straining to hold. He did his best, but he only lasted a few minutes before the riffle clattered across the floor.

"PICK UP THAT WEAPON DALTON AND STAND ON THAT TABLE," the sergeant shouted, pointing to the rifle-cleaning table.

"Sir, yes sir," Frank said shaking as he scooped up his rifle and climbed up on the table.

"Now....hold out your rifle in your right hand and take out your penis with your left!" McVey ordered with a slight smile that tugged at one corner of his mouth.

"Sir? Excuse me sir?" questioned Frank.

"YOU HEARD ME....TAKE OUT YOUR PENIS!"

Hesitantly, Frank unzipped his pants and took out his penis. He had never been so humiliated in his life as he stood there in front of the entire squad with his dick in his hand.

"Now repeat this for fifteen minutes! My rifle is for fighting and my dick is for fun."

Speechless, Frank just stood there.

"NOW SAY IT PRIVATE!" McVey shouted as he prodded Frank in the stomach with the point of his swagger stick.

"My rifle is for fighting and my dick is for fun."

"AGAIN, LOUDER DALTON!"

"MY RIFLE IS FOR FIGHTING AND MY DICK IS FOR FUN," Frank repeated for the next fifteen minutes struggling to hold his rifle steady, but there was no way he was going to drop it this time. His arms would fall off before he would ever allow himself to drop his weapon again.

Next up came the training on the parade field for marching. McVey and his Leaders would take the men out to teach them to march. The four Leaders would assemble the squad into four lines with a Leader at the head of each line. The other enlisted men taunted the Leaders with names such as 'kiss-asses' and 'brown-noser,' however the Leaders did their best to ignore the gibes and do their job so they wouldn't be replaced at the whim of Drill Instructor McVey.

When they started marching, Frank unfailingly had trouble getting into step. So, McVey was perpetually in his face causing Frank to stare at his feet, trying his best to concentrate on the rhythm of the march.

"Dalton, you march like a monkey having sex with a coconut football!" McVey laughed at his own joke as he made fun of Frank desperately trying to stay in step. "What do you have to say for yourself Dalton?"

"Sir....thank you sir," answered Frank nervously.

"You fool....that was no compliment, asshole," McVey screamed in his face.

"Sir....sorry sir."

It seemed that Drill Inspector McVey had a bug up his ass for Frank and he wondered what he'd gotten himself into. Now someone other than his mother was controlling his life and constantly hollering at him. The question really was, which was worse his mother, or this pompos ass who had decided to make a fool of him every chance he got— pretty much the same way Virginia had. Frank didn't mind so much the strict routine of boot camp, but he wasn't certain which bugged him more—the sergeant in his face screaming at him and poking him with his pointed stick, or the no-see-ums, or sand flies, that seemed to love devouring him every time he went outside. And of course, he was forbidden to swat at them or scratch while he was in formation. It was a sick sort of torture the drill instructor used to make the men crazy, screaming, "Okay, you've had your lunch, now you let them have theirs!"

They would be out marching drills in the hot sun for hours on end. Frank had bad knees and sometimes the marches would go on for up to four hours at a time. They would be required to carry their 'deuce gear' or their 'seven eighty-two pack' with their entrenchment shovel and other tools, as well as humping their supplies and bedroll in their heavy backpacks. One of the squad members, Joey, a Navy recruit who wore a Naval uniform, had been assigned to be the corpsman or medic for Frank's squad. He was a small guy, only about five-foot-six and his helmet looked huge on his small head. It was his job to look after the guys who got heat prostration and give them water or anything else they needed. Men would fall or pass out from the heat and it was his job to get them up and keep them going. It was amazing to Frank how he never seemed to be affected by the heat or the miles like the other men. The men called him corpsman and they respected him, realizing how tough he was given the conditions that kicked many a man's ass in the squad. Frank admired Joey for his stamina and compassion for the other men. Although during many a trek, Frank was hurting from the marching and he was sure he wouldn't make it, but somehow he always managed to pull through without requiring help from Corpsman Joey.

CHAPTER SEVENTEEN

Becoming a Marine

1953 – Parris Island to Pendleton

The next ten weeks were a blur with classes, weapons training, and field trips into the swamp. It was miserable hiking through the swampy waters with the mosquitoes and no-see-ums eating them alive, even though they had old sticky military repellent that they used on the face, neck, and ears. It seemed however, that no matter how much they put on, it didn't stop the bugs from biting; it only seemed to provide them with one more thing to attract them. When they were sleeping out in the field, each man carried a half a tent and their assigned rack partner carried the other half. The men slept head to foot in the tents and learned to live in the swamp for days on end. Needless to say, Dalton and Donahue became pretty well-acquainted as tent mates. Frank realized that even though Donahue was a tough guy, he was a loyal friend and did his best to help Frank whenever he needed him.

The squad was trained in hand-to-hand combat, as well as heavy equipment training, such as using hand-grenades, mortars, mines, and VAR's (automatic rifles). Then, toward the end of their training they were taken one day to an Olympic-size pool on the base to do water training. Even though many of the men claimed they didn't know how to swim, they were thrown in and told to swim the width of the pool. Guys with poles would push the men back in the water as they scrambled to climb out and those who truly couldn't swim would climb up the poles begging to be let out of the pool. They were told they would have to be able to swim the width of the pool to pass and to move forward as a Marine. So, they forced the men to stay in the water until they at least learned to dog paddle. Luckily, Frank had long ago learned to swim in the Saluda River when his Aunt Jeannette's husband Edward, had thrown him into the middle of the river. Frank somehow managed to splash around until he figured out how to pull himself back to the bank looking like a drowned rat. Frank remembered how he and Edward would go fishing using an old fashioned crank telephone, which used two wires to create electricity in the water sending the fish to the surface so they could scoop them up in a net. His memory was one of the few good ones from his childhood and it actually made him feel a little homesick.

Boxing matches, called 'smokers,' were a regular, 'off duty' activity for Company A—Frank's squad, which arranged to fight Company B—their competitors. They were held in platform boxing rings, called 'smoker's boxes,' with ropes that were set up between the barracks. The matches would last about an hour, or until someone was knocked out, or knocked down for the count. The fights and fighters were randomly selected, with each squad picking the man they felt was capable of holding his own in the ring. The men had no real money to bet; however their sergeant's pride was at stake. Amazingly enough, their stern, by-the-book drill instructor, McVey, allowed these fights to take place and even placed bets on a regular basis on his men.

The last thing Frank wanted was to be chosen by his squad to participate in one of these smokers, but after a week or so, Frank was picked to fight. He was scared to death since he really had no boxing experience—he'd never been a scrapper, unlike his uncle Earl. Encouraged by his squad-mates, they strapped his gloves on and after he'd gotten the first punch in, his adrenalin was flowing and he began to feel more confident in the ring. He not only held his own throughout the fight, he even managed to knock-down his opponent, who gave up not wanting any more abuse. When Frank was declared the winner and his men shouted praise for his win, he finally felt like a real man for the first time in his life. Suddenly, he was proud to be part of his company and finally understood what being a Marine was truly all about. The praise he received from the men made him feel like he was important to them and the unit. Frank was, for the first time in his life, beginning to believe that he was a valued human being—not just someone's slave. Up until then, he'd always felt like the odd man out, but now he was finally coming out from under his mother's suppression and control—he was coming into his own. He had become a man, not a helpless kid whom others trod on like dirt.

There was a loud-mouthed guy from New Jersey named Reilly, in Frank's squad, who bragged and claimed to be a professional boxer. So the men in the squad assumed they had a ringer and placed a lot of bets on him when they paired him with another man from Company B. His opponent was a man often chosen by his squad to fight in the smoker events. He was a huge black man with unusually long arms—fondly called by his squad, Killer Tex. The men repeatedly forced Tex to fight in these matches, even though he didn't really want to participate since he was a peaceful man who kept to himself. The men would goad him into the matches however, by taunting him with claims of being a sissy. In previous fights, he'd always managed to knockout his opponent in the first few minutes, but loud-mouthed Reilly boasted large about how Tex wouldn't stand a chance up against him—a professional from New Jersey.

When the match with Reilly started, it wasn't five minutes after Killer Tex stepped into the ring with the 'ringer' from New Jersey, that the obnoxious loudmouth was lying out cold on the canvas, with the bell ringing loud and clear in Tex's favor. They tried, but were unsuccessful in waking Reilly, so they took him to the barracks and laid him out on a table. It took about an hour of wet cloths and ice before the man finally regained consciousness. The guys in the platoon were so pissed about losing their money on the guy, that later that night the men, disguised in camouflage ponchos took him from his bunk to the showers to beat the tar out of him. The next morning at attention when Riley tried to report the incident to Sergeant McVey, who got in his bruised and battered face and screamed, "REILLY! This is a case where you mouth is overloading your ass! You're lucky they didn't kill you! Maybe this'll teach you to keep your big mouth shut!" From that day on, the men rarely heard a peep out of Reilly who managed to later get himself drummed out of the Corps.

Killer Tex's size and brawn scared Frank and he prayed he'd never be called to fight against the giant of a man. After his success in his first fight, Frank was selected to fight three more 'smokers.' He held his own and was successful at knocking down his opponent in each fight until the last, when unfortunately, his opponent turned out to be Killer Tex. Frank was certain he wouldn't last a round and did his best to convince his squad to choose another man for the fight, but they wouldn't hear of it. Luckily, he'd watched Tex enough to know how to stay out of reach of his enormous arms whenever possible. He even surprised himself as he managed to hold his own—getting one really good punch in, but he was hurting bad from the man's pummeling. As much as Frank danced to avoid the man's reach, his arms managed to easily slip through Frank's defensive blocks and connect with his left jaw. But, no matter how many times Frank got hit, he was still standing and in the end the fight was declared a draw. The two men even shook hands before leaving the ring.

Killer Tex was an odd duck with feet too large for any shoes available to the United States Marine Corps and when someone saluted him, he would only wave back at them, refusing to return the required salute. Because of that and the fact that there was no foot-ware large enough to fit him, the Marines made the decision, near the end of boot camp, that he just wasn't Marine Corps material and they voted to give him an honorable discharge. For some reason when he was released from duty, Frank was assigned to escort Tex to the administration building, to be discharged off the base. Frank was really nervous as he walked in the shadow of this huge man—scared that that Tex would take his dismissal from the Marine Corps out on him. Frank was uncomfortable with being assigned as MP (Military Police), since he'd had no training for the position, nor had they ever assigned him such a duty before. But Frank got to talking to Tex on the way to the building and he realized that the man was actually a really nice guy with a great sense of humor. He told Frank he held no ill will against him, or the Marine Corps, and he was looking forward to heading home to Texas to see his family. He wanted to go home and cook barbecue for a living, not be fighting for a living. Frank sort of wished that Tex was staying, since he realized that this was the kind of guy he wanted to have his back when push came to shove, or when his life was on the line. It was the first time in his life he had ever respected a man of the Negro race, since where he'd come from, one was born with a deep-seated prejudice against anyone whose skin was any other color than white, or anyone who was considered a foreigner.

It had been a hellacious long twelve weeks at boot camp and every step of the way, Frank was certain he'd be drummed out, as his buddy Glen had been. Surprisingly, one morning after the final grueling weeks of drills and tests McVey lined them in formation and announced that all of the remaining men in their squad had made it through to graduation and had been promoted to private first class from a lowly private. McVey ordered the men 'at ease,' as they waited on their assignments. Then he announced that they were to be flown to Camp Pendleton in San Diego, California the following week for further training, before they would receive their final assignments. Only six of the men, including Frank, were issued one set of dress blues, better known as 'Hollywood Blues.' Marines called them that since the dress uniform was generally worn by those at Camp Pendleton, who were assigned to important posts, such as sea duty or a special assignment such as the president's watch. Frank was thrilled to hear that his next stop would finally be his end-goal—to make it to California and see the Pacific Ocean. Not only was he going to the land of milk and honey—he'd be going in style on an airplane.

As the men headed back to barracks to dress in their new uniforms for graduation, McVey called Frank aside. Frank was concerned that the man who had made his life hell for the last twelve weeks had decided to single him out. As he stepped up to the sergeant he smartly stepped to attention.

"Yes SIR, you wanted to see me, SiR?"

"At ease Dalton....I just wanted to give you back this," McVey said kindly as he handed Frank a satchel. "It seemed pretty important to you at the time."

Confused Frank pulled out a book—his Dalton Gang book, which had been confiscated his first day on base. Frank was overwhelmed to see his precious book again and he choked back tears. For a moment he wasn't sure what to say to the man who'd seemed to constantly go out of his way to humiliate him in front of his peers. "Thank you sir, you don't know how much this means to me."

"I assume that you are related to these brave men in this book."

"Yes, sir, it seems I am, sir."

"I hope you don't mind that I read it. They were an interesting bunch, those Dalton boys. Too bad they turned to the criminal side of the road, but I see a lot of their good in you. I want you to know that I singled you out because I felt you had great potential. That's why I assigned you the duty of Military Police. I figured that if anyone would understand the job, it would be you."

"Well....thank you sir. I really appreciate your confidence in me, sir."

"Now go out there and make me proud, son," McVey said as he held out his hand to shake—unusual conduct for a superior officer.

Frank grasped his hand in a handshake that he would never forget. He felt as if he had just graduated into manhood and this tough Marine had acknowledged his ascension from the kid he'd been when he'd been driven through those gates just twelve weeks before.

Back at the barracks Frank dressed in his green wool trousers, black socks, long-sleeved khaki shirt tucked in and on top, a blouse-like button-up jacket and a matching wool woven belt with a brass buckle shined to perfection with blitz-cloth. He checked himself in the mirror and thought he looked quite sharp. The person he saw looking back at him was a proud man—not the young, naive kid that had shown up on that bus from another lifetime ago. All the men in Frank's squad had been issued the standard winter uniform with a green hat with a visor and a USMC emblem, not the tan, summer, 'piss cutter' casual hat.

Graduation included standing at attention with their arms at their sides, as well as marching in the parade with their rifles raised to 'right-shoulder-arms." The festivities took place around the Iwo Jima monuments. The men looked smart at their graduation and Frank was thrilled he had successfully completed something that he could be proud of, even if he hadn't really planned to become a Marine in the first place. No matter, he'd done it—completed something important and he no longer felt like the inferior, stupid kid he'd imagined himself to be when he arrived at Parris Island. He now felt that he had been given the chance to represent something far bigger than himself—his country. After the parade was over, the men, including stone-faced McVey, lightened up, and the men stripped off their wool jackets in the heat of the summer afternoon.

Before they left South Carolina they told the Marines they needed a class on what to expect from the peculiar people they were about to encounter in Southern California. The lieutenant that was assigned to review the topic proceeded to explain about gay men or 'queers,' as he put it, and how to identify them. He told the men they were not to associate with them under any circumstances. He explained that gay men performed unsacred acts of deviant behavior on each other including anal and oral sex or intercourse, as well as other disgusting behaviors. Frank had heard the term cornhole for a queer man having sex, so Frank was aware of such behavior. Overall there was a rousing round of shock from the squad as one of the new Marines from the sticks shouted, "God damned queers do what?! That's the most disgusting thing I eva' heard. I'm gonna kill myself a queer when I get to California!"

Most of the men in the squad now looked uncomfortable to say the least, spawning the response the lieutenant had been looking for since the U.S. government frowned on such 'deviant' behavior.

At the end of WWII, the U.S. government had implemented a witch hunt to rid the country of suspected communists and 'queers.' On February 9, 1950, Senator Joseph McCarthy, a man with the biggest bullhorn on the safari to eliminate the 'enemies within,' gave his speech in West Virginia. He had insisted that 'queer' people were predisposed to be susceptible to being indoctrinated as communists.

"They are a dangerous threat to our society and the U.S. government so beware of anyone appearing, 'light on their feet,' if you know what I mean," the lieutenant finished to a round of nervous laughter.

After their California debriefing, the men were loaded onto a DC 3-s military transport plane, which only offered benches for seats and no seat belts. Frank was in awe when he first saw the plane and even more exhilarated when the plane raced down the runway and lifted off the ground taking to the sky. It felt as though the pit of his stomach had dropped out of his body. As the plane climbed he gulped for air and swallowed hard, trying to clear his ears. He'd never before been at six thousand feet and as he peered out of one of the windows, he remembered watching the skywriting plane back in Pickens. He finally understood what it felt like to feel weightless like a bird gliding on the wind, even if they were being propelled by two fourteen cylinder, thirteen hundred-fifty horsepower, radial engines. The plane landed in Houston, Texas for refueling and the men were allowed a break to buy snacks at the commissary. Frank bought a packet of crackers and a Coca-Cola and they were loaded back onto the plane for the second leg of their flight to Pendleton Marine Corps Air Station in San Diego, California—a sub-unit of El Toro—the Marine Corps aviation center on the west coast. As they circled in for a landing, Frank got his second glimpse of and ocean after Parris Island. This time it was the Pacific. Once again, he was in awe.

The squad was stationed at Pendleton for two weeks. While there the men were given liberty off base on the weekends, but Frank never left the base after the lieutenant's fearful warning of 'queers and communists' lurking the streets of San Diego. For the last week at Pendleton, they were taken up to the Sierra Nevada Mountains for cold weather, high terrain training in the snow-covered mountains at a USMC base called Pickle Meadows. It was the Marine Corps' official Mountain Warfare Training Center, located in a barely accessible area of the Humboldt Toiyabe National Forrest. They loaded the men onto a bus, taking California State Route one hundred-eight, high up into the Sierras. As they climbed in elevation, the warm coastal weather grew colder and colder and Frank wondered why cold weather training in the mountains would be required if they were to be sent to the Hawaiian Islands.

Day one in the field it was snowing heavily. It was the first time in a number of years that Frank had seen such a heavy snowfall. The men were issued two pairs of padded socks and reminded what to do with them should they get wet. They camped in tents at high altitudes and dug fox-holes with frozen hands. The fare was not very appetizing since they were fed only C-rations and the melted snow for water to fill their canteens. It was even more uncomfortable there in the icy cold winds than it had been in the hot swamps of South Carolina being eaten alive by unseen insects.

After the squad arrived back at Pendleton, they started getting the men ready for duty, even though they still hadn't yet been told if they were going to Hawaii or to a warzone. The Marines insisted that due to the secrecy of wartime they were unable to reveal who would be stationed where. They lined the men up outside with shirts off to receive three vaccinations in each arm from the corpsman. Donahue bravely went ahead of Frank for his shots—rubbing his arm as he walked away when he suddenly realized he still had a needle stuck in his arm that had come loose from the syringe. On the spot, the tough guy passed out cold on the ground. The corpsman saw him hit the ground and he ran over and looked down at him, "So there's my needle," he said matter-of-factly as he yanked it from Donahue's arm and slapped his face to revive him.

Frank could see a newer ship anchored in the harbor that was set to sail to the Marine base in Hawaii. Rumblings amongst the men warned that the last thing they wanted to be assigned to was the second ship which sat the harbor—an old, refitted freighter, the USNS General R. L. Howze. If they were unlucky enough to draw that straw, they would then find themselves at the DMZ (demilitarized zone) in Korea. Due to the fact that he had received his set of dress Hollywood Blues, Frank felt confident that he would indeed be one of the lucky ones and land himself a cushy assignment in the Hawaiian Islands the men coveted.

CHAPTER EIGHTEEN

The General Howze — Korea

1953 – War or Peace – Inchon – DMZ

The General Howze had been used during WWII by the Navy as a transport ship and it was still about as basic as a troop carrier could get. The luck of the draw was not in Frank's favor as he was taken to board the Howze with forty-five hundred other Marines. The minute it was clear that he was Korea bound, he was certain that he was on a one-way trip to a foreign land from which he would never return. The first thought in his mind was the Daltons' 'invocation to the gods of chance.' His second was, would this indeed be his first and last adventure to a foreign land? For that matter, Frank was invoking help from and pleading with God to somehow make them discover that they had made a mistake—that he was really supposed to be on the new ship bound for the tropical island of Hawaii.

Alas, once he stepped foot onto the Howze he knew that there was no mistake—this was the ship of his destiny which would take him to a not so certain future. He was headed to a war zone. A war of which he'd heard terrible stories. Once onboard he quickly also realized how bad the accommodations were aboard ship. The men were to sleep in canvas hammocks, hung one on top of the other up to eight feet high. In order to crawl into their berth, one had to climb up the stringers along the hull to get to their hammock. Luckily, Frank was quick to select his sleeping arrangements this time and managed to secure a top berth, so that no one would be crawling over him to get into bed. Once onboard, they still weren't a hundred percent certain that they were destined for Korea, since no officer had actually spoken the 'K' word but Frank had a sinking feeling in the pit of his stomach and he was sure that he was destined to die in a war he understood absolutely nothing about.

The Korean War had started when North Korea invaded South Korea on June twenty-fifth, 1950. There had been escalating clashes along the border between the two countries—the North—communist—supported by China and the Soviet Union; and the South—democratic and supported by the United Nations and the United States.

Once out at sea on the Howze the waves were enormous and the ship rolled as it punched through the huge swell. Many a green Marine would stand at the rail seasick from the morning mess while others were too sick to crawl from the floor of their quarters. Frank would stand at the rail for hours fascinated by the sea—so vast—so blue, yet angry and confused. Kind of how Frank felt inside—angry and confused about his life—about his choices, as well as the things he'd had no control over such as his mother and their impoverished beginnings—both in their souls and material stature. He would watch the flying fish sailing far ahead of the bow, racing to get away from the great steel beast that threatened to crush them. He would watch the clouds thinking how strange it was not to see birds in the sky for they were too far out to sea. He'd stand at the stern and watch the cavitation of the massive propeller as it rose out of the water with nothing to bite into but air, as the bow dove deep into the troughs of the giant waves. Some days, the sea was so rough the decks would be awash with seawater and all hatches would be latched down and all ports secured. The men on deck found it necessary to wear their cold-weather field jackets after three weeks on the water. The further the ship traveled, the cooler it became making Frank certain that they were indeed headed for Korea and not the warm waters of the South Pacific.

The only other thing to do on the ship from morning 'til reveille was to line up for chow, waiting hours to eventually get to their food and then try their best to keep it on the

tray as the ship pounded up and down and rolled side to
side. By the time they were finished eating, it would be
time to get back in line again for their next meal. As they
neared the coast of Japan, Frank started to notice the presence of seabirds that greatly resembled the loons in South
Carolina. He assumed they must be nearing land—a fact
that was confirmed when islands of what looked like floating boulders appeared ahead of them, rising straight up out
of the ocean. A sergeant finally explained to the men that
they were off the coast of Japan and that they'd soon be
approaching Inchon, South Korea, where they would disembark to go to Seoul. There they would receive their
assignments. Now Frank was certain that he was heading
to his demise and that he would never have the chance to
return home again. Maybe that wasn't such a bad thing, not
going home ever again. But, the alternative—death, was a
frightening thing for a young man who had never had the
chance to live.

When the ship arrived in Inchon harbor, on the western
side of the Korean peninsula the tide was so low the ship
was unable to tie up to the dock, making it necessary for
the men disembark into large rafts that ferried them
ashore. Once everyone was off the ship, the men were
marched through the port town of Inchon to camp. Frank's
squad spent two weeks in Inchon, living in tents set up at
the Marine encampment. There they learned that on September fifteenth 1950—U.S. Marines had landed at Inchon,
led by Douglas MacArthur, one hundred miles south of the
thirty-eighth parallel, only twenty-five miles from Seoul,
which had been taken by communists in June of that year.
By early evening, the Marines had overcome the resistance
in Inchon and had the area secured. It still remained secure
under American control, as did Seoul. They also learned
that they would be taken to Seoul and then on to the DMZ
to replace men who were being discharged to return to the
states. Frank was panicked that they were taking him to
the front lines after all—what did he know about fighting a

war? Hunting with rifles and war games were great fun, but this was a real life war and he was sure that his life was about to be over. His greatest relief came when, Sergeant Rick, from Company B, explained that fighting had officially halted with an armistice signed on July twenty-seventh of that year, only three months prior to their landing. Frank's squad was to be assigned to the DMZ to enforce the cease-fire. Frank and the other men heaved a breath of relief when they heard that they were not heading into an active war zone.

Sergeant Rick selected twelve men and loaded Frank's First Marine Division—Foxtrot Company, onto an old shot-up truck to take them to Seoul and then on to their unit at the DMZ. The fact that the truck was full of bullet holes didn't instill any comfort as they climbed aboard and headed through the city on dirt streets, filled with bomb craters and nasty standing water. Sergeant Rick was to head home in a month and he was a wealth of information about how to survive in Korea. As they drove over a bridge, they saw two Korean men viciously fighting down below in the water. One man was hitting the other downed man with a brick and trying to drown him.

"Damnit, it looks like they intend to kill each other. Shouldn't we stop and do something?" asked Frank.

"If you want to survive this war there are two very important things to remember....never ever show compassion....and most importantly, never, ever show fear. They're the two things that will surely get you killed."

They drove on down the dirt road to Seoul, which had a ditch running down the middle for sewage. The stench burned Frank's eyes and nostrils as he looked out the window at the sorry state of affairs. Unbelievable poverty spread before them, scarred by destruction, with little improvement anywhere to be found. He considered the sergeant's advice. It seemed that he would have plenty of time to contemplate his future actions in hopes of surviving his stay here in this godforsaken place. He would have to find a way to turn a blind eye to all the suffering he was about to witness in the devastated country. Korea was like going back in the deep woods—although it was the worst place he'd ever seen in his life. And he thought he'd come from impoverished beginnings. The images of life that unfolded before him as they drove through the thick dusty tracks humbled him and made him realize that maybe his poverty-stricken life had been rich in comparison to this destitute population. Their homes were nothing more than five-foot-tall huts made of sticks and mud—warmed by small fire pits built underneath for warmth. He felt as if he'd stepped two hundred years into the past. Frank thanked God for the little he'd had growing up, since compared to these poor souls, his life had been rich in many ways. It was as if their dire poverty hadn't been enough suffering—now they had been cast into a war that they never asked for and might never recover from.

When they arrived in Seoul and the Sergeant dropped them off, they walked through the city to the train station. Nothing but devastation surrounded them—much like pictures of Europe after WWII that Frank had seen in the newspapers. Hundreds of young kids in gangs huddled under a destroyed bridge. Their means of survival were limited to scavenging and stealing anything they could find for sustenance. Rick had warned the men to stay away from the harmless looking kids since, like a hungry, rabid pack of dogs, they would do serious damage. When they got to the north side of Seoul, the men were loaded onto a train that would take them close to the front lines at the DMZ. As they boarded the train, an officer checked their credentials and loaded them into one of the crowded passenger cars. "Don't stick your arm or head out the windows unless you want it cut off....there's no clearance," the man said curtly, as if it were his normal welcoming speech for those heading to the end of the line. When the train pulled into the switchyard at their destination, the men were picked up by truck and driven as close as they could get to the front lines to join Frank's unit of one hundred-ten men—many of whom had been there for over eight months already.

South Korean Marine troops passed them on the road in American issued new Willys jeeps, wearing crisp new American uniforms. Everything they had came from the Americans, including their new holsters and 45mm pistols. The Koreans even chrome plated their helmets. Frank's unit on the other hand wore worn out uniforms with holes and had no holsters in which to carry their weapons. So the men made do. They were forced to carry their weapons in their belts. After all they weren't there for a fashion-show, as the South Koreans.

Their unit of one hundred and ten men had been on an eight-month rotation, but since the ceasefire had started, they had frozen the rotation and now the men were ordered to stay a minimum of eighteen months in Korea at their posts. Frank suddenly realized that his tour of duty in Korea had just more than doubled. The unit size might rise and fall a dozen or so due to deaths and casualties, but with this new crop of 'boots,' *(beginning of one's tour)* as they were called. Their unit was back to its full capacity. When Frank and the others arrived at the DMZ, they were met with a large sign that announced the recent armistice agreement and cease-fire between North and South Korea. The men in camp appeared to be idle, since the fighting had stopped.

The new men were immediately put to work digging foxholes to sleep in and large ammunition bunkers. Inside they would store ammo and mortar rounds and then they would cover them with a metal or log roof about twenty-by-twenty feet and then spread dirt over the area. The men would actually sleep in these ammo bunkers on air mattresses and a sleeping bag. By morning the men would find that during the night the air would have leaked out of the mattress and they were sleeping on the cold damp ground. They lived on old C-rations, which consisted of two crackers, a small container of meatball spaghetti, two cigarettes and a small piece of chocolate. One hot meal a day—chili was brought to their camp in jeeps and each man would receive one scoop, which only left them wanting more. Since he didn't smoke, Frank would trade his cigs for chocolate, or any other food that someone didn't want. Word had gotten around that someone was selling bread on the black market, that was being stolen from the military, and the men did everything they could to buy what little was available.

Once a month the men lined up at the paymaster's table and each private would be given sixty-three MPCs (military payment certificates) a month. The only place it could be used was at the commissary in Seoul, or for gambling purposes amongst the men and since Seoul wasn't right around the corner, a lot of gambling took place behind closed tent flaps. The men could actually be court-martialed if they were caught carrying American money. Another court martial offense was for the men to fraternize with Korean women, or any women for that matter. In fact, it was a court martial offense to have any friendly dealings with Korean civilians, either men or women. Even so, many an Army soldier had taken themselves either young, male houseboys, or what they called a mouse—a female Korean housekeeper who offered many services other than just keeping a man's tent tidy.

Additional tents were set up behind the lines—one tent for a M1911 or Colt 1911 semi-automatic pistols—AKA Colt .45, and another tent for BARs (Browning Automatic Rifle), Springfield M1 rifles, Thompson sub machine guns, and flak-jackets from wounded, dead or rotated soldiers. No guards were ever put in the weapons tents so the men could simply walk in and take whatever they wanted. Frank would stop and swap his weapons out for newer, cleaner weapons if something was wrong with them. He chose to carry the Thompson submachine gun and he would swing by the ammunitions bunker and pick up boxes of cartridges and punch them into the clip, which held thirty each. He would also carry extra cartridges, ready to fire as a backup if needed. He practiced with his weapons as little as possible since the sound severely hurt his ears, but in time he would find his lack of practice to be a huge mistake.

A week or so later they sent bulldozers in to scrape flat areas for canvas tents to be constructed over wooden frames for troop housing, a mess hall, and a M.A.S.H. unit (Mobile Army Surgical Hospital). Latrines, or 'piss-tubes' were nothing more than a mortar-shell sunk in the ground with a canvas tarp around it up to one's waist. All of the new men who had arrived with Frank were assigned some sort of duty at the mess hall, which was not a popular assignment since everyone hated doing dishes and preparing food. Frank however was assigned mine duty, which didn't sound all too safe to him, so he offered to swap it with another man named, Curtis, who'd drawn dish duty. Curtis jumped at the chance to get out of doing dishes and liked the idea of learning how to set mines that would keep the enemy at bay. Their commanding officer (C.O.) Sergeant Fidorkey, approved their swap, so the next day Frank went to work at the mess hall and Curtis went to mine school. Only a few days into the class a mine blew up by the students' bleachers and everyone was killed, including Curtis. Frank felt awful—guilty for making the trade with his friend. At the same time he felt terribly lucky, even though he'd believed he'd gotten the short straw by being assigned duty on the front lines to begin with, even if there was a truce at the moment. As far as he knew fighting could start again at anytime and he'd be right in the thick of it with little chance of survival. Quickly, Frank became a true believer that he had indeed acquired himself a guardian angel, or the gods of chance. That was until he received his next assignment.

Frank was assigned to a forward-watch observers-point on a regular rotation in the DMZ mountains. Five men at time would spend a week patrolling the DMZ. Across the DMZ spanned a large valley with the Imjin River flowing through it—across which was the Freedom Bridge, one of the few physical connections between North and South Korea. The Armistice Agreement had required that each side move troops one-point-two-miles back from the front line, providing a buffer zone—two-and-a-half miles wide. An exchange of POWs had started around the time Frank had arrived, to bring UN, South Korean, and American prisoners back to the newly established Red Cross camp on the south side of the DMZ. Frank watched as they drove a train across the Freedom Bridge and returned with not only American and Allied POW's, but also many North Koreans hopping aboard hoping to defect to the South. At the same time the train carried Northern POWs back across the line, releasing them to the North Korean and Chinese Armies.

Frank was assigned to put up barbed wire along the DMZ at night and to patrol the area from one area to another when he was off rotation—uphill past the company headquarters and as far down as the Freedom Bridge. It was a scary assignment for Frank to cross into the DMZ zone as lookout since the Chinese Army seemed unaware of the cease-fire and they often took potshots at Americans in uniform. Every night he went on patrol he was certain would be his last. He was sure that he was going to die there and he made peace with that. He simply resigned himself to the fact that he would never return from his duty here in this godforsaken country alive. He'd never seen anything like it before and thought that the hell he'd learned about in bible school must have looked like this hellhole called Korea. He believed he must have done something to be punished for, since he was still alive and living in hell. With this understood, he was able to stand up to whatever he encountered and he always remembered his first lesson there—not to show fear or compassion. Frank always kept his pistol loaded and cocked and ready to fire right through his field jacket pocket and he would pull the hood on his jacket tight around his face at night so that as to be less conspicuous in the dark.

Of course, American snipers would watch and wait to return fire on occasion, picking off Chinese officers with a powerful riflescope, while they were sitting in the latrine— blowing them right out of their skivvies. This would simply cause them to dig deeper foxholes as well as latrines. At night, groups of Chinese would often sneak across the DMZ and ambush, abuse, and kill Americans and hang their bodies over the barbed wire fences, then sneak back across to the North. Frank ran across several unlucky bastards that ended up as bird carrion hanging from barbed wire fences. Their patrols would find them come morning, after the men had been tortured and killed by the Chinese the night before.

On his trips into the DMZ, the forward observer would go forty to fifty yards ahead of Frank and his unit in order to push the Chinese back behind the required buffer zone. If the forward observer found it necessary to send in a round he would shout, "Drop me a round one hundred yards out from your position." Frank was the gunner who set the scope as his assistant dropped the fragment rounds, with Willy Pete (white phosphorous), into the mortar launcher. Frank would call out to the forward observer to drop and they would simply fire right over his head. When ignited, white phosphorous could not be extinguished and the Chinese would frantically pull back, or be burned alive. "Look at those S.O.B.s run," the forward observer would shout and laugh as the Chinese quickly pulled back their troops to the agreed position. There was no communication with headquarters other than runners and the phone lines the men laid over and over again were also cut by the Northern army every chance they got.

CHAPTER NINETEEN

Military Police

1953 – A Name Change – Korea

Frank had been in Korea a few months when his CO called him into his tent one morning. He was unsure why and was worried that maybe he'd done something wrong. When he arrived he was surprised to find, not only his commanding officer of B-Company, Colonel Anderson, but a chaplain and a Red Cross representative waiting for him. Now he was really concerned and started to panic. Maybe someone had died back home, but then as far as he knew, no one was even aware that he'd joined the Marines.

"Sit down son," said his CO as Frank nervously took a seat. The others also sat across from him in camp chairs surrounding Frank, making him feel as if he were ready to be roasted at some sort of tribunal. He knew something serious was up since his CO had called him son, not private first class.

"We've been contacted by your mother, Virginia Holliday....she's been looking for you." his CO started as if encouraging Frank to comment.

The moment her name rolled off his COs tongue, Frank's heart sank. She'd found him and he was panicked the Marines would send him back home to the woman who'd tormented him for the last ten years. How the hell did she find him, he wondered? Even Bessy didn't know he'd enlisted.

"She claims that you were only sixteen when you enlisted....is that true?"

Frank sat there like a deer in the headlamp of an oncoming train, uncertain whether to continue his lie or confess that he was indeed underage when he'd enlisted. Studying the concerned faces before him, he decided to proceed with the truth. Not only the truth about his age, but also the truth about the abuse he'd suffered under her roof. By the end of his story he had the men before him nearly in tears—moved by what he'd endured as a child. He also pointed out that he had recently turned seventeen and could now make his own decisions as an adult.

"So then....," continued Anderson, who looked at the other two counselors, "....since you are now seventeen, we will give you the choice....to stay and continue your duties as a United States Marine, or you may return home to your family."

Returning home would certainly get him out of harm's way, but the last thing he wanted was to be controlled by Virginia again. As tempting as the thought of leaving Korea was, Frank knew that he didn't need time to mull it over. "No sir....I'd like to stay here and continue my duties as a Marine, sir."

His CO stood, as did the others and they shook his hand. "Well then Private First Class Dalton. You have orders to report to the Military Police Command Post in Seoul."

Once again, he was concerned that unbeknownst to him, he had done something wrong. However, when he arrived by truck at the headquarters, he discovered that he had been sent there to report for Military Police duty. It seemed that he'd been randomly assigned to serve as an MP with little or no training. Or, had they decided it best to move him away from the DMZ since he was so young? Maybe it was because they felt sorry for him after his story about his upbringing. He was surprised by his new assignment, yet relieved that he would not be patrolling the front lines at night anymore. He was issued an armband, a helmet, a knife, and a 45 mm, standard issue Springfield pistol. They recommended that he carry a large rock in a sock inside his jacket pocket to aid in his defense should he get into a hand-to-hand scuffle. He was then paired up with a partner by the name of Raymond. Best of all, they were issued an old, beat-up Willys jeep and sent out to do their job, with no idea what that job really entailed. Frank was stunned that he would be entrusted with such an important position so soon after arriving in Korea, and at such a young age. But, if the truth be known—he was scared to death, even though he couldn't believe his luck. Now he would wield some authority in his role as a Marine, even though he was still only a private first class. Here, a poor, small-town kid, with little or no experience had been appointed the important position of Military Police. He knew that many of the men in his unit would resent him, but at the same time, he also knew that his position would garner him respect as long he handled it right.

Their first assignment was to park at an intersection and stop busses and board them, in search of contraband—mostly cigarettes. The local buses would be terribly overloaded with eighty to ninety people aboard. The MP's order was to lighten the load and take the excess people off the bus, however as soon as the buses would pull away, the stranded passengers would run ahead and climb right back onboard. Many of the MPs were pissed about being forced to stay longer in Korea due to the armistice and they took out their frustration on the local people by harassing them for no reason. Frank did his best to treat them fairly, however he always kept Sergeant Rick's advice in the forefront of his mind about the perils of showing compassion. They would surely take advantage of anyone who showed what they might detect to be weakness. Frank continued to make certain to always keep his pistol cocked with a round in the chamber, and he carried the weapon in his field-jacket pocket with his finger on the trigger at all times. That way he wouldn't even have to take his weapon out if he needed to fire, he could simply shoot through his jacket taking his target totally off guard.

A month later Frank was once again called into the CO's office, and as before, the priest and the Red Cross representative awaited him. All Frank could think was, 'What had Virginia done now?"

"Take a seat private," his CO said in a less concerned and more jovial tone than the last time he was there. "It seems that your mother has legally changed your name."

"I don't understand....how could she do that?"

"Well, until you're eighteen, you're technically considered a minor and she has the right. It seems she went to court and filed a name change for you back in Pickens County."

"But I don't want to change my name," insisted Frank. "What did she change it to?"

"Well....it reads here, Carl Franklin Holliday."

"I don't want to be named after that lazy good-for-nothin' husband of hers. I'm a Dalton, kin of Frank Dalton the U.S. Marshal," Frank boasted proudly.

"Well then I don't blame you. That's an impressive lineage. But, there's nothing you can do about it until you get back to the States. Then, if you want, you can legally change it back to Dalton. In the meantime I have no choice but to change your official name to Carl Franklin Holliday," he said finitely as he handed the court document to Frank. "Here's a letter she sent you," he said as he gave him an unopened envelope. "You're required to write home occasionally, son. You can give the letters to Father Russell and he will mail them home for you."

"Do I have to?" Frank asked unhappy with the thought.

"I'm afraid so son. It's not a request it's an order."

Frank nodded and hesitantly took the letter from the colonel.

When Frank left, his first instinct was to burn the letter from Virginia, but instead he just buried deep it in his duffle, as well as in his mind and forgot about it for a while. He would accumulate three letters from her over the next three months, and he remained unwilling to read them. It surprised him that she was even capable of composing a letter, considering her limited education. The last thing he wanted to do was to write her back and he seriously con-

sidered returning her letters unopened, but he was afraid
he'd get in trouble with his CO. It was hard getting used to
it, but from that day forward the men were instructed to
call Frank by his new name, Holliday.

One night, Frank was sent into a small village, with six
other MPs and an officer on a raid to find a U.S. Army deserter. The MPs were to split up to search every hut in the
village. Frank entered a communal area behind one of the
huts, but he found no one outside, so he kicked in the door.
On the other side was a hysterical old woman screaming at
him in Korean as she beat him over the head with a broom
and hit his chest with her fists. Frank pushed past her to
sweep the room then opened the door to leave to find a
young, large Korean man standing on the other side with
arms crossed, screaming at Frank. It was one of the few
times that Frank didn't have his gun cocked, so reacting to
the threat, Frank pulled his pistol from his pocket and
pointed it at the huge man. However, when he pulled the
slide back to load a round into the chamber it accidently
fired. It was the first time he had ever had to pull his
weapon on anyone and he had been terribly nervous.
There was a blinding flash and a round tore open the man's
chest, throwing him backwards, right off his feet. All Frank
could see in the flash of bright light were the soles of the
man's feet and blood—everywhere. He froze—realizing
what he'd just done, although accidently. Frank was blind-
ed by the flash and deafened by the shot in the confined
space and his ears were ringing a deafening drone. The old
woman continued screaming and attacking him from behind with the broom so Frank turned and pointed the gun
in the woman's face. Terrified, she ran and cowered in the
back of the hut. When Frank turned to see if the man was
still alive, he was stunned to find the man had simply dis-

appeared, as had all other villagers, who had started gathering around. With his heart pounding, Frank quickly ran from the hut and rejoined the other MPs as if nothing had never ever happened.

"Hey Frank....you hear a gunshot back there?" asked one the guys.

"Na....didn't hear nothing," Frank said shaking his head attempting to clear his ringing ears. Indeed, at that moment, Frank couldn't hear a thing due to the blast from the pistol. He was also in a state of shock trying to process the fact that he'd just shot an innocent man—one that was likely dead considering the point blank impact—so powerful that it had blown the man right off his feet. But, where had he gone? It was as if he had vanished into thin air. Could he have possibly been able to stand and run in his condition? Or, had someone simply pulled him away while Frank was dealing with the old lady. Had she distracted him so that the man, likely her son, had time to get away?

They continued on that evening from hut to hut, never finding the deserter. Frank struggled to concentrate on the task at hand, afraid to enter any more huts so he teamed up with his partner to stand watch outside, while Raymond entered the shanties. Frank decided right then and there that he would never tell anyone what he'd done. He was afraid he'd be court-martialed, or worse. He did however feel he would have to do penance for his deed, even if it had been accidental. It was then that he realized the need for some serious practice at handling a pistol. After all he'd only grown up with rifles and now the Marines handed him a weapon for which he sorely lacked training. He thought of the Daltons and realized he'd have to become a crack shot like them, if he stood any chance of surviving his stint in Korea.

In his spare time, Frank practiced with his forty-five and in the remaining free time he had, he studied the locals and how they lived—attempting to understand them. He had been warned not to show compassion, however he felt he needed to learn more about them in order to do his job—for his own safety as well as theirs. The shanties the people lived in were nothing more than hovels for the most part. Their toilets were indoor honeypots, as they called them, which they poured into one large drum to use as fertilizer. Everyone wore the same light colored trousers and jackets with a typical Asian collar, making it difficult to tell them apart. Their shoes were called Iddywa shoes—rubber galoshes with straps laced from the ankle up the calf to the knees, with a heavy sock underneath. The rubber shoes aided the population in navigating the extremes of four inches of mud or dust, depending on the season. The older men—grandfathers or Papasans, wore long white chin hair, yet grew no other facial hair, making them look like something out of the Ming Dynasty.

One day they were sent to a village to gather up all of the residents and put them in a stockade. Then one by one, they had doctors check them over. After their physical exam, they would hold each person down and spray them with DDT using a compressor hose. The people were scared to death by the smell and the fact they had no idea what they were doing to them. Or, that it was the military's way of ridding these infested people of lice. Of course, at the time the military had no idea that they were dousing the population with a deadly poison.

It was getting colder and wetter by the day at the DMZ and the men found it necessary to dress in layers of clothing and burn a stove in their tents at night. Marine troops had finally been issued rubber insulated boots, called Mickey Mouse boots. They were designed to prevent frostbite, since many troops before them had suffered severely from frostbitten toes and feet. The Marines had no showers for the men, so Frank and Raymond would swing by the Army tents and use their hot showers whenever they felt like it. At least the chance to remove the grime from their bodies gave them some sense of humanity in that filthy hellhole. The days were long and the nights were longer. Many a night consisted of gambling and card games in their tents until wee the hours of the morning. A normal day in Korea for Frank consisted primarily of him riding shotgun in the jeep with his partner, Raymond, keeping the peace with the local population in the surrounding villages. One afternoon a call came through on the radio to go and check out a disturbance. Upon their arrival, a crowd of South Koreans had formed around a local man wearing an American military jacket. As Frank and Raymond approached the man, Frank shouted, "What's going on here?"

The cornered man spun on his heels, pointing a Marine-issued forty-five pistol at Frank's head. Instinctively, Frank threw up his arms in front of his face to protect himself and the gun discharged—pointblank. Raymond tackled the man to the ground, taking his weapon away. Dazed and confused, Frank felt a searing pain in his arm and his ear pounded terribly. It took several moments for him to realize that he'd been shot. It wasn't until he saw the blood streaming down his left arm from inside his jacket sleeve that he understood what had happened. When Frank took his jacket off and tore open his sleeve, he was shocked to find a large wad of muscle hanging from the through-and-through bullet hole in his upper left arm. Tearing the sleeve from his shirt, Frank wrapped the sleeve around his wound, while Raymond called for backup to take in their prisoner. Then he drove Frank directly to a M.A.S.H. unit for attention to his wound.

Frank sat in the passenger seat of the jeep in a daze as he realized how lucky he'd been not to have taken the bullet pointblank in his face. Instead, his quick instincts had deflected the bullet just past his head—slightly grazing his ear. When he arrived at the medical unit, the doctor was able to see him immediately thanks to the ceasefire. Because of the ceasefire the revolving door to the operating room with injuries and deaths had been temporarily closed and most of the doctors sat around their camp twiddling their thumbs, or looking after those with infected insect bites and diarrhea. The young doctor took a quick look at the muscle and fat hanging from the hole in his arm and casually cleaned it with iodine and then casually took a tongue depressor and pushed the meat back into the hole, then sewed him up. Unfortunately, the doctor didn't bother injecting the area with a little lidocaine before he began the operation, nor did he send Frank back to base with any sort of pain medication for his injury. That night as Frank tried to sleep, the pain from his wound gnawed at him and radiated up his arm to his shoulder and down to his fingertips. He wondered how the lawmen in the old west handled getting shot and having the bullets removed without any form of pain medication. Then he thought about his predecessor, Frank Dalton, being shot multiple times and how he suffered in pain until he took his last breath. At least Frank's wound wasn't life threatening or disfiguring, as it easily could have been, but it still hurt like hell and Frank lay in his tent fighting hard to hold back tears due to the intense pain. During the night he broke into a cold sweat and his body shivered and shook so hard, Raymond got up to check on him.

"Hey buddy....you all right?"

"Yeah....I'll be okay," Frank answered in a weak, raspy voice.

Then Raymond pulled out a flask of whiskey he kept hidden in his pack and screwed the lid off, then kneeled down and helped Frank take a big swig.

"This'll help you sleep."

Frank gulped down a couple more good swigs, "Thanks buddy," Frank replied choking on the rough, cheap booze. Then he lay back in his rack and waited for the alcohol to take effect. Once again he realized how lucky he was, yet foolish to be so careless as to walk into a disturbance unarmed and unprepared. From that point on he would assume every seemingly nonthreatening event to be a life or death situation. It was a long night and luckily Frank wasn't required to report to duty the next morning due to his injury, so he went in search of some confiscated contraband to ease his pain. Although he had been wounded in the line of duty, to Frank's disappointment, he would not receive a Purple Heart since his injury was not combat related due to the ceasefire.

After that, Frank was allowed leave with a few other men to go to Kobe, Japan for a week's R and R (rest and relaxation). The men were given an orientation when they arrived in this new country and they were given recommendations on where to go, what hotel to stay in, and they were told in detail about pleasure girls. They were there for anything the men's hearts desired—sex any time of the day or night, or simply to be their tour guide. Frank took a sweet little thing named, Sue, for the entire week. He drank American beer while she drank sake, but most importantly, she focused on making him happy. Frank thought he'd died and gone to heaven. He liked Japan—the people were courteous, polite, and helpful. He could get whatever he wanted and he even entertained thoughts of going to live there after he got out of the Marines. Only one of the guys that went with them didn't want a girl. Instead, he wanted to simply see Japan. While he was there he bought a pet white rat to take back to Korea with him. It didn't take long for the men to kill it to see if they could make him cry and on that account they were successful.

When they returned to their unit in Korea Frank realized how much he hated it there. He had gotten a taste of something beautiful and then abruptly returned to that hellhole on the DMZ. Everyone hated the enemy and everyone was trying to kill each other. Even though the Americans were thousands of miles from home fighting and dying for them, the South Koreans picked on the Americans. Many South Koreans had deserted and simply run away to let the Americans fight their war for them. The Americans had brought in equipment for the Korean Army and troops however there appeared to be little or no appreciation for their support.

It felt like years, but finally Frank was approaching the end of his eighteen-month stint in Korea. Since there were new recruits arriving at the DMZ they decided to take Frank's unit, as well as other returning Marines, back to Incheon and load them onto an old training ship. They were told they were going on marine training exercises on the eastern side of the Korean peninsula but that's all anyone seemed to know about their early exodus from the DMZ. Honestly thought Frank, just about any reason to leave the front lines early was a good one and he breathed a sigh of relief. Maybe the gods of chance had smiled on him after all.

Frank's unit joined a group already onboard the ship and headed around the tip of the peninsula past Japan to the eastern side of Korea. Several landing craft vessels had been loaded onto the deck of the ship before they sailed so that they could do landing drills once they arrived at their destination. On the sail around to the tip of the peninsula Frank and two other guys stood at the rail near the beam of the ship, watching the flying fish sail ahead of the wake from the bow. A sailor working on the landing craft directly behind them suddenly shouted," Look out below!" as the steel ramp on the front of the landing craft crashed down the ship's rail where the three men were standing. Chip, the man most forward of Frank and his buddy, Raymond was crushed between the steel ramp and the ship's gunwale, nearly cutting him in half. Frank stood staring at the young boy's body as blood gushed onto the deck around his feet—his life-blood flooding out of him as Frank looked on. Frank and Raymond had just turned to leave their friend, Chip, when the ramp had dropped down from above. Once again, Frank realized how lucky he'd been in that split second as if a guardian angel had told him to move out of the way of certain death. A split second earlier and the huge steel ramp would have also cut them in two.

After the ship reached the harbor, the men were allowed a short rest before they were ordered to gear up, climb down the net draped from the bow and swim to shore. Although he sort of knew how to swim, Frank wasn't all that comfortable with climbing the netting draped across the bow of the ship and jumping into the icy ocean waters. When he hit the water, it took his breath away as he sank deep down with all his gear on. Out of breath he frantically clawed his way to the surface and gasped for air as his face broke through to fresh air. Frank was sure he'd drown before he made to shore—his gear weighed him down so much he could barely keep his head above water. He was so cold in the icy waters he could hardly force the air into his lungs as he summoned everything he had to keep on swimming. There were more than fifty men floundering in the water—struggling to get to shore and there was no one there to make certain they didn't drown. Frank thought for sure he would die right there in that freezing-cold harbor before he made it to land. When his feet finally touched the bottom of the shoreline he crawled onto the sand and just lay there heaving and throwing up icy seawater. It was then that he wished he'd taken learning to swim much more seriously.

Of course, who would have ever taught him to swim with more than fifty pounds of gear on?

When they arrived onshore exhausted, wet, and shivering, their next arduous drill was beyond what Frank could even have even imagined they would be asked to do. Suddenly he became even more suspicious about what the Marines really had in store for their next assignment. He had signed up for four years and there were still two-plus left for him to serve. The men were marched to a large hill in the woods in the pouring rain, where they were told to climb to the top with severe mudslides running down the steep slope. It was a grueling and bone-chilling exercise as Frank clawed his way up in full gear—sliding down over and over again, until he finally made it to the top. He wondered why after all his basic training they would be putting them through this now that he was supposedly headed back to the U.S. Maybe the Marines had something else in store for them and they hadn't yet dropped the bomb. After all, they hadn't even known they were going to Korea until they were more than half way there. When they were finally done with the climbing exercise, they were hardly given a rest before they were ordered to march back to the shore.

The weather was even colder and the rain was coming down so hard they could no longer see the ship in the harbor. They were then ordered to swim back out to the ship and climb back up the netting on the topsides to the deck of the troop carrier. Shivering and climbing with numb hands and feet, Frank somehow managed to find himself upside down, tangled in the netting, with his helmet across his face. He could see nothing and he struggled to simply hang on. He felt his hands slipping from the wet netting and started to panic, certain that he would fall on top of the other men and simply sink to the bottom of this icy harbor with all of his gear from sheer exhaustion. His buddy, Raymond, saw Frank's panic attack and climbed back down the net to talk him through his crisis. After a few minutes, Frank's breathing calmed and he righted his helmet and himself and started to climb one rung after the other, until he finally made it to the top and crawled over the gunwale—simply falling to the deck. He lay on his back out of breath and shivering with hypothermia, as did many of the men. A number of corpsmen scurried around the deck doing their best to help as many of the men as possible.

After the exercises were over, they were taken back to Incheon to board the USS General Howze to head back to the U.S. At least that's where they assumed they were going. Frank was relieved to finally be leaving when three Red Cross trucks pulled up to the docks. They set up to distribute coffee and donuts and the men were looking forward to an America treat before departing. However, it seemed that the America soldiers were not allowed to have any coffee or donuts—it seemed that they were only being offered to the Korean soldiers. Frank thought of the Marine slogan, Semper Fi (Semper Fidelis = Aways Faithful).

CHAPTER TWENTY

An Unimaginable Surprise

1954 – Treasure Island, San Francisco, California

Frank had spent two Christmases and eighteen months in Korea and the entire time he was certain he'd never see the United States again. When he caught sight of the Golden Gate Bridge he was overwhelmed with emotion that ranged from relief to absolute euphoria. He was soon to be back on American soil and he was grateful that whoever had been watching over him, had succeeded in keeping him alive. He swore that the moment he was granted leave, he would head home to try to right his wrong of leaving without telling anyone where he was going. Making peace with his mother was quite another thing, however, and he decided he would confront her about his name change when and if he saw her. He had finally gotten up the nerve to read her letters on the ship and he wasn't surprised to find that she blamed him for their terrible relationship. It was the third letter that sent him reeling.

When he started to read he was dumbfounded —

"I got a visit from that Judith Maxwell girl that moved to Anderson to live with her Grandma. Says you were more than friendly with her and got her pregnant. I didn't believe her til she brought the little bastard round. Took one look at him and realized he looked just like you when you was born. Not only that, her family's making an awful ruckus 'round here. So first chance you'd best get back here and do your duty and marry the girl since she's a telling everyone we know you're the little bastards father."

Inside the envelope Virginia had stuffed Judith's note. All it said was—

"Dear Frank, I had a baby boy and it's yours. His name is Terry Gene, he just turned one. You gotta come marry me and give him a last name. I'll be waiting for you at my Grandma's house in Anderson.

Love,

Judith"

Pregnant?! How was that possible, thought a naive Frank who was extremely inexperienced when it came to sex and the reproductive system of a young woman. They'd only been together once and as far as Frank remembered it, he was so nervous, his horse had crossed the finish line before the race had even started. As far as he knew, his boner-brew, as his buddies called it, had never gotten close enough to the required stable to get her pregnant. Maybe his mother's first instincts were right and the kid wasn't really his. He felt sick to his stomach. Marriage....?! He barely knew the girl and one thing was for certain—he was nowhere near ready to marry someone, let alone have a baby. At first he was angry that the first real time he'd had sex with a girl he could have gotten her pregnant. He felt his actual first time with his cousin didn't really count. She had come to him and had her way with him, telling him she was teaching him about the birds and the bees. Funny, but he didn't remember learning anything that night about bees or birds. He just remembered how pleasurable it was since he didn't really have to do anything—she'd done all the work for him. And that time he knew he'd gotten the horse into the stable on time, but it surely didn't result in any baby. At least none he'd heard about. Hell, he was even too shy to have sex with his pleasure girl in Japan, even though she'd made it very clear that 'it' was available for the taking anytime he wanted. Once again, Frank thought his life, as he knew it, was over.

When the Howze finally arrived at the dock on Treasure Island in the San Francisco harbor, a Marine band was playing. As soon as the men disembarked, there was a small military presentation award ceremony held, welcoming the returning Marines. All the men received a Presidential Unit Citation Ribbon and Frank was awarded six campaign ribbons. After the ceremony they were given the most elaborate lunch Frank had ever seen. It was by far the best food he'd ever eaten in his life. After the ceremony it was all quite anticlimactic Frank thought, especially since there were civilians on the street shouting, throwing things at the men, and picketing the Korean War. He was disappointed that America was not welcoming them back home with open arms.

After the luncheon, his unit was taken to the Treasure Island Marine Corps barracks to await orders for their next assignment. The best aspect of their temporary station was the magnificent food of every kind for them to eat at Treasure Island's chow hall. After the C-rations in Korea the men were in heaven—able to eat pretty much anything their hearts desired.

Frank and four other guys were assigned to duty at the mattress warehouse, but they really had nothing much to do there other than sleep. It seemed that their newest assignment provided the perfect place to SKATE on the job. After the grueling cold and discomfort, Frank was finally enjoying the fine art of S.K.A.T.I.N.G. in the Marines— (Stay out of trouble; Keep a low profile; Avoid higher-ups; Take your time; and last but not least, Enjoy yourself.)

He was excited to be back in California, especially since he was even closer to the ranch of Bill Dalton near Paso Robles, in San Luis Obispo County, California. He thought that maybe he would find time to visit there on leave should they be stationed here for a while. When the men were finally allowed to go off the base on liberty, it was for only two days. They were warned that there was a serious anti-war sentiment running rampant in the city, as well as in the rest of the country, and that they wouldn't be treated well by civilians. It seemed that most Americans were down on the United States' participation in the Korean War in general. The men were restricted from wearing their uniforms off the base and told to buy civilian clothing at the commissary just in case their uniforms should spark controversy or violence in the city so Frank bought civilian clothes at the commissary. They also warned the men to be ready to defend themselves, so Frank stuck his rock sock in his pocket for protection. He'd exchanged the rock however, for a large bar of soap so that he wouldn't do too much damage in case he had to use it his homemade weapon.

Their first night out at a local bar, Frank hit a guy with his fist for intentionally scuffing his shoes and dropping a meatball on it. He had also called Frank 'a baby killer.' His buddies pulled Frank back, preventing the altercation from turning into something more serious and they told Frank to go outside and calm down. He was so frustrated that civilians didn't understand how hard it was to spend a year and a half in that hellhole. Frank had truly expected they'd come back from Korea and be treated as heroes. He couldn't have been more wrong—it was just the opposite.

Frank was in San Francisco only a month before he was issued a two-week pass. Although his heart told him to explore California, his head told him to hitchhike home to Pickens to sort out his family issues. His trip across-country took about five days, but the journey was well worth it since he traveled across the majestic, jagged mountain range of the Sierra Nevada's as the Dalton brothers had, then down though the desert plains of the Nevadas and past the statuesque, red buttes of Utah and Arizona. From there he traveled across New Mexico, where Emmett had nearly gone to jail, then on across the top of Texas and into the state which had been home to his infamous kin—Oklahoma. As badly as he wanted to search out all the Dalton brothers' old haunts and home, he knew his time was limited and felt not only an obligatory pull to get home, but some small pang of homesickness that he was hesitant to admit to. After all, it had only been a few years since he'd left in quiet desperation to escape his life there and everything it represented. But, life is funny that way. Sometimes the miles of road traveled can dim the heartache of the past and shine brightly on those things one once cared about that still remain tucked somewhere in a corner of one's heart. He traveled through Arkansas, Mississippi, Alabama, Georgia, and home into South Carolina. Most of the time he slept by the roadside, but every now and again he'd hitch a ride in a big truck where he could get some shut-eye on the road. But, Frank didn't want to miss much, so when he was mobile he did his best to stay awake, unless it was night and he couldn't see much anyway. When Frank arrived in Pickens he made the decision to go straight to the McVey house. If his mother wanted him home, then she was about to get her wish.

When he arrived at the house in the middle of the day, without warning, only Wes was home. Frank was shocked to learn he'd been sick with diabetes and they had amputated his right leg. Now Wes had a good reason to sit around all day doing nothing, Frank thought. He honestly felt sorry for Wes who'd spent the best years of his life putting up with Virginia. Now, he was a broken man, appearing twice his age sitting in that tattered easy chair. Surprisingly, Wes acted as if it wasn't anything for Frank to just walk through the door like he'd just seen him earlier that morning.

When Frank asked Wes why Virginia had changed his name to Holliday, Wes' name, his answer shocked Frank.

"Seems I'm the only dad you got, son. Sure didn't see that Dalton fellow comin' around when you was little to clothe you, feed you, and see how you was doin'. Virginia tole me the bastard didn't want nothin' ta do with ya when you tracked him down. Even left the county the day after you went to see him. So's best you be happy with what you got here, son. You go on now and chaw on that for a spell."

Frank was surprised to hear Wes speak so many words at once. In fact, it was the first time he'd really heard him talk at all without Virginia around. But his words made an impression on him. Even though he was a sorry excuse for a father, at least he'd been present when he was growing up—even if he'd allowed Virginia to whip him senseless. But then Frank realized that Wes was nothing more than a whipped puppy himself under Virginia's rule.

Frank knew that his first order of business was to face the music and go visit Judith and the baby, who was more than a year old by then. It only took one look at the child, and like Virginia, Frank knew that it was his offspring. The kid was a Dalton sure enough. In fact, the baby even had Frank's strange ears. Now that he was a Marine, Frank knew he had to man-up and do the right thing. So, the two were married the next day at the Pickens County Justice of the Peace with no one else in attendance, except the secretary as witness. Frank thought about changing his name back to Dalton at the same time, but he had more important things to tend to now that he was a father. So, Judith took his new name, Holliday, as did his son.

When Frank and Judith returned to the house on McVey that afternoon, Virginia was there and he introduced her to his new wife and son. Virginia simply responded with a surprised look and a quick brush-off, "Yeah we've met before," she replied with a hint of sarcasm and disdain in her voice. "Planning on staying this time?" she asked looking at his pack and the girl's bags.

"Well that depends," Frank spoke carefully. "Could we stay here until my leave is over?" He was surprised when Virginia said yes, but then added, "Sure I'd be happy to take in family, Frank. That is if you can pay room and board. So, instead of giving Virginia more of his hard earned money, he and his family went to stay in town at the boarding house for the few days until he had to head back to San Francisco. After all, he thought it was only fair that he take the chance to consummate his marriage properly, so he took a few days and got to know his son, and his wife for that matter, since he really knew nothing about the woman. In fact, she was pretty much a stranger to Frank.

A few days later, Virginia actually made them dinner. There was never any sort of congratulatory gesture for his new child or his marriage, but then Frank knew that Virginia didn't have that sort of kindness in her. It was a strange feeling for Frank being back under Virginia's roof, but this time it was on his terms. Virginia was surprisingly civil to him, but he was relieved to leave as soon as they'd finished eating. Maybe knowing that he was now considered a war veteran of the United States Marine Corps, she would be more afraid of him as well as give him a little respect.

Virginia told Frank about the family and how Jeannette had left Edward Campbell remarried a man named Carl Brazil and moved to Pickens. Earl had left home when Bessy had moved and there was still no word from Coleman Virginia said, but Frank assumed he'd also joined the military, like himself. It would be five more years before Coleman would show his face again in Pickens. She told him about Bessy leaving the farm to go and live with Leroy and Geneva—basically as their full-time babysitter while they worked at Owens Corning. Frank really wanted to see Bessy, since he owed her an apology. He still felt guilty about her losing the farm and thought he should have tried to do more to help. But Frank had less than a week before he had to start hitchhiking back to base and he felt obligated to spend that time with his new wife and son.

Frank was pushing it close on time to get back to his

unit, so he decided to splurge and fly back to San Francisco. He hadn't really had much to spend his pay on since he'd gotten back and he was running out of time. Before Frank left, he gave Judith most of the money he had and put her and the baby on a bus to Atlanta to live with her parents while he waited for his next assignment. Once he was assigned, he figured he'd be able to bring his new wife and baby to wherever he was stationed. Most likely, it would be right back there in North Carolina at Camp Lejeune.

When he arrived back at Treasure Island, his buddies were shocked to learn that he'd been married while he was away and that he had a new baby. It seemed to change their opinion of him since they all believed him to be shy with women and likely a virgin. He thought that maybe marriage and a family wouldn't be such a terrible thing for him after all, so he decided he'd make a serious effort to make the best of it. Frank only served two more months at Treasure Island before he was sent to the Marine Corps Air Facility at Quantico, Virginia for two weeks of additional training.

CHAPTER TWENTY-ONE

The Honeymoon

1954 – Back at Camp Lejeune

After that, Frank was assigned, as he expected, to the Marine Corps Air Station New River located near Camp Lejeune, in North Carolina. It was a thirty-year-old base, which had had zero upgrades in the facility. Its airfield had been somewhat dormant for years and was then being used for practice landings and takeoffs, as well as an emergency airstrip. Overall, it was also used as a training and repair base for old aircraft and the hangers there served as facilities to do the repairs on aircraft owned by the Marine Corps.

A month after arriving in North Carolina, Frank was promoted to sergeant to his surprise. His promotion meant that he'd be making eighty-three dollars a month, so rented he a furnished off-base trailer for Judith and his son. He couldn't believe that he'd found himself right back in such close proximity to the home he'd tried so hard to escape from. The thing that bothered him most was that he'd never really gotten to see California the way he'd hoped and now he was saddled with a wife and child. He swore that some day he'd get back out west to really explore the lands of his forefathers.

It wasn't long before he was assigned as commander of the guard (COG). His job was to investigate crimes or disturbances, take men to and from their post, and to raise and lower the flag every day. It seemed the worst crimes he handled were men walking, running, or driving on the base's grass. The Navy gave him a new battleship grey, Chevy pick-up to drive, however he could only use it on base, unless there was some sort of pick up he was ordered to make off base. He knew he was going to have to buy himself a car if he was going to live off base and bring his family there. He had a great schedule of one day on and one day off—another Sergeant shared his COG position serving on Frank's days off. There were twelve guys in Frank's unit, some of whom lived on base and some off in rented trailers. As commander of the guard, Frank would often take them on arms and marching drills, conduct weapons inspections, and the most dreaded assignment— 'Field Day'—usually a Thursday, when they had to completely clean the barracks from top to bottom, which involved moving the furniture clean outside. It brought back long forgotten memories for Frank of Virginia insisting he remove all furnishings in the house and scrub the floors until she was satisfied. Virginia would have fit right in, in the Marines—making one hell of a nasty drill sergeant, thought Frank. Except her swagger stick would surely be a strong switch.

Frank bought a 1953 Ford Fairlane and proudly telephoned Judith to tell her the good news about the trailer and the car, but she didn't sound all too pleased about the trailer. She felt a small house would be a better choice for them, but Frank explained that on his meager salary, it was the best he could afford for the time being. He agreed to drive to Atlanta to pick her up on his next leave and she hesitantly agreed to move there with him.

In his idle time Frank would sneak into the woods—on and off duty—with a Thompson submachine gun to do some target practice. He'd found he really enjoyed using the weapon as long as he wore earplugs to protect his ears. But more importantly, Frank kept practicing with a Colt forty-five single-action revolver he'd purchased—known as a Peacemaker. It was much like the one his ancestor Frank Dalton had used when he was alive.

Finally, Frank was granted a long enough liberty to make the drive to Atlanta to fetch his wife and son. They hadn't really had a honeymoon and Frank was excited to see them. He had high hopes of a loving family relationship, even if he'd never had his own personal example of such. Judith complained during most of the drive to the base and upon their arrival, she was extremely put out by the condition of the old trailer. She complained the moment she walked through the front door with the top screen hanging loose from its frame and continued until she finally fell asleep at night. Frank gave Judith pretty much all the money he made and her job was to take care of the bills.

Judith didn't stay long in North Carolina, however. She simply took the car one day when Frank was at work and returned to Atlanta to be with her parents. Frank was surprised that day when she didn't show up to pick him up on base, so he caught a ride with one of his buddies to the trailer. When he arrived to find the car gone he got worried. After hours of waiting and worrying that she and the baby had been in an accident, the phone rang. He held his breath and picked it up—expecting it to be the police or a hospital. Instead, it was Judith on the other end saying that she'd just decided to drive back home to Atlanta to see her parents—she was homesick. Frank was hopping mad and nearly hung up on her. Now he didn't have his family there with him, but worse—he didn't have his new car. Since he would now have to rely on rides from the base to the trailer, Frank usually just stayed at the barracks until Judith decided to return at her whim. She rarely consulted him on her decisions to leave and she stayed away in Atlanta more often than not. She had control of his money and was spending it faster than he was earning it—so it was at that point he decided not to reenlist. He couldn't afford to be married to Judith and be a Marine living on a restrictive, meager income. He had only one active year to go on his commission, so he did his best to stay out of the poorhouse.

Things eventually got pretty relaxed at the base and there were many days that Frank didn't even bother to do roll call in the mornings. Although Judith was a pain in the ass, he kind of missed having his son Terry around and watching him grow. He'd be walking soon and Frank was afraid he wouldn't be there to see his first steps.

Frank and the guys kept wishing for some excitement around the base, but most days were hum-drum with little to do, other than go to the officers' slop-shute—a bar that sold only warm beer and pop. One day Frank got a call over his radio from one of the base guards that a mixed race fellow, from New Orleans, named Brussard, was running down the runway during takeoffs and landings. Frank knew the man well, so he figured he could easily take care of the situation. When Frank arrived on-scene in his truck, Brussard was acting totally crazy—holding his hands over his ears and screaming, while chasing the planes down the runway as they taxied.

Frank stepped out of the truck and walked over to the man "Hey buddy, you okay?" Frank questioned, concerned.

The man was slobbering and non-responsive—as if was if he was hallucinating and unaware of his surroundings.

"Henry, what in the hell has gotten into you? Are you sick? It's Frank...tell me what's wrong."

Brussard backed away from Frank with a fearful look in his eye and took off running again. Frank realized the man was far too large to subdue alone, so he radioed for backup. Brussard was a hulk of a man—about six-foot-four and two hundred-sixty pounds. Five officers arrived with the MP van and they did their best to cuff him, but the man fought them off like a trapped animal. It took all six men to subdue him and wrestle him to the ground—a few having been hit, kicked, and bitten by the crazed Marine in the process. Finally, they managed to handcuff him and get him in the van. Then they drove him to sick bay and struggled to get him in to see the medical officer. The men picked him up by the arms and legs, since he was still fighting them and refused to comply. When the doctor saw the man's condition he immediately tried to give him a sedative, but Brussard wouldn't hold still long enough for the injection. The doctor then ordered them to put him in a canvas straightjacket, but Brussard kept getting out before they could get it secured. Finally, the medic drew up another sedative and stuck the man in the neck as he struggled. After a few minutes he started to calm down and it eventually knocked him out. Several months later Frank saw Brussard hitchhiking in civilian clothing in town, apparently after a medical discharge. Frank felt bad for his friend and he always wondered what more he could have done to help the man through his difficulties. He had never really found out what was wrong with the man, but he assumed that it had been some sort of psychological disorder.

It seemed that Brussard wouldn't be the last of the psych patients around the base. A month later, another really smart Marine named, Imus, stacked wooden blocks at the top of the staircase and pushed them off onto the head of the officer of the day, who was doing rounds with his logbook. This time, when Frank was called to arrest another out-of-control Marine and take him to the brig, Frank made more of an effort to talk the guy down. He knew that something like this could ruin the man's career so he drove Imus around for a few hours until he started acting himself again. Frank was beginning to wonder if there wasn't something in the food or water on base that was making the men act extremely out of character. Or he wondered, were they simply looking for a quick way out of the military?

It was early October of 1954 when the base received word that Hurricane Hazel was headed for a direct hit with the North Carolina coast. The base gave an order for all families to be evacuated from the area, giving Judith the perfect excuse to take Terry back to Atlanta in Frank's car. Frank was assigned to stay on base to handle any emergencies or damage that might arise from the storm. The next day the storm came through with a vengeance, pummeling the Carolina coast like a prizefighter. It hit as a category four hurricane and did a tremendous amount of damage to the area. Frank was actually grateful his family hadn't stayed, since many of the trailers had been pretty badly torn up, not to mention the hangars and aircraft at the base. It seemed there was plenty of repair work to be done, so Frank got to work and tried to stop worrying about Judith and her whereabouts for a while.

Before Judith's next visit Frank decided that he'd surprise her with a used black and white television for the trailer so that she could watch the daytime shows she always talked about. He was hoping it would keep her in town longer so he'd have use of his car, but even that didn't please her. She bitched because the tubes kept blowing and to change the channels one had to go outside and turn the entire antenna to tune in or change stations. They only had three channels to watch anyway so Frank couldn't really understand what difference it made. So once again, Judith returned to Atlanta to stay with her parents, but this time Frank drove her there and brought his car back to the base.

One day Frank was called on a report of a theft on base. It seemed a Marine had been stealing meat from the food mess and selling it off base. Frank was told to pick the sergeant up, arrest him, and take him to the brig. Weeks later the man had been court-martialed and was being drummed out of the Marines. Frank was ordered to assemble the men on the parade field in formation, close to the guard shack, then to pick up the prisoner from the brig and bring him to be drummed out. Frank returned with the man in tow—wearing civilian clothes and handcuffs, and walked him to the front of the unit to be read his charges. The man stood there awaiting sentencing—only able to look at the dirt underneath his feet. As Frank watched the man, it reminded him of the way he would look at his own feet when being scolded by Virginia as she sentenced him for some crime she thought he'd committed.

They read off the man's sentence of a dishonorable discharge and stripped him of everything but his ID. Then with a drummer walking ahead of him drumming his every step, the man was escorted through the gates of the base for the very last time. The prisoner was still in cuffs when the drummer halted—removed the cuffs and kicked him the rest of the way off the property onto the railroad tracks, which represented the property-line.

Frank had been waiting and watching the painful spectacle from his truck next to the gate. The stupid thing, thought Frank, was that the man had made it to the rank of sergeant and he'd served his time. If he'd wanted out of his service, all he had to do was to muster out. Could he have really been so foolish as to think they wouldn't punish him for his dishonorable act? It was the core virtue of the Marines—honor, courage, and commitment. And stealing wasn't honorable. Had the man owned up and made right his egregious actions maybe his commander would have simply NJPd him, or ninja-punched him (Non-judicial punishment = knocked down a rank with less pay).

This time Judith was gone for nearly three months when he received a call at the base. It was Judith calling to tell him the happy news—she was pregnant with twins no less, and Frank's heart suddenly sank to the pit of his stomach. Now he would have five mouths to feed. Frank was so shocked that before he could even respond to her, her father yanked the phone away and yelled over the line in Frank's ear. "How the hell do you plan on supporting my daughter and her kids on that lousy Marine salary you're making?! If you think I'm going to feed three of your screaming kids you're sorely mistaken! You're a low-down, sorry scoundrel."

Frank assured him that he'd already decided to move to Atlanta at the end of his commission and find a good paying job. That seemed to calm him somewhat, but he was still grumbling when Judith snatched the phone back. "Don't mind daddy, he'll get used to you someday, Frank."

"But, twins?" questioned Frank, "Are you sure?"

"You don't sound happy I'm carrying two more of your children, Frank."

"How do they know it's two?"

"There are two heartbeats silly," Judith replied.

Frank hung up dumbfounded. Once again could he be sure they were his? After all, she wasn't around much and as far as he knew, twins didn't run in his family. He didn't know his situation could get any worse, but here he was now saddled with three children and he hadn't really had a chance to live his life. Unbeknownst to Frank however, a few weeks later, Mr. and Mrs. Maxwell made the decision that three were two too many children for Frank to support and they took Judith to get an abortion at nearly six months pregnant. Frank was never told about the termination of the pregnancy. He only learned about the demise of the fetuses when the funeral home called Frank to pay for their burial. Frank was speechless when the man told him he was sorry about the death of his two daughters, but since the miscarriage occurred so far into the pregnancy, they could not just dispose of them—they were required by law to bury the babies.

"Miscarriage?" asked Frank. "My wife hasn't told me anything about this. What do you mean so far into the pregnancy? She couldn't have been more than three or four months pregnant."

"I'm sorry to be the bearer of bad news, sir, but these two babies appear to be nearly fully developed. They would have to be six to seven months it appears."

Frank was speechless. He was shocked that Judith had told him nothing about the babies and worse—that she was apparently much further along than she'd said. He'd just thought she was gaining weight. Frank didn't have the money the funeral home was asking for the burial, so he tried getting assistance from the Red Cross, but they wouldn't help. Being a veteran of the Korean War he was advised that he was entitled to have a burial in the Georgia National Cemetery for free. He would also be able to bury his children in the same plot. The Marine Corps ended up awarding him the plot with Frank's name and rank engraved on a headstone. It wasn't until Frank arrived in Atlanta after he'd mustered out of the Marines, that he learned the truth. The babies had been aborted. The thought of it made him sick to his stomach. They had intentionally killed his two little girls.

A few months after the funeral Frank had served his three years, so he officially left active duty. That meant that until he reached retirement age, he would no longer receive a paycheck from the Marine Corps. He would, however, have to remain in the reserves for the next five years. Should they call him up, he knew that he would have to drop everything and go back to active duty. He also knew that he had to find a good paying job and find it fast.

CHAPTER TWENTY-TWO

An Atlanta Policeman

1956 – '57 – Back to Law Enforcement

Frank had no plans or job offers when he retired from the Marine Corps. He was worried. After all he had a wife and child to support, so he moved to Atlanta hoping for the best. Judith was already living with her parents, Reverend Raymond and Saphire Maxwell in their house next to a mill, so Frank moved in until he could find a job and rent their own place. It brought back vivid memories of Frank's earlier life—living at the Mill Hill House with Virginia abusing him. Frank was to say the least, not Reverend Raymond's favorite person so in some ways life there was as difficult as living with Virginia, albeit he was not receiving his weekly lashings—at least not with a stick. However, tongue-lashings were pretty much a daily dose served up by her father. He now had his father-in-law down his throat, twenty-four-seven, as well as Judith and her difficult mother.

Reverend Raymond ran a congregation, he had organized in the suburbs of Atlanta. His son, Max, had found an acre of land for a new church site and his followers had anted up the money to build a modest house of worship. He held services there for his newly formed congregation for a number of years until they started questioning the way he was running things and they formally asked him to step down as minister, hoping to replace him. Somehow however, Reverend Raymond had managed to put the land in his own name, so he refused to leave on the grounds that he owned the land and thus, the church itself. He suggested that if they weren't happy with his sermons and management, they should move on to a new parish. This caused a great deal of dissension among his sixty-some parishioners and many ended up leaving the congregation. He brought his holier-than-thou, overbearing Christian ethics to Sunday meetings and ruled his parish as well as his home with his belief that he was truly God's messenger and whatever he said was the iron-clad law of the land. Although Frank considered himself a Christian, his now blossoming sense of self set Reverend Raymond and Frank at odds most of the time. That and Judith's prudish up-bringing, made life quite difficult in the Maxwell home for Frank and he started to realize the urgency of finding a new vocation and means of earning a living. He wanted to get out from under the Reverend's roof as soon as possible.

Every morning, Judith's father rode him, "So, Frank-lin....what are you going to do today about finding a job to support my daughter and grandson?"

"Well sir....I was just heading down to the employment office to see what they might have for me."

"Son, you need to do a might better than these daily minimum wage jobs if you're going to get by in this world. Just because you come from a family of underachievers don't mean you should follow in their footsteps. I told Judith you came from white trash and wouldn't amount to anythin'!"

"Sorry you feel that way sir. I agree I'm not from money or a successful family, but I'm proud of my service in the Marine Corps."

"Well no daughter of mine is going to be married to a soldier making peanuts. Now you get out there and find something that pays better! You hear?!"

So once again, Frank went to where it had all started in Atlanta—the local unemployment office. They sent him to a string of below minimum wage jobs such as a paper company, loading giant rolls of paper into railway containers, making only a dollar an hour; a job printing Marietta Bread covers for about the same pay; then finally a job at Lockheed Martin, in Marieitta, Georgia a few months after he'd arrived, earning two dollars and five cents per hour. Lockheed offered him promising prospects since they were willing to train him for work in the aeronautical industry. Even Judith's father was impressed by the possibilities of his future at the company.

A month after starting at Lockheed Frank rented a part of a house consisting of one bedroom, a bath, and a kitchen for his family. He immediately started Lockheed's one-year training program. While in their employment he learned to read blueprints, solder wires, shoot rivets, and run hydraulic pipes throughout their aircraft. They also trained him to install electronics in their planes. It offered a bright future for Frank to learn a new trade, since civilian aviation was starting to take off, both figuratively and literally. The plant employed over one hundred thousand people making it the largest plant in the U.S. under one roof. Some of Frank's co-workers even paid Frank to drive them to work in his Ford Fairlane, giving him a little extra income on the side. Frank had always been good at finding profitable side-hustles.

Things seemed to be going well for Frank and Judith with his new job and their little rented flat. She had even quelled her bitching a bit and had become, if not pleasant, at least tolerable to live with. However, about the time he completed his training and was about to receive a two-dollar an hour raise, Lockheed laid off sixty thousand employees with no notice—including Frank. It was a Friday afternoon at four o'clock when they announced their cutbacks. It seemed they were being forced to remodel the C-130 transports, thus production would be halted for some time to come. It was a devastating blow, since Frank thought he was set for life in a secure job, which would provide exponential growth. Although half of the county had suddenly found themselves unemployed, he was lucky enough to find a job in the labor pool at the Ford assembly plant, in nearby Hapeville, south of Atlanta. When he got there the plant personnel guy took applicants upstairs to the roof of the plant and asked to see everyone's hands. Only the guys with rough hands got hired. The starting pay was about the same as Lockheed's had been so he felt lucky just to be employed in a sea of struggling unemployment. The county had taken a hard hit in the wake of Lockheed's temporary demise and Frank thought it best to leave the area, but Judith wouldn't hear of it. She wanted nothing to do with moving away from her family again.

Judith's brother, Max, worked as an officer of the law on the Atlanta police force and he encouraged Frank to put in his application. Since he'd had Military Police experience while serving in the Marine Corps, he said Frank was a shoe-in. Of course, Judith and her parents were against it since it was a dangerous job and they already had enough worry with their son working as a cop. No matter, Frank went down to the precinct, with Max's recommendation, and put in his application for police training. He was told however, that it could take up to a year to work his way through the red tape of their hiring process, since there were over one hundred applicants.

In the meantime Frank continued with his job at Ford— replacing employees who were out—a frustrating and stressful job. He'd be put on the assembly line doing many different jobs with little or no knowledge of what the job entailed. His first assignment was installing taillight wires when the cars were red hot right out of the lacquer ovens. It was grueling, hot, and exhausting work and the only time during the day that the assembly line shut down was for a thirty-minute lunch break. He did this six days a week, twelve hours a day. The hardest job there was hanging doors in the body shop and Frank seemed to get stuck in that position more than not. Trying to position the doors hanging from a cable above and align them onto the door hinges with six screws was to say the least, a challenging and awkward job. Everyday he swore he wouldn't go back, but he always did when he assessed his mounting bills and

Judith's overspending. But, after a year-and-a-half he was abruptly laid off. Luckily, at about the same time he received a fourth callback from the Atlanta police force to come down for one last interview. He had already been interviewed twice, had a physical, and taken a written test. It seemed that his brother-in-law, Max, had greatly influenced their decision to hire him—telling his superiors that he would personally oversee Frank's training. It seemed that the Atlanta Police Department had no official training program. They simply put men out on the street and hoped they survived. It was their usual procedure to team up new rookies with a veteran cops and hope that they would catch on quickly without getting killed in the interim. Luckily, Frank's experience as an MP in Korea and at Lejuene came in handy. The work came easy to him, since it was so similar to his job in the Marines. Except for the fact that out on the street the crazy ones were carrying guns.

Max and Frank had been assigned to canvas a bad part of downtown Atlanta around Pryor St., known to the locals as, Blackbottom—a contemptuous, offensive, and disparaging name, but nonetheless, one used by most in the city. The odds weren't good for cops working those neighborhoods that one would survive long enough to retire from the police force, since shootings of police officers were extremely common. In general, police were not highly regarded or liked by the population of Atlanta, which made it a mandatory requirement to leave their uniforms, shoulder brownie belts (Sam Browne belt shoulder strap), and weapons at work when they were off duty. So since his friends and neighbors never saw him in uniform, many never knew that Frank was even a cop. This actually came in handy at times since people felt comfortable speaking freely to Frank about any and all news around town and Frank would put that indiscriminate information to good use.

Max and Frank's main job was to run random raids on

the beer joints, especially the Negro establishments. In essence they were told to harass the Negro population and keep them 'in check.' Their second order of business was to serve warrants in Greenwood—a run-down Negro neighborhood. One day while serving a warrant, Frank went to the front of the house, while Max covered the rear. There was a female of about twenty sitting on the front porch glider as Frank walked up the rickety steps. The house was constructed of naked boards, with few remaining patches of paint over the rotting wood. Some of the windows were even boarded up with scraps of wood.

"Afternoon miss, does a Matthew Brown still live here?" Frank asked the woman politely, but sternly. The woman sat studying him a moment as if deciding whether to respond to his question.

She then leaned towards the screened door and shouted over her shoulder, almost as a warning, "Does Matthew Brown still live here?"

From the back room a man's voice responded with, "Who's askin'?"

"The powleece," answered the woman matter-of-factly.

Suddenly, the backdoor slammed and Frank quickly turned and ran down the side of the house to find Max already on the ground on top of a young Negro man. Max was welding his nightstick beating the man into submission. Frank grabbed the stick from Max and quickly handcuffed the man.

"What'd you have to go and do that for? I was just havin' me a little fun," complained Max, brushing himself off as he stood and pushed the bleeding man ahead of him towards the police cruiser.

"Ain't necessary to beat the man to death, Max. You already had him on the ground."

"What's wrong with you Frankie, got a soft heart, do ya?" Max prodded.

"Let's just get him downtown and book 'em," responded

Frank.

"Seems you have too much of a conscience there, Frankie-boy. Ha....won't last long doin' this job," Max laughed.

"What, me or my conscience?" questioned Frank.

"Neither," chortled Max.

Another night, the Frank and Max were on patrol around Pryor Street. The radio had been especially quiet that night since it was Sunday and the neighborhood lay at the heart of the bible belt. Out of sheer boredom, Max and Frank decided to make a run on a juke-joint—a back-bar establishment for colored folk. When the two police walked through the door the loud laughter and communion promptly terminated and you could hear a pin drop in the bar, as everyone turned to look at the two 'pigs,' as they called them—a term that originated in England in the early eighteen hundreds. Like pigs, who take more than their fair share—police would often skim the illicit gains of thieves for themselves. Listening to the hushed silence, Max and Frank relished the control and power their badges provided as they stood there studying the attentive room. Max walked over to a guy on a barstool and yanked him to his feet by his shirt collar and spun him around against the wall spread-eagled, while he patted him down. As he'd guessed, the man was packing a thirty-eight detective special, which meant an automatic five years in the slammer.

After booking the guy, Frank decided to keep the gun for his own personal use, since he liked the weight and feel of the piece. It was common practice for officers to keep contraband weapons. In fact, they had lockers full of guns and ammunition that managed to remain 'off the books,' so to speak. In fact, Max had many sawed-off shotguns, in addition to handguns, stashed in his locker. It was important for them to have a stash of opportune weapons—'drop guns' they called them. In cases of an officer involved shooting where they shot and later learned that the criminal in question, had actually been unarmed, the cop would simply drop one of the confiscated weapons on the dead or injured man. This ensured that, if the criminal wasn't destined for an address six foot-under, then he would surely land himself a five-year stint in the county penitentiary with little or no trial. It was also important insurance to get the officer who did the unwarranted shooting off the hook. Frank questioned the legality of their actions, not to mention the moral behavior, but he knew if he expressed his concerns to his superiors over Max, he would only cause consternation within the ranks and no longer be considered a team player. In fact, he was certain that he'd be shunned by his co-workers if he didn't play the game the way it had always been played. Not only did Frank need the paycheck, he kind of liked the power his complicit liability bought him.

Another night as Frank and Max were riding around bored and responding to fruitless reports of prowlers in a neighborhood populated by older residents living in lower income apartment buildings, they rolled through the streets in their fifty-five Ford Fairlane patrol car with a bubble on top. Dogs barked and lights flicked on in surrounding windows as residents shouted at dog owners to quiet their canines. They were just discussing the idea of creating some excitement at one of the local bars when Frank spotted a suspicious Negro man walking down the sidewalk well after midnight. The man heard the car approaching and glanced over his shoulder, then continued walking as if he were doing nothing wrong and had no reason to run.

"I think we should check this guy out, wha'd'ya think Frank?"

"Well, the guy seems okay....he's not running so he doesn't seem too worried 'bout us."

Max suddenly slammed on the brakes throwing the three-on-the-tree gearshift into park and jumped out of the car confronting the man, before Frank could follow him.

"What'ya think you're doin' walkin' around this time of night?" demanded Max, spinning him around by the shoulder and getting in the man's face.

It only took two shakes for the tough man to pin Max on the ground, prompting Frank to jump from the passenger seat of the cruiser—gundrawn as Max and the man scuffled on the ground. As Frank attempted to pull the man off of Max, he punched Max hard on the jaw knocking him off, then grabbed Frank and pulled him to the ground. Now straddling Frank he struggled for control of Frank's gun. Suddenly, the cocked gun fired hitting Frank in the same arm that had taken the bullet in Korea. Frightened, the man quickly rolled off Frank scrambling to his feet. Before Max and Frank could get back on theirs the man was sprinting down the street, then dashed into the bushes between two houses. Dogs were barking and howling and doors were slamming shut all over the neighborhood. Both Frank and Max were so dazed by the gunshot they didn't realize at first that Frank had been shot. Then Frank felt the blood trickling down his arm and onto his hand. When he finally realized he'd been hit he exclaimed, "Damn....that's the same arm took a bullet in Korea." He and Max studied his upper arm realizing it was luckily nothing more than a graze. Max insisted they take care of it themselves with their limited medical kit in the cruiser, so as not to have all of that unwanted paperwork that an officer shooting would require. And as for the culprit, the last thing they wanted to do was pursue the witness on foot.

Once his arm was bandaged they continued their shift in the patrol car, canvassing the streets of Blackbottom but there were no signs of the man.

"Thanks for the help back there Frank. That son of a bitch was one tough bastard. I could have gotten him off you know. You didn't have to go an' get yourself shot."

"Yeah you're right....he was a strong one. And since we're not filing a report on this I'd like to keep it from Judith and your family if you don't mind."

"I'm with you on that Frank. I'd never hear the end of it if they thought I went and got you shot," Max said shaking his head.

"Let's just tell everyone I cut myself on a fence pursuing a potential suspect. I wouldn't really want it known I got shot with my own weapon."

"Sounds good to me," Max agreed. "Especially when you were saving my ass," Max chortled.

Frank lay in bed that night thinking how lucky he'd been not once, but twice. He'd been shot twice with little consequence and he realized that both times could have been much worse, even fatal. He knew he had luck on his side, as well as some very busy guardian angel protecting him from mortal harm. He'd survived his stint in Korea with the help of that angel—If only she'd had been able to protect him from Virginia what a difference it would have made in his life. But maybe, he thought, that's what had ultimately made him strong. Although he felt law enforcement was his calling in life, he began to wonder how healthy it would be for him in the long run. The last thing he wanted was to end up like his relative Frank Dalton.

Frank and Judith were still living in the three rented rooms, which was close quarters for a couple that was always quarreling. If it wasn't her dislike of his chosen vocation as a cop, then she was accusing Frank of cheating on her and having sex with other women. They never seemed to get along. Nothing he said to her seemed to convince her that he had been faithful, yet he still had to suffer the consequences of her vivid imagination. There were days that he wondered if he shouldn't just go ahead and have an affair. If he was going to get blamed for it, he thought that he should at least get some pleasure out of spending most of his time in the doghouse. Even some of his friends, including Max, Judith's own brother thought he was crazy not to step out on her. After all, much of the police force was guilty of infidelity, not to mention other mortal sins.

In fact, there was a great deal of chaos in the Atlanta police department. Not many of the men were clean and Frank had been there long enough to learn the underbelly of the inner workings of the force. It was a tough and risky job as a cop in Atlanta. Frank tried hard to keep his nose clean, but there were many temptations—as well as many scandals—especially from shootings of unarmed suspects while police were making arrests. Cops were quick on the draw, much like the old west and now Frank felt like one of those who had jumped to rely on his weapon rather than trying to defuse a heightened situation. The men looked after their own and if the criminal who was shot was indeed unarmed, one of his friends would simply drop a gun on the dead man, or even a wounded one as long as there were no witnesses.

The biggest scandal while Frank was riding shotgun was when a drunken Sergeant ran over and killed two people on a motorcycle while on duty in his patrol car. He tried to get his friends to lie for him, but they refused to get involved. He was known to often come to work drunk and was never reprimanded for his lack of sobriety. Of course, the incident was covered up by the police commissioner and nothing was ever done to punish the sergeant. After all, the two dead victims were only Negroes and their life wasn't worth much in the eyes of most of the city in those days.

After the incident, however, the Atlanta Journal started a huge campaign to clean up corruption in the police department by exposing it to the public. That's when all hell broke loose in Atlanta. The Journal tried to expose the issues of 'drop-guns' as well as police abuse. It concerned Frank that he was pulled into the fringes of questionable practices on a daily basis, and it made him start thinking about the liabilities of being a police officer. Of course, even Frank took advantage of Max's political ability to fix Judith's speeding tickets and thought little of it. But he did wonder if that was that just a step away from delving into larger abuses of the badge and uniform.

Afraid of his own weakness to succumb to the many offers of back-handed payoffs, Frank started carrying a thirty-eight police special. Everyone knew that if you wanted to commit a crime or kill someone and get away with it you would use a revolver since the casings would stay in the chamber, leaving the scene devoid of evidence. So, just in case he found himself in another situation where he found it necessary to shoot someone, or found himself in the middle of some form of police corruption, he wanted to be certain that he had some means of leaving no trace behind. All these things made him feel bad about his participation in what would have been considered corruption of the badge. But most of all, he felt uncomfortable about how racist his co-workers were. Frank had never really been close-friends with a Negro, however he'd served with a few in Korea and found them to be outstanding soldiers. He didn't use racist slurs such as Max's insistence on calling them the 'N' word, but he still didn't understand that words such as 'darkie' were also considered derogatory.

Frank had been there a year and was only making two hundred and ninety-five dollars a month as a civil servant in uniform. He thought long and hard about the many bribes and offers that were made. Then he thought about the Dalton brothers and how they had turned from law upholding marshals to outlaws due to underpayment, or non-payment, and the life–threatening risks they took every day—like the risk his namesake Frank Dalton had taken while arresting the bootlegger and losing his life in the process. That Frank Dalton and his family certainly weren't compensated for his loss of life and he knew that his family wouldn't be either should he be killed in the line of duty. Judith and her mother and father harped on him constantly, asking, "Where would Judith and your son be if you were shot and killed?" Of course, Judith's family wanted him to quit the force since they were all afraid he was going to die and leave the family with the burden of taking care of Judith and Terry.

Somehow, Frank had survived Korea even though he was convinced he'd never return alive. Once again, he supposed there was a strong possibility that he'd be killed working as a cop on the lawless streets of Atlanta. So he started second-guessing his choice to join the force. When he thought long and hard about it, it seemed to Frank that not much had changed since the days of the Daltons, except the caliber of their guns and the horsepower of their transportation.

As risky as it was, Frank still liked the job better than any of the others he'd worked. It was the closest to being back in the Marine Corps. Being a cop was interesting work and it made him feel he was doing an important job, which helped make up for his inferiority complex about his limited education. But he tried his best to stay humble, even though most police on the force wore a superior attitude as an invincible cloak. Frank understood the reasoning behind making them shed their weapons, badge, and uniforms at the end of the day. Frank knew that many would surely use their status in their daily lives to the detriment of the city's population.

Police brutality on the streets was one thing, but it commonly carried over as domestic violence into the homes of officers. Frank had witnessed it with his Uncle and Aunt Carol, but Max was pretty brutal with his wife, Beth. Frank had heard other officers and Judith's mother

Sapphire talk about it, but Max and Frank never socialized after work, even though they were brothers-in-law. However, Frank had seen the remnants of their fights the few times he'd gone to pick up Max for work. Their house was always torn up from their fighting and Beth didn't fare much better. Being a nurse, he was surprised that someone at her job at the hospital hadn't done something about it, since she'd been treated over the years for multiple broken bones and lacerations. Frank tried to make him stop but couldn't reason with him. At that time, wife beating was no big deal, especially to the police, so everyone at work simply turned a blind eye to Max's sins of domestic abuse.

Max seemed to be stuck in a dead-end career as a patrolman until he caught a bank robber one day and he was instantly promoted to lieutenant, due to the positive press he had received on television for his brave act. However, Frank knew the real story of his amazing arrest. It seemed that Max was on his way to the bank one Saturday morning to deposit his paycheck. He had parked in front of the bank and headed in just as a man ran out of the bank and directly into Max knocking himself to the ground. Max picked him up apologizing as the man ran away when suddenly the banker ran out the door screaming, "That was the bank robber, you fool! He just took all our money! Go after him!"

Max, who was grossly overweight, ran after the man still limping from his collision, so catching up to the robber wasn't such a tough feat. When he finally caught him, Max arrested him even though he was out of uniform. On Sunday morning, a television reporter caught up with him attending church with his wife and mother. He interviewed Max on the spot and photographed him with his arm around his mother and wife. It seemed that Max was an instant hero who loved his mother and wife dearly, as well as a churchgoer to boot—a real family man in the eyes of the city.

Eventually, Max left Beth for his girlfriend who worked at the Conyers Hunt Club and Beth filed for divorce. Max actually paid his child support on time, but it didn't stop him from beating Beth every chance he got. He later died mysteriously, and no one really delved into the investigation of his death. It seemed that maybe his brutality had eventually gotten the best of him.

CHAPTER TWENTY-THREE

The Beer Business

1960s – Carling Brewery – Busch Brewery

After a year and a half of risking his life, Frank left the police department and applied for work at Carling Brewery. When he arrived for his interview the receptionist directed him to the personnel office. While he was waiting, a stalwart-looking, middle-aged man came down the stairs dressed in a suit and tie and introduced himself as Lieutenant-General A. R. Bowling. He asked if Frank had been in the service and Frank proudly told him he'd been a sergeant in the Marine Corps. "Well then, I've got a job for you," Bowling said, shaking Frank's hand and without so much as an interview, Frank was hired. He immediately walked Frank to the packing department and introduced him to the department manager.

"Tom Fay, meet your new foreman. What'd you say your name was," Bowling asked, turning to Frank.

Frank put out his hand to shake and introduced himself, "Frank....Frank Dalton Holliday."

"Frank Dalton, ehh? Like the U.S. Marshal?" Fay replied, nodding his head.

"Yes indeed," Frank answered, happy he'd made the connection.

"So Frank, when can you start?" asked Fay.

"Well I suppose....two weeks once I give notice at the police department."

"Okay, then....you're hired."

Frank made a lot of friends at the brewery but Frank and Judith had little or no social life as a couple. She just didn't seem to get along with anyone, so they didn't have many friends and neighbors kept their distance. In essence, everyone seemed to avoid her. On the rare occasion they

were invited somewhere, she would act like a fool—
bragging all the time about her high-end furniture, or some
such nonsense. Frank was embarrassed to take her anywhere since she usually managed to commit one faux pas
after another no matter what the setting. In general she
seemed to imagine people were after her. She even thought
the owner of the rooms they were letting was trying to
break in when Frank was working the night shift. She was
convinced that he was after her and insisted that they find
another place to live.

To please her, Frank decided to buy a house in Jonesboro on the GI bill and become his own landlord. He was
tired of paying rent with zero equity and even more tired
of Judith's constant complaining about why they didn't
have their own home. It was a modest, new, brick-veneer,
three-bedroom house with one bath and no garage. Judith
got pregnant again and their daughter, Sherree, was born
while they were living there. They weren't in that house
more than a few years when Judith grew unhappy with it
and insisted they move to Fayetteville. So Frank bought
two lots in a subdivision and built her a nice two-story
home, but she still managed to complain. She also constantly accused him of looking at every woman he passed
on the street and sleeping with every woman he worked
with at Carling. He would have lunch at the Dwarf House
Restaurant with a few guys from work, at least once or
twice a week and she would always insist that he was win-
ning and dining some of the female employees from the
brewery, instead of his sharing a brew with his buddies
from work.

A man named Truett Cathy owned the Dwarf House and
later opened a few new fast-food restaurants called, Chick-
fil-A. He would have Frank taste-test dishes for him and
often invited him to bring his family in for dinner. Unfortunately, Frank was mistaken in thinking that Judith would
be thrilled to have a night out. Instead, she got all riled-
up—jealous over the fact that everyone treated him as a

regular and she figured they all knew it was where he carried on his liaisons with other women. She was rude to the staff as well as to Mr. Cathy and wanted to leave even before they'd finished their main course. Even though her suspicions were totally unwarranted, Frank made certain not to take her to establishments where folks knew him in the future. He later apologized to Mr. Cathy and made excuses for her bad behavior.

One of the employees of the Dwarf House, with whom Frank had become good friends, ran for sheriff of Mountain View and won, so he made Frank a deputy issuing him a badge and gun. Frank was thrilled to be able have his fingers in law enforcement again, while still working at his good paying job at Carling. However, the election was recalled and the votes recounted and it seemed his friend hadn't really won the election after all. Once the real winner of the election had been sworn in, Frank was disappointed that he was asked to return the badge and weapon back to the little town of Mountain View. So much for him keeping his fingers in law enforcement.

One day when Frank returned home from the brewery, he was surprised to find his Uncle Coleman sitting in his living room chatting to his wife. Judith had called to tell Frank that she had a surprise for him when be got home, but the last thing Frank could have ever imagined was that his favorite uncle had turned up after all those years of being missing. It was if he'd vanished from the face of the earth without a trace. Frank was so elated to see him—a tall and strong man and he felt as though a huge wound in his heart had suddenly been healed. They spent the evening catching up and Coleman told Frank that he'd joined the Air Force when he left Bessy's and had served for four years until he met his wife, Laura. They had married and moved to Arkansas to be close to her parents. They had decided not to have children so they opened a successful diner that they ran together. The bond that Frank had desperately missed with Coleman came back to him instantly as they caught up on old times. Coleman asked about home, but Frank hadn't really kept up much since he married Judith and moved to Atlanta. He told Coleman about Earl's early drinking problems and how he'd simply disappeared one day and no one had heard from him since. All he really knew about Bessy was that she'd gone to live with Leroy and Geneva when Austin had gambled away her farm. Since then, her mind had quickly deteriorated and they had put her in a nursing home where she had passed away not long after. Frank expressed his guilt over not going to see her when he went home to marry Judith, and for that reason, he'd not been to see her during a few subsequent visits he'd made home. He told him that he'd stayed with Virginia and Wes, who'd lost his leg to diabetes, in a new home that Austin had built them a home on a large parcel of land. Virginia had purchased a trailer and put it in on the lot next door for her son Johnny and his wife Grace. Frank brought Coleman up to date on the events leading up to his departure from Pickens County as well as his adventures in the Marines and Korea, but as far as the rest of the family went, Frank knew very little. He wasn't exactly good with keeping up, nor were they. No one in the family really seemed to care to keep in touch, so Frank had pretty much done the same.

When Coleman left to return to Arkansas they both promised to stay in touch. Aside from Bessy, Coleman was the only member of the family Frank cared to remain in close touch with. It had broken Frank's heart when Coleman ran away. He had felt deserted by him and wished that he'd taken him with him—even if he totally understood the reason he'd left.

Frank's and Judith's house in Jonesboro was in a quiet neighborhood and they managed to live a somewhat quiet and civil life together for a while as the children grew. However, when Sherree was around ten, she came home one day, crying because a boy down the street, who was always picking on her, had thrown clods of dirt in her face. Frank went with Sherree to speak to the boy's mother, who was very arrogant and denied he had thrown the dirt in the first place. He insisted that she was making it up. Frank had words with the mother and made it very clear that the boy had damn well better stop picking on his daughter or he would do something to stop it himself. It seemed that the woman had connections at the courthouse and the police showed up the next morning and arrested Frank for cursing in front of the woman. It was okay it seemed for the boy to accost his daughter both verbally and physically almost daily, but illegal for Frank to use the word 'damn' in a woman's presence. Frank thought it to be a joke and explained the situation to the police, as well as the fact that he had been on the police force in Atlanta, but nonetheless, they took him to jail and locked him up anyway. Suddenly, he had become a criminal in the eyes of the law for defending his own daughter. Judith arrived at the courthouse and posted a bond to release him and Frank opted for a jury trial, as opposed to one with an obviously biased judge who happened to be related to the woman. Frank went to court representing himself and the twelve jurors found him not guilty. It seemed that Frank had had his first taste of being on the other side of the law and he didn't like it one bit, especially when he knew he'd done nothing that any good father wouldn't have done protect his daughter.

Although Frank was a law abiding citizen, he seemed to find himself on the wrong side of the law again one night when Frank and Judith were driving home on a two-lane highway from Atlanta, in their new GTO. A state trooper pulled him over for no apparent reason. Frank was doing well under the fifty-five-mile-per-hour speed limit, however the officer wrote him a ticket for speeding anyway. When the older officer handed Frank the citation, he looked at it curiously, "But officer, you know I was only doing fifty at best. That's five miles under the speed limit."

"Well in this county, the speed limit drops ten miles per hour after dark."

"I was an officer of the law in the city of Atlanta and I've never heard such a thing. Is this reduction of speed posted somewhere?"

"You city cops, you think your above the law now don't ya?" scolded the trooper.

"Well no sir, but--"

"--What's wrong with you?!" Judith piped in. "My husband risked his life every night on the streets of Atlanta and you think you can disrespect him that way?!"

Frank did his best to get Judith to shut up, but then she called the cop a 'stupid son of a bitch.'

With that, the furious officer slammed his ticket book closed and said, "That's it! You're going to jail. Follow me back to the Coweta County courthouse!"

Frank was furious with Judith for opening her big trap. By the time they arrived, thirty minutes later, no one was in the Courthouse, so the Trooper called the sheriff, who showed up an hour later. Frank just happened to have a friend in that county named, Bill Brown, so he called him asking if Bill could post a bond for him. Bill arrived a little while later and signed the bond so they would release Frank. Even though it had been Judith that had cursed at the cop, it was Frank who had to suffer the humiliation of being arrested. A week later, Frank was summoned with a notice for his trial and when he arrived in court in front of the fat, sweating judge, he wasn't allowed to say a single word in his own defense. The judge simply sat there reading the docket, then slammed down his gavel and simply pronounced judgment, "Pay the woman at the window a hundred, or go to jail." Needless to say Frank paid the fine and left the county as quickly as he could keeping his speed to ten miles under the speed limit.

It seemed strange to Frank that since he had left the police force he kept finding himself on the wrong side of the law. Sort of like the Dalton boys, except he wasn't intentionally aggravating the law by robbing banks or trains.

After four years at Carling, Frank had been made packaging manager and as management he was allowed to drink for free in the Carling Room located in the brewery, as well as attend all functions there. Carling owned the Atlanta Braves and Hank Aaron, their top player of all time, came for the Little League field dedication at the plant. After the ceremony, Aaron and most of the team went to the Carling Room for drinks with the top employees. Hank's wife had been in the paper a lot regarding her multiple speeding violations and knowing that Frank had been a cop in Atlanta, Hank talked to him about how to handle her many tickets. She was insistent that she was getting pulled over a lot for traffic violations, because she was being singled out as a black woman driving an expensive Caddy. Hank was tired of always having to defend her in court and Frank said if he were still a cop he might be able to help her, but since he'd left the force he'd had little to do with his buddies, or even Max his brother in law, for that matter. Hank shook hands with Frank as he was leaving and went to put his uniform cap back on, but he changed his mind and handed it to Frank. 'Here's a souvenir," Hank said, smiling as he left the room.

After all the years of reading his book about the Dalton

brothers, Frank decided to fulfill one of his childhood dreams and buy his own horse. So he bought an old house in Rex, Georgia, with a big barn and ten acres of pasture and crops. A friend of his named Ralph Hogan had bought a mare and a one-year-old black colt that was more like a puppy than a horse, since he would follow everyone around at their heels. Ralph agreed to sell the colt to Frank for only fifty dollars, so Frank jumped at the chance to buy the yearling. Frank splurged and bought a fancy saddle and tack for the kids to ride, but they weren't the least bit interested, and unfortunately Frank was far too large for the yearling. The kids did however decide they wanted to name him—they called him Choggie. He was pretty wild and had never been saddle broken, so Frank would do his best to climb on him by climbing over the stall partitions to mount him, hoping to break him. But Choggie was having none of it. So Frank just released the young horse to run free in the cornfield wearing only a halter.

Frank was working long hours and had little time to deal with a stubborn pony, so he gave up on his dream of riding into the sunset like the Dalton Gang. Choggie was not yet shod or gelded so Frank decided it best to sell him for three hundred dollars, with the saddle and tack, rather than spend more money on him. The buyer insisted that Frank deliver Choggie to a horse farm at Stone Mountain. Frank knew that getting the untamed animal to the farm was going to be a challenging feat, but he borrowed cattle sides for his truck and hooked the horse's bridle to a come-along, then simply ratcheted him up a ramp, into the bed of the truck. The man owned a number of other horses, so when he arrived at the farm, Frank simply backed his truck into the guy's pasture and turned the horse loose. Choggie immediately went after the mares in the field and Frank got an irate call from the buyer claiming that Frank had sold him a wild stallion that he couldn't even catch. On top of that the damned thing was mounting all his mares. Frank just chuckled knowing that Choggie was likely having the time of his life.

Out of the blue, Carling suddenly announced that they were closing the brewery in Atlanta and they planned to move many of their employees north to their Baltimore plant. Judith was furious and insisted that she was not moving that far away from her parents. Regardless, Frank went there anyway, on Carling's dime, to check it out but quickly decided that living up north wasn't really for him. He didn't like the area, nor did he like the cold weather of that part of the eastern seaboard. He'd heard, however, that Anheuser-Busch Breweries was building a new plant by highway eighty-five in Jacksonville, Florida and they were hiring. So he decided to fly to Jacksonville after booking an interview with the personnel manager. He was hired on the spot as a salaried, non-union manager and he immediately gave Carling notice. Frank was thrilled that he wouldn't be forced to move to Baltimore and he thought Judith would be too. Although it was only a few hundred miles away, she was less than happy about his relocation so far away from her parents. She also hated Jacksonville. But then, she hated just about everything so Frank took the job anyway.

Busch sent Frank to St. Louis, Missouri for training and then transferred him down to the new Jacksonville plant as soon as it opened. Judith arrived soon after with the family. Unfortunately, Busch had made an unfortunate choice of locations for their new plant, thanks to the awful smelling paper mill up river, as well as Glidden chemicals that contributed to the unpleasant aroma. Busch had arranged an apartment on the St. Johns River, which turned out to be totally unacceptable to Judith, since it was downwind of the nauseous, toxic odor. She called it a stinking hole and threatened to go back to Atlanta. Frank managed to find them a different apartment on the St. John's River, which was also not to her liking, but slightly more tolerable. She spent more time driving back and forth to Fayetteville than she spent in Jacksonville, which suited Frank just fine since he didn't have to listen to her incessant complaining. At least now she had her own car and could come and go as she wished without compromising Frank's mobility.

Frank went for a drive to the coast one day, while Judith was away, and found an old house for sale, right on the beach. Frank thought he'd hit the jackpot—surely Judith would be happy living in a beach house. It was an older, two-story, wood house with shingle siding but it had just been fully refurbished. It had all new fixtures and wall-to-wall carpeting, so Frank bought it on the spot without consulting Judith. Once again he'd made another huge mistake—assuming that he could possibly please Judith and once again she did not approve of his newest choice of domicile. She especially didn't approve of that particular beach, which had huge boulders piled along the beachfront as a surf break, instead of a clear view of the ocean. Regardless of her complaints, the family moved into their newest residence.

Judith was alone all day while Frank was at work and she grew bored with beach life very quickly. After all, Sherree was now in junior high school all day and Terry was grown and working, leaving Judith with nothing much to do, but sit on the beach and drink. She was nearly an empty-nester and it didn't fare well with her nerves. Frank had gotten Terry a job with his stepbrother, Johnny Holliday, as an electrical apprentice—building a power plant in Carlton, Alabama. He also bought him a car and found him an apartment. Judith was furious with Frank for encouraging Terry to move so far from home, instead of sticking around to keep her company.

Frank came home from work one day after their first month there and found that Judith had cleaned the place out and moved back to Fayetteville. She had quite literally taken everything with her except the wall-to-wall carpeting and the kitchen sink. Not only had she taken one of the cars and all of their personal possessions, she had cleaned out their bank accounts and had taken their daughter out of school and back to Fayetteville with her. Then she proceeded to file for a divorce and a restraining order to keep Frank from seeing his daughter, or from even entering his own house where they were now living. Judith even convinced Terry to leave his job and come home to live in the Fayetteville house with her. Frank attempted to visit the children many times, but she never allowed him in the house again. Her father, who belonged to the Masonic Lodge had a great deal of pull in the community and managed to have Frank arrested every time he tried to visit. Once Frank picked up Sherree and kept her for two weeks. When he took her home, Judith had him arrested and put in jail for one night. Luckily, the sheriff let him out after paying a two hundred dollar fine and dropped the charges, since he knew all about Judith's state of mind.

Luckily, Frank quickly found a buyer for the beach house and turned a profit of sixty-two thousand dollars without Judith getting to it first. He then moved into an apartment in Jacksonville and lived there alone for the next several years. Judith managed to take all of his other investment properties and did her best to get his Marine Corps pension, but was unsuccessful. Somehow she even managed to sell two ocean front lots in Seacrest, Florida that Frank had purchased in his name as investments. Frank struggled to find an attorney to represent him in the divorce, but because of Judith's father, Reverend Raymond's connections and power in the community with his congregation, the only one he could find to represent him was a drunken attorney from Jonesboro. The man dressed like a cowboy and spent most of his days sidled up to the bar in the local Jonesboro tavern. Frank even got a ruling in his favor for one of the lots when he took her to court.

But then, his own attorney managed to swindle him out of the money by selling it off for only for what he was owed on the case.

One day, not long after Frank started working at Busch, August Anheuser Busch Jr., the CEO of Anheuser Busch Companies, LLC, arrived in his helicopter to take a tour and inspect the plant. August didn't like the packaging manager so Jim McGarry asked Frank to escort August on a tour of the new facility, giving Frank an opportunity to speak with August at length. It was immediately obvious to August that Frank had a lot of camaraderie with his fellow workers, even the ones that worked under him in the brewery. Frank had come from meager beginnings and he always treated the men as his equals. In turn, they trusted him. August mostly wanted to talk about Frank's family and Frank was honest about his recent divorce and that his wife and kids were now living in up in Fayetteville. August talked to Frank about his past and his plans for the future and was candid with Frank about his concerns and suspicions about the Jacksonville plant. August was impressed with Frank's military and police background and he asked Frank if he would be a secret liaison, or secret police, for him inside the plant. He wanted him to keep an eye out and report back to him about issues and concerns with employees, as well as methods and procedures. Frank would often catch his workers punching each other's time cards to fake their hours, or drunk after imbibing Buds in the lunch room and then napping on the job. He would always give his men a second chance to redeem themselves, however he never offered them a third chance, since he knew he would then lose his rein on authority, as well as August's respect and trust. After the first month of working undercover in the plant, August gave Frank a leather briefcase for his birthday, which made him feel as if he were a valued and important employee.

In 1969 Judith held court hearings on the divorce with-out Frank ever being notified since they sent notices to his address in Fayetteville, which he not only didn't live in was unable to even visit. They took Frank's savings and bank accounts and both of his GTOs leaving Frank driving his old pick-up. Judith, it seemed, had later taken out a per-sonal loan for fifty-five thousand dollars from a bank in Jacksonville and put Frank's name down as guarantor. When the bank tried to collect from Frank a judge sent it to a jury trial, but after the hearing he never heard any-more about it and assumed that they had dropped the case, perhaps because she had signed his name to the loan doc-uments after their divorce had been final.

As miserable as Frank was with his lack of marital-bliss, he had spent nearly seventeen years of living hell with her. He was seemingly repeating the eleven years of abuse he'd received from Virginia, sans the beatings. It seemed he had never been able to please either woman—he could never do anything right or make them happy. Not only did he and Judith never get along, Frank had found it impossible to get along with her father who called him a no-good scoundrel their entire marriage. Her parents always took her side on any topic related to their marriage, or the chil-dren. Judith also incessantly accused him of sleeping with every woman he ever met. Frank had wanted a divorce for years from Judith, but family was important to the Carling family and he felt that his job would be at risk had he been the one to leave. At that time in the south, a divorced man would be singled out as somewhat of an outcast.

After twenty-eight years of living with unstable women, Frank grew to realize that one just simply couldn't reason with crazy. And on top of it, Judith had a jealous streak that just wouldn't quit. Unfortunately, thought Frank, he had been too stupid to actually cheat on her all those years, but he still had to live with the consequences of her vivid im-agination. It was then that he started to question his own

motivations for staying. Maybe he actually felt the abuse
was normal since he didn't really know anything else.
Frank hadn't been raised on love, he was raised on survival, and it seemed that was all he knew how to do—to
survive. So, he buried himself in his work and plowed forward to make a new life for himself. He lived alone in his
Jacksonville apartment and after he'd had a little time to
recover from the divorce, he started to date on occasion.
He was new to the concept of dating, since he'd married
and had a baby after only one date in his teenage years. So,
it took a little coaching from some of his friends to understand what was involved in dating and also how to
romance a woman.

CHAPTER TWENTY-FOUR

Round Two

1960s - 70s – On the Wrong Side of the Law

Frank eventually bought an old, cheap house in San Jose, on the north side of Jacksonville—far from the right side of the tracks. It was a simple little house with a tar and rock roof, three bedrooms and one bath. He was now living the life of a bachelor and driving a new Corvette to boost his ego and his chances of getting lucky, since his ego was in the toilet where it came to women. He spent most of his time working overtime at the brewery, so he rationalized that he didn't need a fancy house. That was until he met an attractive blonde divorcée named Patricia Barker several years after his divorce from Judith. Prior to that he'd only managed to have a string of one-nighters—nothing worth even a follow-up phone call. The fact that she also had the same middle name as Judith concerned him somewhat, but she was fifteen years younger than Frank and a looker so such trivial details didn't quell his attraction to her. She had more curves than a country road, so dating her was a huge boost for his ego that had been so badly battered by women his entire life. Patricia made good money as an executive secretary for Ryder Truck Rentals, so that was also a plus in his book. This time, he wouldn't have to be her sole source of support as he had been for Judith. Patricia had a teenage daughter named Nancy, who still lived with her in the nice little house that she'd won in the divorce. On occasion, Nancy would go to stay with Patricia's mother or sister, but rarely did she see her father—Patricia's ex-husband. Patricia received no alimony, but he did provide her with child support each month, which meant that Frank wouldn't find himself supporting some other man's child.

Frank had gotten word that his stepbrother's wife, Grace, had died of cancer the year before and then a year later his mother called to tell him that Johnny had suddenly died of an overdose of Grace's cancer meds he'd had taken to deal with his grief. Frank made the trip home to pay his respects to his stepbrother. While he was there he stayed with his mother and Wes, since with one leg, Wes wasn't capable of any sort of work around the house. Frank closed up and winterized the trailer for Virginia and did a few odd jobs around her house before he returned to Jacksonville. He couldn't say that he felt a great deal of loss at Johnny's passing, since he and Johnny had never been close. In fact, he hadn't really spoken to him since his last visit to Easly.

Frank and Patricia dated about six months and they discussed the possibility of him moving into her house, but she insisted that they marry first, using the excuse that it wouldn't be a good example for her daughter if they were living together in sin. She knew that Frank had a stable, good paying job with a pension from work and the military, so she wanted to be certain that she got a long-term commitment out of him. Frank eventually agreed to marry Patricia and they moved in together, then Frank sold the San Jose house making a small profit. Patricia's daughter Nancy lived with them and seemed to cause constant trouble in an attempt to get her mother's attention. But in general, life was good for a few years as they got to know one another better.

Since they were both making good money, Frank was able to save money and make the occasional investment in vintage cars, as well as Real Estate, both of which he'd been lucky enough with to turn a profit. Frank's daughter, Sherree, eventually moved down to live with them to attend school in Jacksonville, after he and Patricia had been married a few years. Frank was glad to have the opportunity to get to know his daughter all over again, however the rift that Judith had driven between them was so deep he knew their relationship would never be the same. Even his relationship with his son had changed. It seemed that Judith had turned them against him by filling their head full of nonsense that wasn't true. She had made them believe that he'd been unfaithful to her during their marriage and that he had likely known Patricia before they'd been separated. It seemed that nothing Frank could say would make them believe any different.

Frank was happy working at Busch as he was climbing the ladder rapidly. Frank and August Jr. got quite friendly over the years as Frank reported to him on a regular basis on how things were running in the plant. It seemed their relationship had grown more personal than business related and he felt that August truly liked him as an equal, which mean the world to Frank. Especially when August gave him a Rolex watch on his first anniversary of working at Busch.

When August Jr. lost his youngest daughter at the end of 1974 he fell into a serious depression, becoming extremely difficult to work with, causing difficulties with the board of directors. Frank remained friends with August and reported to him on the workings of the plant until May of 1975 when August's son, August Busch III, got him ousted in a board-room coup, claiming that his father used the company for his own personal piggy bank and that the corporation needed new, fresh leadership. His son then proceeded to sell off the yacht and the private train car that had been used for the board and August's buddies to party on on their way to California. August was allowed to remain president of the Cardinals as long as he went along with the public's image that his removal had been voluntary. He was also allowed to stay in his home, known as

"The Farm," that housed all of his horses and a small zoo.

When Ryder filed bankruptcy, Patricia went to work for Delta Airlines in reservations at the Atlanta airport. Working for Delta was a nice perk that allowed the two of them to travel to California and Europe whenever Frank could take time off from work. For the first time since Korea, it afforded Frank the opportunity to see the world. Most importantly, he finally had the chance to travel to parts of California to see where the Dalton boys had spent time. Patricia also insisted they go to Hollywood to see the fashionable homes of the rich and famous in Beverly Hills.

After a number of years, Frank and Patricia were still living in the house from her divorce, so once the girls were grown, they decided to look for a house north of Jacksonville on the Nassau River. Frank thought it best to look at properties from the water, so in 1983 they bought a small motorboat and cruised the reed-lined river in search of the perfect property. Eventually, they found a house they both liked on Samples Creek, which sat on the water with wooded lots on either side. It was pretty isolated with a three hundred foot long drive to the property from a cul-de-sac in the small subdivision called The Cape. The house was a modest brick-veneer, one-story house with a two car garage giving Frank space to tinker with his collectible cars that he invested in as a hobby. Due to her new job with Delta, Patricia was able to travel for free whenever she wanted, so she'd often be gone for the weekend with a girl-friend or two from work. She would get bored when Frank was working in the garage on his cars, so she used that as an excuse to quell her boredom and catch up with her girl-friends. Since her trips generally happened once a month, Frank often suspected that the girls' weekend getaways weren't as innocent as Patricia portrayed them to be. So, having felt like a fool for not messing around the first time,

even though Judith constantly accused of being a philan-
derer, he decided to invite a young woman named, Patsy,
down from Atlanta for the weekend. Frank had worked
with Patsy at the Atlanta brewery and he'd attended many
a lunch with her, but only when other employees were
present. One weekend, while Patricia was away and Frank
was bored, he gave Patsy a call and bought her a ticket to
fly down to Jacksonville. He took her to see their house on
the river and made the mistake of succumbing to her ad-
vances in their master bedroom. Once Patsy returned to
Atlanta she kept calling Frank professing her love for him.
When he refused to leave Patricia for her, or even see her
again, she got angry and called Patricia at work and told
her that she was in love with Frank, not to mention the fact
that they'd had sex in her bed. Nothing could have lit her
fuse faster. When Frank showed up that night she tore into
him madder 'n a wet hen. There wasn't much he could do
or say to defuse the situation. The only thing that would
appease her was for him to call Patsy in front of her to tell
her that he wasn't interested in seeing her anymore and to
please stop calling. Even if he'd confessed to his infidelity
with his tail between his legs, he was still evicted from the
master suite and served his sentence in the doghouse by
sleeping in the guest room for the next month.

Things seemed to spiral downward in their relationship
from that point on. When they did finally resume their sex
life once again, Patricia's sexual appetite seemed to have
become more exotic, as if she'd been taste-testing new cui-
sines elsewhere. Her newly acquired tastes and requests
seemed to fall outside of Frank's liking guidelines and he
grew uncomfortable with her and her strange new appetite
in the bedroom.

Once when Frank and Patricia were traveling in Europe,
she suddenly pushed him into traffic at a crosswalk and
then insisted that it had been accidental. Now Frank was
getting concerned that she wanted get him out of the pic-

ture, but still be able to collect on his insurance as well as his two lucrative pensions. Patricia also seemed to be more paranoid about staying at home alone while Frank worked the night shift, since he often worked overtime. His primary concern, since Judith had taken him to the cleaners, was to replenish his bank accounts and make more investments in their future. It became a regular thing for Patricia to exaggerate her fears of someone trying to break into the house while she was there alone. She would call Frank at work whenever she heard the least little noise outside, or when a fox or a deer tripped the sensor on the automatic area lights outside the house. So one night when Frank was on the graveyard shift and he was having a lot of difficulties with the manufacturing line she persisted with calling, saying that someone was definitely trying to break into the house. She was frantically insisting that a Pinto with New Mexico plates had driven down the driveway, and that two young men around seventeen to twenty, in jean jackets, had tried to get in the door, then walked back to the car and backed down the driveway.

When the two men drove partway down the drive again and walked through the woods to the back of the house, Patricia called their neighbor, Homer. Before the neighbor got there, the two men actually did start trying to break in the back door. Just as Patricia was panicking and calling Frank again, Homer knocked on the front door shouting, "Patricia it's Homer, I'm here with my gun." Suddenly, he saw the two men run from the back of the house, through the woods, and back to their car. They jumped in, started the car, and quickly backed out into the cul-de-sac.

Patricia had cried wolf one too many times and Frank didn't take her latest claim of an intruder seriously—at least not until he finally managed to tear himself away from the plant to find Patricia outside their house with Homer.

"Patricia, what's all this nonsense about two men and a Pinto?" Frank asked skeptically as he climbed out of his truck.

"She's right Frank....I seen two men running through the woods earlier, as well as that Pinto she saw, driving around the neighborhood."

"Well then what are you waiting for Homer? Get in," Frank insisted as he climbed back in his truck. Frank took his thirty-eight-revolver from the glove box and plugged his spotlight into the cigarette lighter of his car, then set it on the seat beside him.

"I think I should stay here with Patricia," Homer said nervously looking at the gun in Frank's hand.

"Get inside and call the police, Patricia."

"I already did Frank," insisted Patricia. "You should wait 'til they get here! You're not a cop anymore, remember!"

"Once a cop, always a cop," Frank said as he started the truck and put it in gear. "Now get back inside and lock the damned door. You and Homer stay there 'til I get back!"

Frank circled slowly through the subdivision around the back way until he spotted the Pinto with the New Mexico plate parked on the side of the wooded road. He pulled up next to the car and shined the spotlight into the front seat, but the car appeared to be empty.

"Get that damned light out of my eyes!" shouted a man leaning over in the front seat.

"What the hell do you think you're doing, trying to break into my house?" Frank shouted in return.

Suddenly, the distinct sound of a shotgun being cocked was heard from the backseat as the man in the front exclaimed, "Oh man, don't do that!"

Frank cocked his own weapon as the man in the backseat sat up, pointing a sawed-off shotgun right at Frank's head. Frank leaned over in the seat just as the man opened fire, pumping the shotgun at the passenger window of the truck, raking buckshot through all the windows, and shattering glass everywhere inside the cab. Frank lay on the seat showered by shards of broken glass as the man in the front seat shot six rounds from a handgun, into Frank's truck until he was out of ammunition. For Frank, time seemed to stand like an eternity, knowing that this must be the end. Ironically he'd survived Korea only to die in a shootout defending his own home. Then there was silence as the men stopped shooting to reload. Frank saw his chance and sat up firing into the Pinto until he also ran out of ammunition. He could see the man in the back climbing over the seat and out the driver's side of the car as he re-loaded, so Frank threw the truck into gear and gunned it, ducking as the man shot out his rear window and peppered the truck with more shot. Frank reached through the open back window and fired at the man as he drove away. He arrived back at his house and insisted that Homer get his gun and come with him. He got in the passenger side reluc-tantly after seeing the state of Frank's truck with all the glass blown out, holes everywhere, and the headliner hang-ing down in tatters. All the while, Patricia was hysterically screaming at Frank to wait for the police, who still hadn't arrived, even though she claimed to have called them a second time.

"Man Frank, I think you need to let the police handle this."

"I'm as good a shot as they are and I'm not letting these guys get away so they can come back to rob the place or kill us in our sleep!"

When they drove back to where the Pinto had been parked, it was gone.

Nervously, Homer begged, "Let's go to the gate and wait for the police!"

"Okay, let's go," Frank finally agreed as he put the truck in gear and headed towards the entrance of the subdivi-sion. As they came around the curve, Frank shined his spotlight down a side road to the fish camp illuminating the frontend of the Pinto, which was parked on the wrong side of the road facing him. Frank yanked the wheel left and headed toward the dead end, pulling up in front of the car, shinning both his headlights and the spotlight into the Pinto windshield. The young kid immediately stepped out of the driver's side with his hands up and dropped his handgun. Suddenly, Frank's Marine Corps training kicked in as he jumped from his truck and pinned the man down on the ground with his knee in the middle of his back. "Where's the other guy?" Frank demanded.

"There's no one with me, I swear!"

Frank shouted to Homer, "Stay on this guy while I search the car!"

Homer reluctantly got out and stood over the guy, holding his gun on him while Frank searched the Pinto, finding it empty as the young guy had claimed.

"Seems the guy with the shotgun's gotten away," Frank said shaking his head.

"Hey, this guy's been shot," Homer shouted as he spotted a pool of blood glinting in the glare of the spotlight on the asphalt "Looks like he's been shot in the back."

"Just don't let him up!" ordered Frank as he searched the cul-de-sac with the spotlight. Then Frank jumped back in the truck and drove around shining the light deep into in the woods as he searched for the guy with the shotgun. As he reached the spot where the shoot-out had happened, there were already many red and blue lights flashing from fire, rescue, and police vehicles surrounding the area. Frank pulled up and parked behind a squad car. He got out and approached the six officers standing over a man laying facedown in the palmettos, with the shotgun next to his hand. One of the men looked back at Frank's bullet-riddled truck and shook his head.

"You the one that shot this bastard?" asked the sheriff.

"I guess so....didn't realize I'd hit him since he kept on firing. Just look at the condition of my truck!" Frank exclaimed, pointing back at his newly air-conditioned pickup.

"Let me shake your hand mister," the sheriff exclaimed

extending his hand to Frank. "That's one bad motherfucker laying there....the baddest in Florida. I can't believe he didn't kill you by the looks of that truck," he said as he spit out some tobacco. "He's on parole for murder and robbery. He stole a shotgun earlier today and sawed it off by the looks of it."

"My neighbor's holding the young one back there on Starret Road. Seems he's been shot, too," Frank informed the sheriff.

"Junior take the rescue and go collect that one, not much they can do for this fool. Rodney, go call for the coroner to pick up the stiff."

The sheriff turned to Frank "What'd you say your name was mister?"

"Frank....Frank Dalton Holliday."

"Mr. Holiday, you've done this community a favor here tonight."

"Well just doing what I know best....I was a cop in Atlanta and an MP in the Marines in Korea before that."

"Atlanta you say...." he groaned shaking his head. Atlanta's a tough place to work the streets. Guess you are lucky a man if'n you survived all that as well as walked away from tonight's shootout. Kinda like the wild west," he said continuing to shake his head in disbelief. "Why don't you just head on back to your house? There's a detective waiting there for you to make your statement. I'm sure they'll write this off as a justifiable homicide."

"I should hope so considering how many holes my truck has in it."

When Frank got home an officer was waiting for him with Patricia on the living room sofa. He proceeded to take Frank's statement, as well as Homer's and Patricia's and then told Frank to be down at the courthouse in the morning to talk to the states attorney. Frank was now worried. Would he once again find himself on the wrong side of the law even though he knew he had done nothing more than defend himself, his wife, and his home? He'd just killed a man—of that he was certain, but it was in self-defense—his bullet riddled truck was proof enough of that. As well, another man lay critically wounded in some hospital bed. Come morning he might also become a casualty.

CHAPTER TWENTY-FIVE

The Final Reckoning

1892 – Dalton's Last Call to the Gods of Chance

That night Frank was so rattled by the evening's ruckus events he couldn't even begin to sleep. Patricia had taken a sleeping pill—her nerves so frayed by the events that had unfolded. Instead of crawling in bed with her and staring at the ceiling, Frank went to his study and plucked his worn and tattered Dalton book from the shelf. He looked at it—it had seen a few miles of his life by that point. Its spine was split and the pages were starting to yellow. Some were dog-eared. He sat down in his easy chair and turned on the reading light. He thought about the Daltons' 'invocation to the gods of chance' and he thanked them and every other god he could think of for the fact that he was still alive—he had survived the shootout without a scratch. He flipped through the chapters until he reached the one—the chapter that felt somewhat reminiscent of the evening's series of unexpected, life-affirming events. It was the story of the Dalton Gang's final showdown. And he read through to the end of the book into the wee hours of the morning....

"'*A group of Negro workmen were tearing up a portion of Union Street in the town of Coffeyville a little after nine o'clock on the morning of October 5, 1892.* '

'*We were coming in now on Union Street, the main residential avenue. A few belated children were hastening to school, a woman was digging up some flower bulbs. The blacksmith show was melodious with anvil music. Somebody getting a horse shod. Folks going about their business.*

"*I'll be damned!*" *suddenly spoke Bob.* "*Look, the hitch rack's gone. Torn down to fix the street where them darkies are workin'.*" *This was the rack where we had intended tying our horses beside the Opera House.*

"This street'll be bad to get out of," added Bob. "Horse might stumble. Got to find another place." He peered around quickly, estimating. "Back yonder in the alley," he indicated. We turned and cantered in behind the blacksmith shop and the lumber yard. There the alley widened to a considerable area. And there folks often hitched their horses to a fence rail while they did their trading.'

'Looking east through the alley, which opened on the triangular central plaza, we could see the front of the First National Bank. Adjoining it, and also plainly visible, was Isham Brothers' hardware store. As events turned out we could not have placed the horses in a more dangerous spot.

As we started off, Bob's horse, a big bay, turned his head and whinnied.

"All right, old-timer," Bob called over his shoulder, "we'll be back in a jiffy."

At our left as the five of us strode swiftly out of the alley, walking east, stood the Condon Bank, located in the Luther Perkins Building. It occupied the north end of the plaza, fronting south. On three sides were plate-glass windows. It was like a show case into which the sun streamed brightly. It was perhaps fifty paces from the First National. On our left also, in order from the alley, were McKenna & Adam's clothing store, Wells Brothers' general merchandise store, and the Old Opera House. At our right on this side the plaza were Slausson's drug store, a furniture shop, the post office and Reed Brothers' clothing store. Another tier of stores occupied the southern end of the plaza, and on the eastern frontage, flanking both sides of the First National Bank and Isham's place, stood Boswell's hardware store, Rummell's drug store, and Brown and Cubine's shoe shop. These places then, formed the gallery from which the deadliest street brattle in the West was to be viewed and from which it was to burst in a tornado of fire within a few minutes.

The plaza, thus encompassed by buildings, was paved

entirely with brick. Our feet made a scuffling noise on it as we advanced—Bob and I ahead, Grat, Powers, and Broadwell just behind. Hitching racks lined the sides of the open area. Several teams were there. Draymen were wont to stand in the plaza with their wagons, awaiting business. Drayman Charley Gump was the first on hand this morning. He looked at us with idle curiosity as we neared the banks.

Eighty feet from the alley mouth, Grat, Powers, and Broadwell wheeled sharply and entered the Condon Bank. Bob and I proceeded without looking back, toward the First National. There was a scattering of people on the streets. But thus far we had attracted no special notice. Men walking with rifles in hand was not of itself a suspicious circumstance.

Suddenly Charley Gump's eyes bulged. From where he sat sunning himself on his dray wagon he could look straight into the Condon Bank. He saw the first move of the holdup by Grat, Powers, and Broadwell—saw it like a show from a reserved seat. In a flash he knew.

"The Daltons!" shrilled drayman Gump, leaping from his wagon. Now Bob and I, as we went swiftly toward the First National, had also become significant. Once more he cried out the alarm—"Look out! The Daltons!" It wasn't a matter of recognition but of correct assumption. His startled outcry echoed across the plaza. Immediately a dozen of Coffeyville's many dogs began barking in agitated bedlam. For a moment the few residents who were abroad around the square stood stock-still. Charley Gump's feet scuffled rapidly on the brick pavement as he ran toward Boswell's hardware store.

Bob whirled and fired at Gump in an effort to check the alarm. The bullet took him in the hand. He scuttled into the store. The dogs continued yapping.

If the town of Coffeyville had apprehended a raid by the Daltons, as some have claimed, it was now strangely inert and unprepared. Awakened suddenly to danger by Gump's affrighted yell, the citizenry were held numb with shock and indecision in the stores and along the streets. For minutes no one raised the mustering call to arms.

In the Condon Bank Grat had covered Cashier Charley Ball with his Winchester. Charles T. Carpenter, the vice president, also stood with hands raised. Broadwell and Powers held guns on T. C. Babb, the bookkeeper, and on one other man in the bank. The outlaws scooped fifteen hundred dollars of counter cash into a sack Grat carried.

"Open the safe and open it quick!" Grat commanded the cashier with rifled threat.

Ball hesitated—Ball, the sickly man of cool nerve and rigid discipline.

"It's a time lock," parleyed Ball with courageous wit. "Doesn't open until nine forty-five." He slanted a shrewd look at Grat.

Grat hesitated indecisive. The statement surprised and momentarily baffled him. The moment for swift, unerring decisiveness had come. But Grat, Powers, and Broadwell let it slip.

Nine forty-two now. For a moment every eye clung in fascination on the hands of the wall clock. Suppose it should stop. What then? Fantastic thought!

"We'll wait three minutes," said Grat.

If he or his two companions suspected a ruse, none of them made any effort to verify the cashier's statement or call his audacious bluff. In relating the details later, Ball said he had spoken on impulse. But once having made the fateful assertion he could not retract. Ball realized how precarious his position was. Like all the others in the bank and in the adjacent streets, he had heard the drayman's outcry and Bob's shot. He was certain that the trio of outlaws who held him covered were only part of the raiding force. His life might be forfeit any moment. But he stood pat. He watched the outlaws like a cat. Heard the clock tick off its measured beat. Hoped that the bravest of the townsfolk would yet rally and abort the holdup within the prescribed time. Played for high stakes in the few minutes of perilous respite.

While Grat, Powers, and Broadwell played their waiting

*game, the bank door opened to the rushing entrance of John
D. Levan. He was a money lender. He had heard Charlie
Gump's shout. Without knowing the exact situation Levan
had hastened to warn the Condon Bank people. "the Daltons
are here—" His words choked in a gulp of amazement as Grat
grabbed him and lined him up with the others.*

*Vice President Carpenter quieted Levan's terror with a look
of calm reassurance. Even in this crisis his imperturbable good
nature and resignation to the inevitable could not be jolted.
What was to be would be. Carpenter trusted the Lord.*

*Nine forty-three. Ball's strained face turned a shade whiter.
Outside somewhere along the plaza a gun cracked....Another.
The sweat broke out on the cashier's forehead. Doggedly Grat,
Powers, and Broadwell waited.*

*I have dwelt at some length on Ball's behavior. His was the
decisive act in Coffeyville that day. His shifty falsehood about
the vault—which all the time was open to any hand—was to
save his bank eighteen thousand dollars. It was also to cause
the death of eight men within the next five minutes.*

*Meantime Bob and I had entered the First National. I was a
few feet ahead. In the bank at the time were Thomas G. Ayres,
cashier, Brett S. Ayres, his son and assistant cashier, W. H.
Sheppard, the smiling and gracious teller, and a bookkeeper
whose name I have forgotten. These composed the official
force. In addition, three customers were present: J. H. Brew-
ster, a prominent contractor; C.H. Hollingsworth, and Abe
Knott, a deputy sheriff of Montgomery County.*

*Knott had just cashed a four-dollar check. He stood with
his back to me as Bob and I came through the door. I recognized him as he turned in surprise at my command of "Hands
up!" And immediately I knew that he might have a dangerous
man to deal with in Abe Knott.*

*His hands had gone up, still clutching the four dollars in his
closed fist. He wanted to save that money, as he later told me.*

His hand kept straying downward. He hoped to slip the bills into his vest pocket. I thought he was watching for one split second of relaxed vigilance to grab the six-shooter I saw at his belt. He would have done it with a fraction of a chance. Abe Knott, a Kentuckian and fighting man, had plenty of sand in his craw.

I had learned from experience never to take my gaze off the other fellow in moments of danger, and never to give back a step. As I looked into his steady eye I felt that one of us might have to die.

"Keep 'em high!" I warned, striding closer toward Knott. He grinned with cool effrontery. But he made no more suspicious move. "I don't want your chicken-feed," I said.

Tom Ayers had dodged down behind the counter at my command. I expected him to come up shooting. I had to watch his as well as the deputy sheriff for a tense moment. But Bob, who had entered right behind me, edged around and covered him. The others were standing as ordered.

Throwing Ayres a sack, Bob ordered him to put the money in it. He started dumping in trays of silver. "Keep that silver out," Bob spoke. "It's too heavy to bother with. The vault!" he rapped. "The big stuff!"

Tom Ayres opened the vault and threw the currency into the sack. Things were going like clockwork here at the First National. Not more than a minute had elapsed since Bob and I came through the front door. Here too, a clock was ticking on the wall.

In the stores along the plaza the citizens were coming out of their coma of fright. If they had been slow to start, they were now making up for lost time. There was a scurrying toward the first concentration of resistance. A stealthy mustering. Word of the raid was being flung all across the town: "The Dalton gang—they're holding up both banks! Al-

ready wounded Charley Gump!"

The First National vault had been emptied. Bob and I were marching the bank officers and the three customers toward the front door. Bob was ahead. I brought up the rear, lugging the weighty money sack. Bob stepped out and peered quickly about.

Whang! Came the first opposition shot. The bullet smashed into the door casing. Bob jumped back into the bank, grinned, and said, "Bum shot!"

We herded the bankers and the customers out through the door—all except Sheppard, the teller. Knott was watching like a hawk for a chance to shoot. We hadn't disarmed him. But he edged out, and his chance was gone.

A glance through the front window revealed men scurrying this way and that, everyone acting on his own, like a squad deploying soldiers without an officer. Some were hastening to arms. Others were running to cover. There was a scattering of shots toward the First National as soon as the men we had sent through the front door had gotten in the clear.

Those were the shots the group in the Condon Bank had heard as the minute hand on the wall clock hung at nine forty-three.

The battle had opened.

"Can we get out the back way?" I asked Sheppard, whom I had kept covered while Bob watched the front door for a possible rush.

"The back door's open," calmly announced Sheppard. He had remained coolly unruffled throughout the holdup. Even in these circumstances he could be polite. A fragment of his celebrated smile still clung to his lips. "It leads to the alley," he concluded.

"You come and show us," I insisted. He led us to the rear door. It was open. I finished tying the money sack in the middle so that it would hang securely over my arm. We ordered Sheppard back into the bank. Then Bob and I stepped out into the alley. Out front the crackle of the guns was increasing. But here for a moment everything was clear.

"You look after that money sack," said Bob. I'll do the fighting."

Lucius Baldwin, a young clerk in Boswell's hardware store, emerged from the store into the alley. He came trotting toward us with a revolver in his hand.

"Hold up there!" Bob called, withholding his fire. But the clerk kept on coming, at a dog trot. He did not fire, and he did not speak. Some strange confusion upon him. Like a somnambulist he moved, gun leveled at us.

Bob fired. The ball struck Baldwin in the breast. He crumpled up, the revolver skittering form his hand. Before he died Baldwin said he had heard Bob call to him to halt, but he was too overcome with fear and surprise either to shoot or stop.

We hastened north through the alley behind the bank, turned left on Union Street, and within a few yards had come around to where we were exposed to the gathering storm in the plaza. Now for the first time the citizens saw us and had us a few moments in the clear against the sights of their rifles. On the instant the hitherto desultory and rather aimless shooting burst into a crescendo of fire. Within the sounding box of the store-flanked plaza it bellowed in thunderous crashes. The din became terrific. Teams hitched along the square and in the adjacent streets broke loose and ran helter-skelter. A fear-maddened saddle horse raced across the brick pavement. Citizens up to now hesitant about getting into the fray began blazing away, incited by their more intrepid fellows. Fire-breathing bedlam whirled about the public square as a vortex.

Bob and I had snapshot flashes of heads peering from doorways, appearing at store windows, shouting imprecations; faces in strange grimaces of terror or fighting fury. The shooting was as yet still wild and spasmodic. The townsfolk were still in the first jumpiness of buck fever. For a moment it seemed inexplicable that Bob and I should be the target for so much flailing lead and yet remained unsigned. Then I realized that while some of the shots were coming in our direction, *most of them were being directed into the front of the Condon Bank. Without catching the significance of that, I had a swift sense that Bob and I were being favored by the flip of the luck at the morning camp fire which now seemed ages remote.*

All this—snarling lead, flashes of though, pictures of battle, and the shrill sounds of it—had impinged during the few seconds it took Bob and me to jog across the northern end of the plaza toward the sheltering rear of the Condon Bank. I still carried the money sack, and Bob squinted warily for a chance to score.

Now two of Coffeyville's brave, embattled citizens stepped into the open: George Cubine and Charles T. Brown. They were partners in business. Cubine was an expert bootmaker. He catered to the cowboys' taste in fancy footwear. Years before he had made boots for Bob, Grat and me. He knew us well.

Cubine came out of his shop with Winchester in hand. Brown followed at his heels, himself unarmed. Cubine swung down on us. As he did so Bob took a flash shot. Cubine fell dead before he could fire. Brown, undaunted, stooped down and took the rifle from the dead man's hands. He leveled at us. No buck fever in Cubine and brown. Bob shot again. Brown died beside his partner.

At the moment I was slightly ahead of Bob. Hampered by the heavy money sack I had reached cover behind the corner of the Perkins building.

It was for the death of Cubine that I was later convicted, although I had not fired a shot at him.

"Go slow," Bob said as he came to my side. "Take it easy—I can whip the whole damn town!" We jogged around into the alley behind Wells Brothers' general store, momentarily secure. We did not yet know how thoroughly roused and determined the citizens were. Even their hectic fire hadn't greatly alarmed us, although it was the first time we had met such general resistance.

At the moment we had no inkling of how Grat, Broadwell, and Powers had fared. We did not yet know of their fatal mis-

take in accepting Ball's statement about the time lock on the Condon Bank vault. We assumed they had already come back to the horses toward which we were now hastening.

As we came down the alley behind Well's store, little Bobby Wells, fourteen years old, ran out of the back doo with a.22 revolver in his hands. Waving it at us with boyish menace, he demanded truculently:

"What're you fellers doing here?"

For a moment the boy's sudden appearance flabbergasted us.

"You run home, boy, or you're liable to get hurt," said Bob. He spanked the lad lightly on the seat of the pants with his rifle. Frightened but game, Bobby retreated—and lived to become one of my best friends. We were surprised not to find Grat, Broadwell, and Powers at the hitching rack. A thundering crash of shots sounded from the plaza.

"What's keeping the boys?" Bob muttered anxiously as I tied the money sack to the saddle.

The Isham hardware store, adjoining the First National Bank, afforded the best cover for the fighting citizens, and there a crowd had gathered. From the show cases they had armed themselves with rifles and revolvers. They had spotted us as we came to the horses. The open alley gave them an unimpeded range. Bullets were whining about our ears even before I had made the money sack secure. Bob began pumping his Winchester, swinging it this way that that in rapid arc, still believing he might be able to terrify the opposition.

But by this time the citizenry were beyond intimidation. A fog of acrid gunpowder smoke began to swirl lazily in the October sunshine. And still no sign of our three comrades.

"Boys must be in trouble," exclaimed Bob. "We better go and help 'em out."

Here we were, Bob and I, with good assurance of safety only a few yards down that alleyway. All we had to do was fling a leg to saddle and make a dash for it. The shooting was still inaccurate, although we were fair targets from the Isham *arsenal.*

"*Come on,*" *said Bob, walking into the line of fire.* "*We'll go and help 'em.*" *I don't believe it was even a test of Bob's loyalty, in the sense that test implies deliberation. If he thought for an instant that he might be tossing his life away to range back through a hail of lead to stand by out three companions, that thought was accepted as the inevitable consequence of "one for all, and all for one." I went by his side. For myself, I recall no definite sensation of fear or anxiety. We were still on the swelling tide of battle.*

The fight burst once more with a sudden crash in front of the Condon Bank as we came toward the head of the alley on the plaza. It was Grat, Powers, and Broadwell coming out.

With foolish but magnificent courage Grat had been counting the ticks of the clock on the wall. What was happening in that deadly show case had been as plain as day to a hundred hidden and squinting eyes on three sides of the plaza. Despite the danger to the bank officials, lead had poured like hail against the bank front, shattering windows, pitting the woodwork. At the first crash Grat had ordered all except Cashier Ball to flatten on the floor.

"*Get down, or you might get killed,*" *he roared. Grat himself stood behind a window casement. Partially protected. Broadwell and Powers were under precarious cover. Broadwell had in his hand the sack with the counter cash, about fifteen hundred dollars—the meager silver measure of his life and of Grat's and Powers.*

Ball stood by the safety vault, continuing his magnificent bluff. He too watched the hands of the clock. Half a minute more. The sickly, taciturn man who had closed his mind against everything except that rigid conception of his duty did not flinch. And Ball won his grim gamble.

Before the clock had ticked off the few remaining seconds the fire had become so intense and the rally of the citizens so ominous that even Grat, for all his reckless nerve, considered it best to make a desperate retreat. Glass was falling about them, wood splintering—bedlam and inferno. Death was fanning hot and close. Eighty bullet holes were later counted in Condon Bank Building. Suddenly all the gold in the Condon vault had no value to the outlaw trio. They drew together for the rush.

And now they were coming out. From our exposed position in the alley we saw them break cover. They came out shooting. Their guns talked fast.

For a moment the attention of Bob and myself was distracted. The firing zone spread. Behind the back doors and windows of the stores to our left there was a stir, a movement of skulking figures. A Negro porter, startled, made a confused break from the rear of Slauson's drug store. Bob whanged at him. The Negro dived back in through a window. A few scattering shots were beginning to come from this new quarter. Bob pumped his gun at the doors and windows, and at every sign of mobilizing menace, partly to protect himself and me, and also to keep the way of retreat clear from possible enfilading fire for Grat, Powers, and Broadwell. They were now backing across the sixty feet of exposed plaza toward the alley in which we waited.

They came very slowly, it seemed to me, but their Winchesters kept pouring leaden hail toward the Isham store. They were in turn receiving more than they sent. It was during this hot exchange that Cashier Ayres of the First National fell wounded. He and the others who had been in the bank had taken refuge in this store after we had turned them loose.

Over at the Condon Bank the men who had flattened on the floor rose cautiously amid the wreckage and peered out to watch the battle. Cashier Ball stepped away from the vault, wiped the sweat from his forehead, brushed the dust from his coat, and mechanically walked to the counter, as if ready to resume business. Ball, as I have said, was a man of disciplined routine.

Another historian of the Coffeyville street fight asserts that Broadwell had been shot through the arm before he emerged from the Condon Bank. I do not think this was the case, but if so he did not seem hampered as he and Grat and Powers came down the alley in a haze of lifting smoke. We had no time to comment on what was happening.

The kaleidoscope was gyrating in swift detonating flashes. Movements and attitudes of ourselves and our swarming antagonists, whenever they showed themselves, stood out in sharp, looming picture. Everything seemed crystal clear. My brain registered multiple images. I could see the boys reloading their Winchesters. I could see the swing of the glistening barrels. The somber strained faces of my companions. The dull gleam of the shadowy plate glass under the overhanging sidewalk porch of Isham's store, whence flashed lances of flame.

Powers had come perhaps twenty feet into the alley mouth when he was hit in the arm. I saw him return the shot, after he had regained his balance from the violent impact of the bullet. For a moment he took refuge in a doorway of the McKenna-Adams store, reloading.

I suddenly realized this was to be a fight to the death. All the time I had expected the firing to die away, to feel myself on the back of my horse plunging away, presently, with the others—expecting relaxation from this terrible tension.

But there was no let-up. The terrible frenzy of an aroused citizenry was now upon us in full avalanche. They too knew that some of them must die. But they were not deterred. Out of many scattered individuals they had suddenly been compacted into a mob, welded by fire. For us the tide of battle was ebbing. This was its crisis and turning point.

Bob and I covered the retreat while Grat and Broadwell hastened toward the horses in our rear. Powers too passed us after he had recovered from the first shock of his wound. We were all together at last. In those few seconds it must have been incredible—some devil's miracle—to the citizens that we were all still on our feet and by way of escaping after so much lead had been flung at us. Powers had been hit and was still alive. Broadwell had been hit, and he too was still in the fight. Were the lives of the Dalton band charmed? For a moment the defenders of Coffeyville may have been awed. The firing lulled. Then it broke out again with renewed fury.

A team hitched to a Standard Oil wagon, one of the runaways, broke into new panic at the crash. The driver had taken cover at the start of the fight. The team plunged madly into the alley from behind the ice house. It stampeded straight for the spot where our horses were tied. Our own horses reared and plunged. Any instant they might break loose and leave us on foot. But Grat was thinking fast and straight now. In a flash he shot one of the oil-wagon horses in the head, bringing him down and halting the runaway.

The firing from Isham's store was accurate now. The range was about one hundred yards.

I saw Bob stiffen and reel a little. An instant later, as I had my gun at aim, a Winchester ball took me through the upper arm, shattering the bone. The blow knocked the rifle from my hand. I stooped over and picked it up with my left hand. My right hung useless. Bob sagged down against a pile of rocks in the alley, against a high board fence. He didn't say anything.

As I turned in a temporary daze to reach the horses, I got a second rifle bullet. It smashed through my back of my hip, between two shells in my cartridge belt, and passed out through the groin. For a moment it partially paralyzed my leg.

Meantime City Marshall Charles T. Connelly had maneuvered around into the alley behind us toward the west. Connelly was a brave man. He came right out into the open among us. When he was shot and by whom I do not know. Various members of our band were accredited with the killing. When I saw him he lay on the ground. He had appeared at about the time that deadly volley from Isham's store mowed through the alley. Connelly had been a school professor in a neighboring town. He had come to Coffeyville on a furlough. The town had made him a temporary officer. This had been *his first fight. I have never known a gamer man.*

Although now twice wounded, I felt no pain; just a numbness which hampered me as I started untying my horse. I recollect it made me furious. Somehow I got the horse loose. All the animals were snorting and skittish. Powers, who was starting to mount beside me, was having trouble controlling his big dapple-gray. Just as he got his leg over the saddle I saw him pitch headlong. A second bullet had killed him instantly.

Broadwell and I were up together. For this moment every man was thinking of himself. Broadwell reeled in his saddle.

"I'm hit bad," he muttered. Clutching the saddle horn he put spurs to his horse and clattered down the alley westward. I followed him a few yards. Suddenly I realized Bob wasn't with us. I didn't know he had been badly wounded. Looking back I saw him still huddled there against the rocks.

"You go on," I called to Broadwell, I'm going back."

The alleyway was screaming with shots from Isham's and the plaza—from everywhere, it seemed. Bob and Power's horses were killed. Our own firing had left a drifting fog of smoke. It hung over the inert figures of Grat and Powers and the huddled form of Bob. Two of us dead now. One mortally wounded. Myself hard hit.

I had trouble getting my horse to face into the smoke. The money sack still hung there on the saddle, ironically. I had no thought now of shooting. Had no thought of anything except to reach Bob. To haul him up behind me, if still he lived, and try to break clear from that inferno. My own life seemed of no importance—was of no importance. In ten eternal minutes the world had crashed down about me. Our "all for one" had dwindled under incessant gun fire to "One for one." It wasn't a matter of courage. It was a matter of affection for the one brother of all my kin with whom I had the closest bond. I couldn't let him lie there. I spurred my horse forward.

Perhaps it is well to quote Emerson Hough at this point, lest I might be accused of some macabre boast.

"Emmett Dalton," Hough in his *Story of the Outlaw* says, "was not the only one of the band left alive....He still kept his nerve and his wits, even under such pressure of peril. He might have escaped, but instead he rode back to where Bob was lying, and reached down his hand to help him up behind himself on the horse...."

My wounds were bringing me nausea. It was all I could do to control my animal. Bullets were still singing. That I was not riddled in that short zigzag ride to Bob was a miracle.

Meantime Carey Seaman, the barber, had come into action. Seaman had returned from a hunting trip in the Indian Territory just before the battle began. He was unhitching his team at his stable, a block away, when the firing started. In his buckboard was a shotgun, loaded with buckshot. Grabbing it up, he had skirted back though an open lot to the alley. There he was screened from our view by a high board fence. During the deadly volley through the alley he had reached the cover of an outhouse. There he must have been standing as I wheeled to ride back toward Bob. Now he stepped out into the alley, hammers cocked above a double load of buckshot.

"Don't mind me, Emmett," Bob whispered as I leaned down toward him. "I'm done for. Don't surrender, boy. Die game!"

He seemed to realize, although already far gone, that it would be impossible for me to get away now. It was in his mind to give me a supporting word in this business of dying.

Behind me a crashing roar resounded above the thinner din of rifles. Twice it sounded. Carey Seaman had pulled his triggers.

It was all over. With eighteen buckshot in my back, from hip to head, I slid down. The double impact had taken me as I was bending over to catch Bob's last admonition. I clutched at the money sack in my agony. It came loose. I fell on it in a huddle beside Bob. In his last throe Bob turned laboriously on his side, propped himself weakly on one elbow. With eyes already glazing he fired one last wild shot. And so he died.

Sieved with twenty wounds, I still managed to cling to consciousness. But the world swam far away. For a moment longer the sound of guns continued, faint and monotonous, as *if the frenzy of the citizens could not be surfeited. Then the detonations ceased. The quarry was all down.*

For a moment everything was deathly quiet.

Then rose a dreadful yelping of the dogs. Many dogs. Howling an eerie dirge. And through the lifting smoke fog they began to come—the citizens of Coffeyville, the men who had exterminated the Dalton band. Their feet scuffled hesitantly across the brick plaza and down the alley. Vaguely I saw them in a swimming haze. Coming to count the dead. Coming to recover the sacked loot, some twenty thousand dollars.

Dick Broadwell, fatally wounded, had ridden a mile from town, where he toppled dead from the saddle.

Less than ten minutes had elapsed from the time the five of us had entered the banks. The shadows of the buildings across the alley hadn't shifted more than an inch. The clock in the Condon Bank had moved its black hands but a brief span since Grat had first glanced at it.

In that short interval eight men had died: Bob and Grat Dalton, Dick Broadwell and Bill Powers of the outlaw band; Cubine, Brown, Baldwin, and Connelly, among the citizens.

Four had been wounded: three citizens—Thomas G. Ayres, of the First National Bank; T. A. Reynolds, a clerk at Isham's, and Charley Gump, the drayman—and myself. The remarkable thing was that not an unarmed man had been either killed or wounded, despite the fact that more than one hundred shots had been fired.

Colonel D. S. Elliot, G. A. R. veteran and owner of the Coffeyville Journal, made the statement that for the number of men engaged and the time consumed the casualties were heavier here than in any battle of the Civil War.

The curtain had come down on the most deadly street battle of the West.'"

CHAPTER TWENTY-SIX

A Price on His Head

1970s – 1985 – Back on the Right Side of the Law

The next day when Frank got to the courthouse he learned the district attorney was a woman, which concerned him. Normally women don't condone unwarranted violence to solve an issue. Would she feel that he had taken the law into his own hands, he wondered? It only took ten minutes of his statement for her to stamp the man's death as a justifiable homicide. He also learned that the younger man he'd shot, Eugene C. Robinson III, was only seventeen years old and that Robinson's father was a hit man for the mob, who worked out of the Tropicana in Miami. This last bit of information concerned Frank, gravely. Before the D.A. had even warned him that this man might seek retribution on the man who'd shot his son, the thought of a contract hit was already swimming around in his head. Suddenly, there was also a little niggling trace of suspicion in the back of Frank's mind that just maybe, Patricia had hired Robinson or Clements to kill him, but he kept that terrible thought to himself instead of sharing his suspicion with the police.

The sheriff had taken Frank's revolver the night of the shooting so he stopped by the office and asked him if they could return it to him. Surprisingly, the sheriff told Frank where he could pick it up since he'd been cleared of all charges. When he turned in the claim for his truck to the insurance company, they replaced all the glass, but refused to fix the bullet holes in the body and roof. Strangely, the remnants of the shoot-out had apparently added to the value of the truck when he decided to sell it and get one that wasn't riddled with extra air conditioning in the headliner and roof.

A month after Frank's shootout in May, Sherriff Dale

Carson came to the brewery to tell Frank that Robinson's father had indeed put a contract out on him. He told Frank to stop by his office after work and he would give him the paperwork he needed to carry a concealed weapon in order to protect himself since they would not be able to provide him constant police protection. When he got to the sheriff's office, Frank was also given a badge as a special deputy policeman. This gave Frank some measure of comfort, however, he was quite concerned about living in such a secluded area. Patricia was petrified to even stay in the house alone anymore. She often stayed with girlfriends in town and traveled more and more alone, while Frank was working. It didn't take long for their marriage to become nothing more than a marriage of convenience.

Even Frank was always on-edge living at the house and every time he opened the door to the garage, or stepped out of the house he would have a vision of someone standing there with a gun shooting him. That's when the calls started—leaving messages on the answering machine when he was away and catching him at home at two in the morning. "You killed Clements and injured my son...." a woman's voice clearly stated. "You're next and there's nothing you can do to stop it. We're going to kill you."

Frank often found the imprint of a man's tennis shoe around the house stopping at his bedroom window. Both Frank and Patricia went to the police and called them over and over but they did nothing other than cruise through the neighborhood once in a while. One night while driving home late from work, a dark Oldsmobile Cutlass 442 ran up behind Frank flashing its lights, then pulled alongside, swerving into him attempting to run Frank's truck off the road. The police searched for the vehicle that Frank described, but they never found it. Frank and Patricia finally decided it best to sell the house on the river. Patricia didn't want to stay there ever again and Frank no longer felt safe there. They sold it quickly and bought a house on Christopher Creek in south Jacksonville.

One year later two FBI agents were headed into a diner in Ocala, Florida for lunch. As they were entering the establishment, one of the agents recognized Robinson's father, Clarence Eugene Sr., the hit man, walking out of the restaurant and said something to him. The man shot both of the FBI agents point-blank and took off. A massive manhunt across the state followed the shooting and Eugene was eventually found on a ranch in Ocala and they took him into custody. Later, Frank was at the Busch Christmas party when one of his co-workers told him there was someone they wanted him to meet. As they approached a man he reached out his hand to Frank, "Are you the one who shot that Robinson kid?"

Puzzled, yet cautious Frank answered "Yes I'm the one. How do you know that?"

"I'm one of the FBI agents his dad shot in Ocala," the man said shaking Frank's hand.

"Well I'll be damned if it isn't a small world," Frank said returning the handshake of the man that put away the criminal that had been trying to kill him. "I heard you and your partner had recovered from the shooting. I'm relieved to know you're okay and especially relieved to that you've gotten that guy behind bars like his son. Now I can breathe a little easier knowing he's not going to shoot me on some dark road one night, or in my bed while I'm sleeping."

Frank spent all his time working, since the overtime pay he made was so lucrative and it kept his mind off of his strained relationship with Patricia. Then one day, after twenty-five years of service to Busch, Frank decided it was time to retire so that he could tinker with his collectible automobiles. They had been settled into the Christopher Creek house for several years when Patricia suddenly up and decided to make a transfer to Delta's Tampa office without even discussing it with Frank. Surprisingly for Frank, she purchased a house there using her own money.

Frank stayed in the Christopher Creek house for a while with Nancy, Patricia's daughter, while he tried to sell the place. When it finally did sell, Nancy refused to move out, so Frank was forced to purchase a condo near Jacksonville, on Ponte Vedra Beach, so that Nancy had a place to live while she was going to the University of North Florida.

Frank thought about the trailer on Virginia's land in Easley, South Carolina and how it had been sitting vacant for so many years. So he reached out to Johnny Mark, his brother's son, and negotiated to purchase the trailer with an acre of land for only ten thousand dollars. It was a great deal and the size of the lot allowed him to build a five thousand square-foot garage to use as his workshop for his cars. Frank's Uncle Coleman came and helped him build the garage and it felt good to get to know Coleman again after so many years. He was the only family member, other than Bessy, who'd truly understood him and had his back. Frank saw little of his family, other than Coleman while in Easley, but he especially avoided his Uncle Austin, even when he came to visit his sister, Virginia.

Frank spent most of his time in Easley at the trailer, where he could work on his cars and kick back with little responsibility. However, there was one drawback—it was only one hundred yards from his mother, Virginia's home. She had survived her husband Wes, who'd recently died from diabetes. She was living alone with her dog Boomer and Frank used the fact that she needed help with her property as an excuse to live in such close proximity to the woman who'd tortured him for eleven years of his childhood and had treated him like the red-headed stepchild the rest of his life. But deep down, he felt some need to be near her, as well as to garner her love, even if he knew that she was incapable of giving such a thing.

The trailer was in good shape so it gave Frank a place to

get away from Patricia's daughter who continued to live in his Ponte Vedra condo. This little escape in the woods offered him peace and quiet. And at that point in his life, he felt what he truly needed was time alone. He'd been married pretty much since he'd returned from Korea and he suddenly cherished having some space of his own. Frank would visit Tampa on occasion, but he never felt comfortable or at home there with Patricia, even if she was still his wife.

Virginia spent most of her days sitting on her porch, siccing her mean dog, Boomer, on passersby, as well as doing target practice in the back woods with her double-barreled shotgun. Frank would buy her ammunition and groceries and they managed to settle into a somewhat civil relationship, however distant. One day, Virginia had sicced her dog on a man walking down the road and the dog took a generous bite out of the man's posterior. The police later arrived to pick up the dog to put it down, since it might have been infected with rabies. The dog had no tag or proof of vaccination, so the sheriff insisted to Virginia that the dog be destroyed. Frank heard the ruckus and screaming and came out of his garage to find Virginia pointing her shotgun at the sheriff, insisting that he get off her property, or she'd load his ass with buckshot. Frank hesitated a moment thinking it could be a good thing if Virginia was incarcerated, then he would no longer have to deal with her. After all, if they hadn't let her out of jail in the first place, he might never have met the woman.

"You can get your scrawny ass off my land mister! I don't care who you are, you ain't taking my dog nowheres....do you hear me? I'll shoot you soon as look at you." All the while the dog was barking and baring its teeth at the officer and the officer had his gun trained on the dog—uncertain whether to shoot Virginia or the dog first. "You may take my dog, but I'm going to fill your ass with buckshot."

Frank cautiously walked up to the sheriff with his hand extended, "Officer, I'm her son, Frank Dalton."

The sheriff looked at him sideways uncertain whether to trust him or not. Nervously, "Well Mr. Dalton, your mother is threatening an officer of the law with a deadly weapon, I'm going to have to take out a warrant for her arrest."

"Arrest my ass," Virginia screamed. "You just try to arrest me and see where it gets you."

"I used to be a cop in Atlanta, so I understand where you're coming from, sir. But one thing I can assure you....she will sure as hell do what she says, so you might want to reconsider taking that dog, officer."

"Well sir, I'm going to have to come back up here with reinforcements."

"Good luck with that," Frank continued shaking his head. "Just let me handle her. I'll get that gun away from her and make sure she doesn't use it anymore. And you don't have to worry about that dog having rabies. The only disease he's got is meanness....somethin' he learned from my mother. Neither of them take too kindly to strangers on their property."

With that, the sheriff started backing away from the dog and Virginia's shotgun, never turning his back on either of them. When he finally reached his patrol car he quickly jumped in and rolled down the window as he started the car "I'll be back later!" he said, as he drove away. But, no one ever returned with a warrant for Virginia's arrest or the hound. And with that, Frank took the shotgun as well as the ammunition away from Virginia, even though she raised cane over him taking away her favorite pastime of target practice and scaring police officers half to death.

One day when Virginia got furious with him over something absurd, she raised her hand to hit him upside the head the way she'd done when he was a child—"I ought to knock some sense into you! I'll hit you upside the head," she bellowed, as he caught her wrist and forced her arm down, leaving vivid marks on her skin.

"Let's get one thing straight. If you ever lay a hand on me again, I WILL make certain that the police arrest you and I'll take you to jail myself."

Virginia just looked at him shocked that he had finally stood up to her.

"Don't you even feel the least sorry for the way you beat me as a child?" Frank asked, still restraining her wrist to the point of making her wince.

Virginia thought about his point-blank question for a moment "I did the best I could," she said unashamed, then turned to look away. Frank released her arm, knowing that it was the most he'd ever get out of her. "Ain't no point in talking 'bout it anymore," Virginia said as she rubbed her wrist and walked into the house. The screen door slammed behind her like the crack of the final nail being driven into a coffin.

It was the first and the last time he would ever truly stand up to his mother, but strangely enough, it seemed to make her realize that he meant business. From that day forward Virginia seemed to have some new measure of respect for the man he'd become. Just the simple act of standing up to her for the first time in his life had made Frank feel whole—as if he'd finally come full circle and defended the young boy he'd never had the strength to protect, years before. In a strange way, it made a type of peace between them, as well as in his soul.

Frank would spend his days in Easley alone, working on his cars and eating his daily chilidogs from the local filing station. The rest of the time he spent drinking Buds and watching television. On occasion he would go to stay with Patricia in their Tampa house for a night or two, only to be told by the neighbor how she would often stand at the window stark naked. He asked Frank if he could do something about her obsessive need to expose herself, since the neighbor's wife was constantly accusing him of enjoying the floor show a bit too much. He also found out from others in the neighborhood that Patricia had begun participating in the local swinger's scene, making it impossible for Frank to even share a bed with her any longer. Somehow, he had managed to stay married to Patricia for more than twenty years, but in light of this new information, he decided to file for divorce before he left to return to Easley.

When Patricia found out she quickly sold their Suwanne River house—a house that Frank had purchased as an investment property. At the time she'd wanted nothing to do with the property but when she sold it without his knowledge she simply kept the money rather than dividing it as community property. Then she proceeded to hire the lawyer that had defended the man Frank had wounded in the shoot-out, to be her divorce attorney. Somehow they managed to send the trial notices for the divorce proceedings to their previous address and Frank was never notified to attend the court dates in order to testify in his own divorce hearings. He also discovered that the man he'd shot had only served six months in jail for his attempted murder of Frank in the shoot-out. All of this seemed very suspicious to Frank and he wondered if he shouldn't have just filed for divorce much sooner. Patricia even wanted half of the Easley property and actually brought a camera crew and her lawyer up to take Virginia's deposition. However, Virginia was so confused at the deposition, the lawyer threw up his hands and said, "Forget it, let him keep it!"

Although Frank agreed to allow her to keep the Tampa house, he wanted to sell the condo at Ponte Vedra Beach, but Patricia's daughter refused to move out. In the end he had to give her ten thousand dollars to make a down payment on a house so she would leave and they could sell the condo as community property.

When Patricia testified at their divorce hearing she told an embellished version of the story of the shoot-out with the two criminals that tried to break into their house on Samples Creek. She claimed that Frank had chased them down and shot them in cold blood—taking their side even though at the time she acted as if they were out to get her. Frank explained to the judge that he had simply defended house and home, as well as himself and his wife. He also made it clear that he'd been exonerated by the district attorney who'd determined it was a justifiable shooting. After all he was defending himself as they had shot first. Patricia's newest description of the events only served to instill the feeling in him that maybe she had been the one behind the entire incident in the first place.

CHAPTER TWENTY-SEVEN

A Son's Closure

1980s – Third Chance at Happiness

When the wife of Frank's co-worker from Busch, Larry Sadler's died, Frank drove down to Jacksonville to attend her funeral. Frank and Larry had been close friends over the years and he felt it important to pay his respects. While at the service, Frank met an attractive brunette named Barbara Homsey, and they instantly hit it off. It seemed that Barbara's son, George, was married to Larry's daughter, Susie. Frank and Barbara dated for a year while Frank was living in a four-bedroom house he'd bought on the thirteenth fairway of the Jacksonville Golf & Country Club, off Hodges Blvd. When Barbara's six children learned that she was living with a man, who was still technically married and waiting for his divorce to be finalized, they confronted her, concerned that they were living in sin. Barbara and Frank did their best to explain that his divorce was in the works—that it was just not yet finalized but soon would be. At least Frank hoped that was the case since it kept dragging on and on due to Patricia's continuing demands. The divorce had been a long fight and Patricia's attorney continued redirecting the legal notices to another address, so Frank continued to learn about hearings and actions after the fact. That was about the time the stalking started. It seemed that Patricia was stalking Frank and Barbara attempting to make a case of adultery against him in the divorce, but since they had a legal separation, nothing that she managed to dig up actually stuck in court. The last straw was when Patricia started stalking Frank and Barbara in their new community—driving by in her car and hiding behind bushes to take photos of their comings and goings. She even started stealing mail out of their mailbox and stopping the mailman to intercept their mail before he even got to the house. Frank tried to get a restraining order as well as file charges of mail theft with the US Postal Service, but to no avail.

Eventually, Frank's divorce from Patricia was finalized and he and Barbara were finally married. Together they bought a house on Lake Washington in Melbourne, Florida, so that she could be near her children. They also bought two lots on the same road and built a twenty-two hundred square-foot-house, as well as an eight-car garage to house Frank's many collectible cars.

Virginia was still living alone in the same house in Easley when Frank and Barbara went to see her after their wedding. When they arrived, they found the house in deplorable condition. There was old food in the oven and refrigerator and dirty, moldy dishwater in the sink. Virginia had no one to care for her, since neither her daughter, Carolyn, nor any of her siblings lived nearby. It seemed that no one in the family gave a damn about her anymore. After all, she hadn't been the best sister to her many siblings over the years. Virginia's health had declined rapidly after Frank had moved to Florida and Barbara insisted that Frank do something,

"No matter how she treated you as a child, she's still your mother and you have to help her....it's your responsibility," she insisted.

However, Frank felt little responsibility for Virginia. But there was this little niggling feeling that Barbara's advice was the right thing to do. So against his better judgment, they brought her down to live with them in their home until they could move into their new one. They sold her house and car, as well as Frank's trailer and garage in Easley, and moved all of Frank's cars and their personal belongings down to Melbourne. Once they moved into their new home, Virginia would then have a place of her own nearby, where they could check on her every day.

Virginia seemed to like it there for a while, but then she became increasingly difficult to live with. Frank stayed as busy as he could to avoid spending time with her and allowed Barbara to be the one to deal with her dark moods and tantrums. When the new house was ready and they moved in, Frank and Barbara realized that Virginia was in no condition to be living alone. They made the decision that she would be better off with full time care in a nursing home, since her health, as well as her mind, were failing rapidly. She had only had about one hundred thousand dollars in a CD when she came to live with Frank, as well as the forty thousand he'd sold her house for in Easley and Frank and Barbara knew that wouldn't last long paying five thousand dollars a month for her care in the nursing home.

Once in the home, it didn't take long for Virginia's mean streak to surface and she was asked to leave several nursing homes in the area for threatening to beat up other patients, as well as for cursing at and threatening the staff. When she broke her hip and ended up in a wheelchair, Frank knew that he would have to take her to a place provided by Social Security, since Virginia's money was running out and no other private homes in the area would have her—she'd been tagged as a difficult patient. She was always angry in the new home, since she felt she didn't receive enough attention in the crowded facility. Frank and Barbara would go at least once or twice a month, but Frank couldn't bring himself to do more than that. When he was there, she wouldn't say much to him—only scowl at him for not coming to see her more often. She still blamed him for taking her away from her home in Easley and putting her in that horrible place, but Frank did his best to just let her accusations roll off his back. He knew better than to expect anything more from her. Virginia's heart was failing quickly and Frank knew that she didn't have much time left, so he felt compelled to endure her nasty temperament when he did visit her.

On one of his visits without Barbara, he asked Virginia

once again, "Why did you treat me so badly when I was a child? Why did you beat me?" After all he thought, she's not going to be around much longer and he felt he deserved a better answer to his lifelong question than she'd given before.

Virginia just sat there scowling at him and finally shrugged—"I was a sick woman....I should have gone to jail. I guess I done the best I knew how."

Suddenly, the room grew so quiet you could hear a pin drop. Then she continued introspectively—"But....you know, you're the only man who has ever had the guts to stand up to me, Franklin."

Frank was stunned to hear her acknowledgement that indeed she should have been punished for her sins as a mother. A young boy should have a mother's love—not be whipped like an indentured slave from the pre-Civil War era. He looked at the frail woman who lay in the bed before him that he called mother and realized that the past had a way of catching up to one who has fled their sins, with little resolve or penance. Or, even being called to account for them. Ironically, the fate of her life now lay in his hands, as her soul laid in the hands of God. And God had set a definitive term for everyone. Frank had tried to forgive her over the years, but forgiveness was something that wasn't guaranteed to last forever. Maybe forgiveness had to be a daily exercise—maybe it had to be a work in progress within one's own soul.

When Frank got a call from the nursing home a few days later that Virginia had been taken to the Holmes Hospital with respiratory congestive cardiac failure, he was informed that she had been placed on life support and she'd refused to sign a 'Do Not Resituate' order. That meant, that her life was now truly in Frank's hands since he was her immediate next of kin. When Frank arrived in her room she appeared to be unconscious—hooked up to a respirator. They insisted that it was up to him make the decision to unplug her from life support, or to let her linger at a great expense to Frank, since her money had pretty much run out. It was ironic that it was now his decision to take life from the woman who'd given him his. He wondered if she'd refused to sign the DNR simply to lay the decision in his lap.

He sat in the chair in the darkened room staring at her inert, speechless body—listening to the rhythmic beep of the machine as it pumped life into her lungs. And Frank wondered—what would life have been like if Virginia had never returned to claim him as her child. Would he have understood the concept of love? If only he'd been allowed to stay with his grandmother—a loving woman who'd loved and cared for him when she didn't have two nickels to rub together? But most people learn by example and Virginia had certainly been a bad one. He wondered if he might have been a more responsible and loving husband and father if fate had turned in his favor. Was it too late to try? He had been given a new chance with Barbara, to find out what life might be like with real love in it. Would he succeed at making the most of this new chance for happiness? He hoped he could live up to his vows to love and cherish for the rest of his life.

Frank stood when the doctor walked into the room carrying a clipboard, "Have you made a decision on whether you want to keep her on life support Mr. Holiday?"

"Do what you have to do doctor to take her off that thing. She wouldn't want to live that way."

The doctor handed him the clipboard and a pen, "You'll have to sign there. Frank took the document and signed at the bottom and then handed it back to the doctor who nodded and walked over to the machine and switched it off. Just like that, the machine went dark and stopped its rhythmic beeping. He then untapped the ventilator from her face and removed the hose from her throat. Virginia choked and gasped for air, but still made no conscious response. Frank stood there a few minutes as the doctor finished and walked over to him. He rested his hand on Frank's shoulder. "It could take a while," the doctor said as he left Frank alone in the room with Virginia.

Frank looked at his watch—he had to be at work soon, but he sat down anyway and waited. Suddenly, Virginia opened her eyes—staring straight at him. She'd heard every word without any response—not even the blink of an eye—a tear, nor a sound. She was at peace with the fact that she was to leave this world upon Frank's request. Only a signature on a page to end her life....it was only fitting. She kept her eyes trained on him as she lay there struggling to breathe her last breaths. Uncomfortable, Frank glanced once again at his watch. He stood and Virginia's eyes followed him. Neither of them spoke. Frank just nodded at Virginia—there were no more words he needed to say. Then he turned and walked out of the room. Frank went straight to his car, started it, and drove home. When he walked through the door, Barbara was waiting for him.

"The hospital just called. Your mom's gone," she said regretfully.

He went to her and hugged her. Then he broke down and wept. Not so much in sadness, but in relief that that chapter of his life was finally closed.

THE END

EPILOGUE

Then and Now

<u>Carl's Journey</u>

Carl Franklin Dalton Holliday did finally learn that his real father, James Lewis Dalton, had three sons and a daughter. In 2010, Carl finally met his three half-brothers, Bobby, Jimmy, and Jack Dalton. Bobby wanted little to do with Carl, and Jimmy passed away in 2022, however Jack and Carl remain friends to this day. Jack is anxiously awaiting the publication of this book.

Carl never had the chance to meet or speak to his biological father, James Lewis Dalton.

<u>What happened to the Dalton boys?</u>

Out of the forty thousand dollar reward placed on the Dalton Gang's heads, only two thousand dollars was ever paid out. The three widows of Connelly, Cubine, and Brown were compensated from the reward for their loss.

Julia Johnson, a Mexican-American, Emmett's sweetheart, arrived within two days of the shootout at Coffeyville and stayed by his side in a hotel room where they had left him to die.

The Dalton boy's mother, Adeline Lee (Younger) Dalton, cousin to Jim and John Younger of the James-Younger Gang, arrived three days after the event in Coffeyville—too late to see her sons, Bob and Grat, buried. She also sat with Emmett knowing that three of her sons were now dead, and Emmett was likely to be the fourth. She contemplated that the propensity for her sons to become outlaws may very well have come from her blood, since she was related to those notorious Younger outlaws. Of Adeline's thirteen children, four had stepped across the line from lawmen, to outlaws.

Emmett Dalton passed the crisis of his high fever wounds and was carried to jail at Independence, Kansas. Slowly his body healed, except for his shattered arm. Five months later he appeared before Judge J.D. McCue and was charged with shooting George Cubine and Lucius Baldwin as well as bank robbery. His attorney advised him to plead guilty to the second-degree killing of Cubine and assured him that the other charges would be dropped, and thus he would receive the minimum sentence. Instead, Emmett was sentenced to life imprisonment at the Lansing, Kansas State Penitentiary. At twenty-one years of age, Emmett Dalton went to prison in March 1893.

Emmet was assigned to work in a tailor shop where he learned to cut and fit men's clothes, a job he hated. He had envisioned a cattle ranch on foreign soil, but instead received into a four-by-eight-foot cell. One never knows how a dream may manifest.

During all Emmett's years in prison, Julia waited for him and wrote letters, visiting him in prison as often as possible.

In 1894, Bill Dalton was accused of robbing a bank in Longview, Texas. Deputies shot him while he was seated in a chair at the ranch of Houston Wallace while playing with his daughter.

Emmett Dalton was the last survivor of the notorious western gangs. Eventually, he was assigned to jobs outside the prison wall as a trustee.

In 1907, Governor E. W. Hoch pardoned Emmett, after serving fourteen and a-half-years of his life sentence. Not even the citizens of Coffeyville challenged his pardon. Julia had waited for him faithfully, nearly fifteen years, with no guarantee he would ever be released from prison. They were married in Bartlesville after his release. They then moved to California where Emmett became a building contractor.

Emmett Dalton wrote his first book, *Beyond the Law*, in

1918. His second *When the Dalton's Rode,* was published in 1937. It has since been re-published by the Pelican Publishing Company in 2012, as a public domain title.